ALCOA HANDBOOK OF DESIGN STRESSES FOR ALUMINUM

D0965888

ALUMINUM COMPANY OF AMERICA
PITTSBURGH, PENNSYLVANIA

Contents

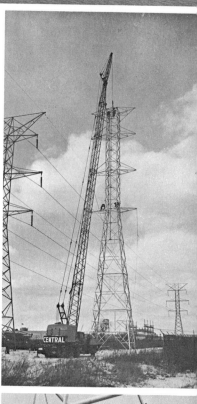

Foreword

THIS HANDBOOK has been prepared for engineers and architects concerned with the design of aluminum strength members. It presents, for the first time, long-needed data on allowable stresses for many alloys commonly used in building construction, and in other applications where aluminum's light weight, durability, appearance and ease of fabrication make its use advantageous. The recommended design stresses are based on factors of safety normally employed in specifications for building structures. This handbook also includes general formulas and strength data from which design stresses can be determined for other alloys, or for other applications where different factors of safety may be appropriate.

In general, the proposed allowable stresses are similar to those recommended for building structures of alloys 6061-T6, 6062-T6 and 6063-T5 and -T6 by the Task Committee on Lightweight Alloys of the American Society of Civil Engineers.

The handbook covers mechanical-property data and buckling constants for more than 150 aluminum alloys, tempers and products, and allowable stresses for 19 alloys and tempers considered of primary interest for structural applications.

The material presented supersedes some of the information in the *Alcoa Structural Handbook* (1960), which nevertheless remains a valid general guide to strength design.

It is not possible to anticipate every application and use that may be made of information contained in this handbook. Aluminum Company of America, therefore, disclaims any responsibility or liability for designs based on this information.

Like all Alcoa publications, this handbook is designed to help the reader to proceed on his own. Nevertheless, Alcoa continues to offer the services of its research and development facilities to customers who desire assistance in the application of aluminum to their products. Assistance may be obtained through the Alcoa sales offices listed in the back of this handbook.

PART I DISCUSSION

Design Data

A WIDE variety of aluminum alloys, tempers and products is used in applications where strength is a basic requirement and design is determined on the basis of allowable stresses. While data on strength of aluminum alloys are available in publications such as the *Alcoa Structural Handbook* and the *Alcoa Aluminum Handbook*, specific recommendations for allowable stresses to be used in various applications are relatively rare. In the structural field, the principal American specifications are those prepared by the Task Committee on Lightweight Alloys of the American Society of Civil Engineers, [1, 2]* which apply to alloys 6061-T6, 6062-T6, 6063-T5 and 6063-T6. The object of this handbook is to present similar allowable-stress data for other commonly used wrought alloys.

ALLOWABLE STRESSES

Suggested allowable stresses for strength members of a number of different types and alloys are listed in Table 1. These stresses are based on the factors of safety used in ASCE Papers 3341 [1] and 3342 [2] for buildings and other structures to which specifications similar to the AISC specifications for steel buildings are applied. Corresponding stresses for aluminum bridges and other structures

---

* Numbers in brackets indicate references listed at the end of the text.

to which specifications similar to the AASHO and AREA specifications for steel bridges are applied are about 11 per cent lower.

For each of the alloys in Table 1, allowable stresses are recommended for 21 different combinations of type of loading and type of structural component. Each of these conditions of stressing is given a specification number. For all alloys except 2014-T6, two sets of suggested allowable stresses are listed for each specification number. The first set applies to any part of a structure that is not affected by the heat of welding. These values are used for all non-welded structures and for welded structures outside the heat-affected zone. The second set of suggested allowable stresses, which is designated by gray shading, applies to the heat-affected zone in welded structures (within 1.0 in. of a weld). Allowable stresses are not suggested for welded 2014-T6, since this alloy is not generally used in welded construction.

Where the term "flat plate" is used in Table 1 and also in Table 4, it refers to any flat element, regardless of whether the element is fabricated from plate (thickness of 0.250 in. or greater) or sheet (thickness less than 0.250 in.), or is part of an extrusion. The specific provisions for allowable stress are reviewed in more detail under "Application of Design Data."

The allowable stresses in Table 1 for alloys 6061-T6, 6063-T5 and 6063-T6, are taken directly from ASCE Papers 3341 and 3342. ASCE Paper 3341 is reproduced in full at the back of this handbook. The tables from Paper 3342 are also reproduced, but the text is omitted, since it is essentially the same as the text of Paper 3341. Allowable stresses for the other alloys were determined from the general formulas discussed in the following section.

Recommended allowable shear stresses on rivets and bolts in building structures are given in Table 2; allowable shear stresses in fillet welds appear in Table 3.

GENERAL FORMULAS FOR ALLOWABLE STRESS

The general formulas used in determining allowable stresses are given in Tables 4 and 5. These are based on the dimensions of the part, the mechanical properties of the material, the buckling formula coefficients for the material (which are based on mechanical properties, as discussed in the subsequent section) and the factor of safety. With the appropriate mechanical properties and factors of safety inserted, the formulas are in essential agreement with the recommendations of the ASCE Task Committee on Lightweight Alloys for the alloys covered by the committee's specifications [1, 2]. In some cases, where recent tests have indicated that the recommendations of the ASCE committee were more conservative than necessary, the allowable stresses given by the formulas in Table 4 are slightly higher than the corresponding values in Papers 3341 and 3342. This applies to compression in welded plates supported on one edge, bending stress in rectangular beams, and compression and bending in round tubes. (See [3] for information on strength of tubes.)

BUCKLING FORMULA CONSTANTS

Allowable compressive stresses are for the most part controlled by the buckling strength of the member or component. For aluminum alloys, buckling strength in the inelastic range can be represented by formulas of the form,

$$F_{cr} = B - D\lambda \qquad (1)$$

where F_{cr} = buckling stress, ksi

$\qquad B, D$ = constants depending upon the compressive stress-strain characteristics of the material, the type of member and the loading conditions, ksi

$\qquad \lambda$ = slenderness ratio or equivalent slenderness ratio, a function of the dimensions of the member

The elastic buckling formula is of the form

$$F_{cr} = \frac{\pi^2 E}{\lambda^2} \qquad (2)$$

where E = compressive modulus of elasticity, ksi. At the intersection of the curves defined by Eq 1 and 2, λ has the value C.

As used in the general formulas for allowable stress in Table 4, the symbols B, D and C are assigned various subscripts to designate the different types of buckling. Table 8 gives equations from which these buckling coefficients can be calculated for any alloy and temper. Values calculated from these formulas can be substituted, together with the factor of safety, in the appropriate expressions in Table 4 to obtain allowable stresses.

For the alloys covered in ASCE Papers 3341 and 3342, the buckling formula constants given by the formulas in Table 8, and listed in Table 9, are not precisely the same as the values which were used by the ASCE Committee in deriving the allowable stresses in Table 1. The differences are negligible for practical purposes, however.

FACTORS OF SAFETY

The specifications for allowable stress in Tables 4 and 5 incorporate three different factors of safety: the factor of safety on ultimate strength, n_u; the factor of safety on yielding, n_y; and the factor of safety on the appearance of buckling, n_a. The latter quantity is employed in cases where buckling does not bring about collapse of the structure, but where the designer does not want the elements of the structure to take on a buckled appearance at design loads.

Values of the three factors of safety used in ASCE Papers 3341 [1] and 3342 [2] are listed in Table 6. The ASCE Papers contain the following statement: "In applications where it is conventional practice to increase allowable stresses for certain types of loads, such as wind loads, the allowable stresses in these specifications should be increased in the same proportions as are the allowable stresses in accepted specifications for steel structures." This statement should also be applied to the formulas and allowable stresses contained in this handbook. Two other quantities appearing in Table 4 should be explained: the coefficients k_t and k_c. The quantity k_t is introduced to increase the factor of safety on tensile strength for some alloys that do not develop quite as high a tensile efficiency in the presence of stress concentrations as do the alloys covered by the specifications in ASCE Papers 3341 and 3342.

The quantity k_c adjusts the factor of safety on compressive yield strength in order to provide a range of slenderness ratios in the short column range for which the allowable stress is independent of the slenderness ratio. This is a convenience to the designer and is consistent with the specifications of the ASCE Committee. Values of k_t and k_c recommended for various alloys are listed in Table 7.

MECHANICAL PROPERTIES

Minimum mechanical properties for a number of commonly used alloys are listed in Table 9. These values can be used in calculating allowable stresses similar to those recommended in Table 1 for alloys not covered in the latter table. Tables of minimum mechanical properties guaranteed by Alcoa are available in the *Alcoa Aluminum Handbook*. Also appearing in Table 9 are values of the various buckling formula constants. These are expected minimum values corresponding to the minimum mechanical properties.

Table 10 gives data on the minimum strength of butt welds and the minimum mechanical properties in the "heat-affected zone." This is the narrow zone near the weld in which the strength of heat-treated or work-hardened material is reduced by the heat of welding. The maximum extent of the heat-affected zone measured from the center of a butt weld or the root of a fillet weld can be considered as 1.0 in. The ultimate strengths in Table 10 are equal to the ASME weld qualification test requirement values [4]. It has been recommended [5] that for general design purposes, the ultimate strength of butt welds be considered as 90 per cent of the weld qualification test value. This assumption was used by the ASCE Task Committee on Lightweight Alloys in preparing its specifications [1, 2]. The tensile and compressive yield strength values for welds in Table 10 correspond to 0.2 per cent offset measured on a gage length of 10 in. across a butt weld [1, 2, 5].

Application of Design Data

TENSION MEMBERS (Specification 1)

Allowable tensile stresses in Specification No. 1 in Table 1 are determined by applying appropriate factors of safety to the yield and the ultimate strength and selecting the lower of the two resulting stress values. The resulting allowable stress is applied to the net section. The net section of a part with rivet or bolt holes is the product of the thickness of the part multiplied by its least net width. The net width for a single line of holes extending across the part may be obtained by deducting from the gross width the sum of the diameters of all the holes in the line. In calculating effective area, the hole diameter is customarily considered to be the actual hole diameter for drilled or reamed holes and the hole diameter plus 1/16 in. for punched holes. Where the holes are staggered in two or more lines across the member, the net width for a broken line of holes may be obtained by deducting from the gross width the sum of the diameters of all the holes in the broken line and adding $s^2/4g$ for each gage space in the chain, where:

s = the spacing parallel to the direction of load (pitch) of any two successive holes in the chain, in., and

g = the spacing perpendicular to the direction of load (gage) of the same holes, in.

The minimum or controlling net section of a part is obtained from that chain of holes which gives the least net width.

In computing the effective section of a single angle connected by one leg only on one side of a gusset plate, it is customary to consider the effective section as the net section of the connected leg plus one-half of the section of the outstanding leg.

The allowable tensile stresses given in Table 1 for areas within 1.0 in. of a weld are lower, in many cases, than the allowable stresses of nonwelded structures because of the reduced mechanical properties in the vicinity of a weld. In some cases, only part of a cross section will be affected by the heat of welding. The allowable stress can then be considered to be the weighted average of the allowable value on the area within 1.0 in. of the weld and the allowable value for non-welded material, which applies to the remainder of the cross section. This is expressed by the following formula:

$$F_{pw} = F_n - \frac{A_w}{A}(F_n - F_w)$$ (3)

where F_{pw} = allowable stress on cross section, part of whose area lies within 1.0 in. of a weld, ksi

F_n = allowable stress for same cross section if there were no welds present, ksi

F_w = allowable stress for same cross section if the entire area were within 1.0 in. of a weld, ksi

A = net area of cross section of a tension member or tension flange of a beam, or gross area of cross section of a compression member or compression flange of a beam, sq in. (A beam flange is considered to consist of that portion of the member further than $2c/3$ from the neutral axis, where c is the distance from the neutral axis to the extreme fiber.)

A_w = area within area A that lies within 1.0 in. of a weld, sq in.

If A_w is less than 15 per cent of A, the effect of welding on the allowable stress can be neglected.

TENSION IN BEAMS (Specifications 2, 3 and 4)

These provisions are similar to those for axial tension, except that for tubular and rectangular shapes a "shape factor" is introduced to take account of the effect of the nonlinear stress distribution in the inelastic stress range. Since a large part of the cross section of such shapes is not stressed as highly as the extreme fiber, the apparent stress (calculated as bending moment divided by section modulus) can exceed the yield strength by an appreciable margin before yielding becomes evident. The apparent stress can also exceed the tensile strength without fracture.

The effects of rivet or bolt holes and the effects of welding are handled in the same way as for tension members. Where only part of a tension flange is affected by welding, Eq 3 can be used to determine the allowable stress.

Example No. 1 — Bending of Flat Sheet

A 3 ft-2 in. $\times$ 9 ft-0 in. flat sheet panel, supported around the edges, must carry a wind load of 30 psf. Check whether the tensile bending stress in 0.125-in. Anoclad $^\circledR$ Sheet, Type 12-H14, will exceed the allowable value.

Neglect membrane stresses. Assume the sheet behaves as a simply supported beam on a 3-ft span. Consider a 1-in.-wide strip.

$$\text{Load, } w = \frac{30}{144} = 0.208 \text{ psi}$$

$$\text{Bending moment, } M = \frac{wL^2}{8} = \frac{0.208(38)^2}{8}$$

$$= 37.5 \text{ in.-lb}$$

$$\text{Section modulus, } S = \frac{bt^2}{6} = \frac{1.0(0.125)^2}{6}$$

$$= 0.00260 \text{ in.}^3$$

$$\text{Bending stress, } f = \frac{M}{S} = \frac{37.5}{0.00260}$$

$$= 14,400 \text{ psi} = 14.4 \text{ ksi}$$

The allowable stress from Table 1, Anoclad Sheet Type 12-H14, Specification 4 (nonwelded), is 13.5 ksi. It is customary to increase this value by one-third for wind loads, giving an allowable stress of $13.5 \times 4/3 = 18.0$ ksi. Since $14.4 < 18.0$, the tensile stress in the sheet is satisfactory.

Notes: In this instance, the controlling allowable stress would be compressive. From Specification 13 in Table 1, this value would be $11 \times 4/3 = 14.7$ ksi.

The foregoing method of computing stresses in flat sheets is generally conservative. In most applications of this kind, membrane action will reduce the stresses and also the deflections.

Example No. 2 — Welded Beam

A welded 5456-H321 girder with the cross section shown is subjected to a bending moment of 11,000 in.-kips. Is the stress in the tension flange within acceptable limits for bridge structures?

$$\text{Moment of inertia, } I_x = 20,060 \text{ in.}^4$$

$$\text{Section modulus, tension side, } S_t = 740 \text{ in.}^3$$

$$\text{Section modulus, compression side, } S_c = 876 \text{ in.}^3$$

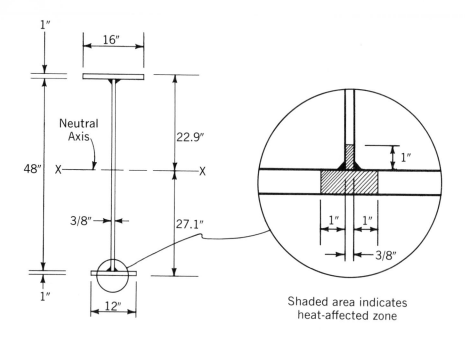

Shaded area indicates
heat-affected zone

From Table 4; substituting values found in Tables 6, 7 and 9:

$$F_n = \frac{F_{ty}}{n_y} \text{ or } \frac{F_{tu}}{k_t n_u}$$

$$= \frac{33}{1.85} \text{ or } \frac{46}{1.0 \times 2.2}$$

$$= 17.8 \text{ or } 20.9. \text{ Use } 17.8 \text{ ksi.}$$

From Table 4; substituting values found in Tables 6, 7 and 10:

$$F_w = \frac{F_{tyw}}{n_y} \text{ or } \frac{0.9 F_{tuw}}{k_t n_u}$$

$$= \frac{26}{1.85} \text{ or } \frac{0.9 \times 42}{1.0 \times 2.2}$$

$$= 14.1 \text{ or } 17.2. \text{ Use } 14.1 \text{ ksi.}$$

Area of tension flange:

Flange plate:	12×1	$= 12.0$
Web:	$\left(\frac{1}{3} \times 27.1 - 1\right) \times \frac{3}{8}$	$= 3.0$
		$A = 15.0 \text{ in.}^2$

Area in heat-affected zone (see sketch):

$$A_w = 2\frac{3}{8} \times 1 + 1 \times \frac{3}{8} = 2.75 \text{ in.}^2$$

$$\frac{A_w}{A} = \frac{2.75}{15.0} = 0.183$$

Allowable stress from Eq 3:

$$F_{pw} = F_n - \frac{A_w}{A}(F_n - F_w)$$

$$= 17.8 - 0.183\,(17.8 - 14.1)$$

$$= 17.1 \text{ ksi}$$

$$\text{Actual stress} = \frac{M}{S} = \frac{11,000}{740} = 14.9 \text{ ksi}$$

Since 14.9 < 17.1, the stress is within allowable limits.

Notes: If there are flange splices or other sources of additional welding on the flange at regions of high bending moment, the effect of this welding on the allowable stresses should be checked.

Allowable compressive stresses in this girder are discussed in Examples 7 and 8.

BEARING (Specifications 5 and 6)

In accordance with the precedent set in ASCE Papers 3341 and 3342 [1, 2], Specification 5 provides the same factor of safety against bearing yield as is used against tensile yield strength, but increases the factor of safety on ultimate strength by 20 per cent. Allowable bearing stresses on milled surfaces and pins are two-thirds of the values permitted on rivets and bolts.

In designing connections for bearing, the effective bearing area of pins, bolts and rivets should be considered to be the effective diameter multiplied by the length in bearing, except that for countersunk rivets, half of the depth of the countersink is deducted from the length. The effective diameter of rivets is taken as the hole diameter, but should not exceed the nominal diameter of the rivet by more than 4 per cent for cold-driven rivets or 7 per cent for hot-driven rivets. The effective diameter for pins and bolts is the nominal diameter of the pin or bolt.

COLUMNS (Specification 7)

The same factor of safety is applied to column strength as is applied to ultimate tensile strength. The formulas for allowable stress are expressed in terms of the ratio L/r, where L is defined as "length of compression member between points of lateral support or twice the length of a cantilever column (except where analysis shows that a shorter length can be used)." The quantity r is the least radius of gyration of the column cross section. In most practical cases, the foregoing definition of L gives results that are conservative but not excessively so. The value of L should not be taken as less than the actual length between points of support except where the member is fastened by rigid connections to other members that are relatively stiff in comparison to the column.

The specifications of the ASCE Committee on Lightweight Alloys [1, 2] contain the following warnings concerning the use of open-section columns and columns with large slenderness ratios:

> "Open-section members that are unsymmetrical about one or both principal axes may be subject to failure by combined torsion and flexure. For single or double angles and tee sections, Specification [8] provides an adequate factor of safety against this type of failure. Other unsymmetrical, open shapes, such as channels, lipped angles or hat shapes should not be used as columns unless a special analysis is made of the resistance to buckling by combined torsion and flexure . . ."

> "Because long columns are relatively flexible, they may be appreciably weakened by the presence of lateral loads that would have little effect on the column strength of stiffer members. For this reason, columns with slenderness ratios greater than 120 should not be used unless special care is taken to insure that the effects of any lateral loads to which the member may be subjected, such as wind, dead load, or the weight of workmen and equipment, are taken into account by using the provision for combined compression and bending . . ."

Welding of compression members is generally confined to locations at the points of support. Such welds have little effect on the column strength as long as the length, L, is considered to be the full length between points of lateral support. For this reason, the allowable stresses for welded columns are the same as those for non-welded columns, except that the horizontal cutoff on the curve for short columns is lower because of the lower yield strength of the welded material. There are three cases, however, where additional account may need to be taken of the effect of welding on column strength: (a) columns with transverse welds at locations other than the supports (say, farther than 0.05 L from the ends), (b) cantilever columns with transverse welds at or near the supported end and (c) columns with longitudinal welds affecting a large proportion of the column cross section (say, with the heat-affected area exceeding 15 per cent of the total area). In the above cases, the effect of welding on column strength can be taken into account by using an increased slenderness ratio, L_w/r, in the column formulas, as indicated by the following equations:

If $\dfrac{L}{r} \geq \sqrt{\dfrac{250,000}{F_{cyw}}}$,

$$\frac{L_w}{r} = \frac{L}{r} \tag{4a}$$

If $\dfrac{L}{r} < \sqrt{\dfrac{250,000}{F_{cyw}}}$,

$$\frac{L_w}{r} = \frac{L}{r} \sqrt{\frac{1 + 100 \dfrac{L_h}{L}}{1 + \left(\dfrac{L_h}{L}\right)\left(\dfrac{L}{r}\right)^2\left(\dfrac{F_{cyw}}{2500}\right)}} \tag{4b}$$

where L = length of column between points of lateral support or twice the length of a cantilever column, in.

L_w = increased length to be substituted in column formula to determine allowable stress for welded column, in.

L_h = total length of portion of column lying within 1.0 in. of a weld (excluding welds at ends of columns that are supported at both ends), in.

r = least radius of gyration of column, in.

F_{cyw} = compressive yield strength across a butt weld, based on 0.2 per cent offset in a 10-in. gage length, ksi

To obtain allowable column stresses for any of Cases (a), (b) or (c) described in the preceding paragraph, the ratio L_w/r is substituted for L/r in the formulas for allowable stresses in welded columns. Eqs 4a and 4b are based on the assumption that the entire cross section within the length L_h is affected by the heat of welding. If only part of the cross section is so affected, the allowable stress based on L_w/r is substituted for F_w in Eq 3.

Example No. 3 — Column Buckling

Design a single-angle chord member for a latticed structure to carry a compressive load of 30 kips with a factor of safety consistent with specifications for building structures. Use alloy 6061-T6.

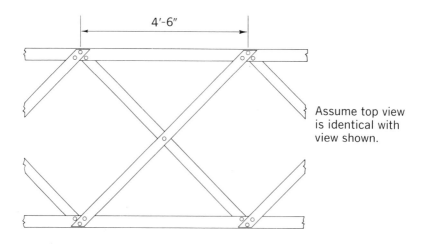

4'-6"

Assume top view is identical with view shown.

Try a $4 \times 4 \times 3/8$-in. angle

$$A = 2.86 \text{ in.}^2$$

$$\text{Least } r = 0.78 \text{ in.}$$

$$\frac{L}{r} = \frac{54}{0.78} = 69.2$$

From Table 1, 6061-T6, Specification No. 7 (nonwelded), $S_2 = 67$.

Since $L/r > S_2$, the allowable stress is

$$\frac{51,000}{(L/r)^2} = \frac{51,000}{(69.2)^2} = 10.6 \text{ ksi}$$

The actual stress, P/A, is $30/2.86 = 10.5$ ksi. The member is satisfactory from the standpoint of column buckling. It should also be checked on the basis of local buckling, using Specification 8 (see Example 5).

Example No. 4—Welded Compression Member

A 9-ft-long, 6-in.-OD by 1/4-in. wall tube of 6070-T6 is used as a compression member in a welded frame. It is joined to the surrounding structure by circumferential welds at the ends. What is the allowable compressive stress, using factors of safety for building structures?

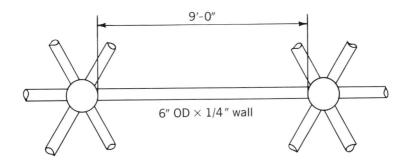

$$r = 2.035 \text{ in.}$$

$$\frac{L}{r} = \frac{9 \times 12}{2.035} = 53.1$$

Allowable stresses for sections within 1.0 in. of the welds at the ends are determined from Table 1, 6070-T6, Specification 7 (welded), while allowable stresses at other locations in the member would be determined from Specification 7 (nonwelded). The former values will govern the permissible load on the member, since the allowable stresses at welds are always equal to or less than the allowable stresses at other locations. From Specification 7 (welded), $S_2 = 59$. Since $L/r < 59$, the allowable stress is 14.5 ksi. The member should also be checked by Specification 10 (see Example 6).

COLUMN COMPONENTS (Specifications 8, 9 and 10)

These specifications are based on the application of the factor of safety on ultimate strength to the local buckling strength of plates and tubes. Welding has relatively little effect on the local buckling strength of plates, so the allowable stresses for welded plates in compression are the same as for nonwelded plates, with the exception of a lower cutoff because of the effect of the welding on yield strength. Circumferential welds in tubes can have an appreciable effect on local buckling strength, however, and this is taken into account by using the inelastic buckling coefficient formulas from Table 8 with the weld yield strength F_{cyw}, substituted for F_y in the formula.

In some cases it is permissible to allow higher stresses on plate components than are given in Specifications 8 and 9, as discussed under "Crippling Strength of Thin Sections."

Example No. 5 – Compressive Local Buckling of Angle Section

Check the $4 \times 4 \times 3/8$-in. angle member of alloy 6061-T6 in Example 3 for allowable stress based on local buckling.

$$\frac{b}{t} = \frac{4 - 0.375}{0.375} = 9.7$$

From Table 1, 6061-T6, Specification 8 (nonwelded), $S_1 = 5.5$ and $S_2 = 12$. Since $S_1 < b/t < S_2$, the allowable stress is

$$23.7 - 0.86 \frac{b}{t} = 23.7 - 0.86 \times 9.7$$

$$= 15.4 \text{ ksi}$$

Since the actual compressive stress is 10.5 ksi, the member is satisfactory from the standpoint of local buckling.

Example No. 6 – Compressive Local Buckling of Round Tube

Determine the allowable compressive stress based on local buckling for the tubular member in Example 4.

$$\frac{R}{t} = \frac{3}{0.25} = 12$$

From Table 1, 6070-T6, Specification 10 (welded), $S_1 = 7.7$ and $S_2 = 247$. Since $7.7 < R/t < 247$, the allowable stress is

$$16.3 - 0.65\sqrt{R/t} = 16.3 - 0.65\sqrt{12}$$

$$= 14.0 \text{ ksi}$$

This value governs the design since it is less than the allowable stress from Specification 7 found in Example 4.

COMPRESSION IN BEAMS (Specifications 11 to 14)

To obtain the allowable stresses for beams in Specifications 11, 13 and 14, the factor of safety on ultimate strength is applied to the stress that will cause lateral-torsional buckling. The local buckling strength of tubes in bending governs the allowable values in Specification 12.

The constants in the formulas for inelastic buckling of single-web shapes and rectangular tubes (Specifications 11 and 14) are the same as the constants in the column formula, B_c and D_c. Higher buckling stresses are obtained for round tubes and solid rectangular shapes because of the "shape factor" effect, and this is taken into account in the buckling formula constants (see Table 8). For tubes whose ratio of radius to thickness, R_b/t, exceeds C_{tb}, the bending stress to cause failure can be considered to be the same as the strength in axial compression. The quantity C_{tb} is equal to the slenderness limit S_2 in Specification 12 of Table 1. For tubes in bending, therefore, Specification 12 is used if R_b/t is less than S_2; otherwise Specification 10 for tubes in end compression applies. Table 8 gives the formula for C_{tb} which was used in calculating the values of S_2 in Specification 12. These values lie between the slenderness limits S_1 and S_2 given in Specification 10 for tubes in axial compression.

The formulas of Specification 11 for single-web beams and girders are based on an approximation in which the term L_b/r_y replaces a more complicated expression involving several different properties of the beam cross section. Because of this approximation, the formulas give very conservative results for certain conditions, namely for values of L_b/r_y exceeding about 50; for load distributions such that the bending moment near the center of the beam is appreciably less than the maximum bending moment in the beam; and for beams with transverse loads applied to the bottom flange. If the designer wishes to compute more precise values of allowable compressive stress for these cases, the value of r_y in Specification 11 may be replaced by an "effective r_y" given by one of the following formulas:

Beam spans subjected to end moment only or to transverse loads applied at the neutral axis of the beam:

$$\text{Effective } r_y = \frac{k_b}{1.7}\sqrt{\frac{I_y d}{S_c}}\sqrt{1 + 0.152\frac{J}{I_y}\left(\frac{L_b}{d}\right)^2} \tag{5}$$

Beams subjected to transverse loads applied on the top or bottom flange (where the load is free to move laterally with the beam if the beam should buckle):

$$\text{Effective } r_y = \frac{k_b}{1.7}\sqrt{\frac{I_y d}{S_c}}\left[\pm 0.5 + \sqrt{1.25 + 0.152\frac{J}{I_y}\left(\frac{L_b}{d}\right)^2}\right] \tag{6}$$

The plus sign in front of the term "0.5" applies if the load is on the bottom flange; the minus sign if the load is on the top flange.

Values of the coefficient k_b in the above formulas are tabulated below:

Description of Loading	Value of Coefficient k_b
Beams restrained against lateral displacement at both ends of span	
Uniform bending moment, uniform transverse load, or two equal concentrated loads equidistant from the center of the span	1.00
Bending moment varying uniformly from a value of M_1 at one end to M_2 at the other end	
$\quad M_1/M_2 = 0.5$	1.14
$\quad M_1/M_2 = 0$	1.33
$\quad M_1/M_2 = -0.5$	1.53
$\quad M_1/M_2 = -1.0$	1.60
Concentrated load at center of span	1.16
Cantilever beams	
Concentrated load at end of span	1.13
Uniform transverse load	1.43

The other terms appearing in Eqs 5 and 6 are defined as follows:

Effective r_y = value to be substituted for r_y in Specification 11, in.

I_y = moment of inertia of beam about axis parallel to web, in.^{4}

d = depth of beam, in.

S_c = section modulus of beam, compression side, in.^{3}

J = torsion constant of beam, in.^{4} (Values of J for standard structural shapes are published in the *Alcoa Structural Handbook*. For other shapes, an approximate value of J may be calculated by assuming the section to be composed of rectangles and letting J equal the sum of the terms $bt^3/3$ for each rectangle, in which b is the length and t the thickness of the rectangle, both in inches. The value of J for a built-up member is the sum of the values of J for the sections of which it is composed.)

L_b = length of beam between points at which the compression flange is supported against lateral movement, or length of cantilever beam from free end to point at which the compression flange is supported against lateral movement, in.

The effect of welding on allowable compressive stresses for beams is analogous to the effect on similar shapes loaded in direct compression.

Example No. 7 — Lateral-Torsional Buckling of Beam

If the compression flange of the welded girder in Example 2 is supported against lateral bending at points 6 ft apart, is the compressive stress within allowable limits for bridge structures?

To obtain r_y, consider both flanges the same as the compression flange.

$$I_y = 2 \times \frac{1}{12} \times 1 \times (16)^3 = 683 \text{ in.}^4$$

$$A = 2 \times 16 \times 1 + 48 \times \frac{3}{8} = 50 \text{ in.}^2$$

$$r_y = \sqrt{\frac{I_y}{A}} = \sqrt{\frac{683}{50}} = 3.70 \text{ in.}$$

$$\frac{L_b}{r_y} = \frac{6 \times 12}{3.70} = 19.5$$

The heat-affected area, A_w, is the same as in Example 2, 2.75 in.^{2} The area of the compression flange is:

Flange plate:	$16 \times 1 =$	16.0
Web:	$\left(\frac{1}{3} \times 22.9 - 1\right) \times \frac{3}{8} =$	2.5
	$A =$	18.5 in.^{2}

$$\frac{A_w}{A} = \frac{2.75}{18.5} = 0.149$$

Since $A_w/A < 0.15$, the effect of welding may be neglected.

Values of S_1 and S_2 can be calculated from the formulas in Table 4. Since these values will be essentially the same for bridge structures as for building structures, they may also be read from Table 1. From Table 1, 5456-H321, Specification 11 (nonwelded), $S_1 = 12$ and $S_2 = 119$. Since $S_1 < L_b/r_y < S_2$, the allowable stress is (see Table 4, Specification 11, and Tables 6 and 9):

$$\frac{1}{n_u}\left(B_c - \frac{D_c L_b}{1.2 r_y}\right) = \frac{1}{2.2}\left(31.4 - \frac{0.212}{1.2} \times 19.5\right)$$

$$= 12.7 \text{ ksi}$$

$$\text{Actual stress} = \frac{M}{S} = \frac{11,000}{876} = 12.6 \text{ ksi}$$

Since $12.6 < 12.7$, the girder is satisfactory from the standpoint of overall buckling. It should also be checked on the basis of local buckling (see Example 8).

COMPRESSION IN BEAM COMPONENTS (Specifications 15 to 19)

As in the case of column components, the allowable stresses in these specifications are based on the local buckling strength. The effects of welding, also, are treated in the same way as for column components. This means that in the case of tubes with circumferential welds, the coefficients in the formulas for inelastic buckling strength are determined by the use of the formulas in Table 8 with the weld yield strength, F_{cyw}, substituted for F_y in the formulas.

Example No. 8 – Compressive Local Buckling of Beam Flange and Web

Check whether the compressive stresses in the flange and web of the girder in Examples 2 and 7 are within allowable limits based on local buckling. Use allowable stresses for bridge structures.

It was demonstrated in Example 7 that the effect on allowable stresses of the weld joining the web and flange on the compression side could be ignored.

Allowable Stress in Flange

$$\frac{b}{t} = \frac{(16 - 3/8)/2}{1} = 7.8$$

As explained in Example 7, values of S_1 and S_2 may be taken from Table 1, 5456-H321. From Specification 15 (nonwelded), $S_1 = 6.7$ and $S_2 = 20$. Since $S_1 < b/t < S_2$, the allowable stress is (see Table 4, Specification 15, and Tables 6 and 9):

$$\frac{1}{n_u}\left(B_p - 4.5 D_p \frac{b}{t}\right) = \frac{1}{2.2}(37.7 - 4.5 \times 0.278 \times 7.8)$$

$$= 12.7 \text{ ksi}$$

From Example 7, the actual stress is 12.6 ksi. Since $12.6 < 12.7$, this stress is satisfactory.

$$\frac{h}{t} = \frac{48}{3/8} = 128$$

From Specification 18 (nonwelded), $S_2 = 126$. Since $h/t > S_2$, the allowable stress is (see Table 4, Specification 18; Tables 6 and 9):

$$\frac{\pi^2 E}{n_a(0.6h/t)^2} = \frac{\pi^2 \times 10,400}{1.35(0.6 \times 128)^2}$$

$$= 12.9 \text{ ksi}$$

The maximum compressive stress in the web is

$$\frac{Mc}{I} = \frac{11,000 \times 21.9}{20,060} = 12.0 \text{ ksi}$$

The stress is within allowable limits.

SHEAR IN WEBS (Specifications 20 and 21)

The factor of safety that is applied to the shear buckling strength to obtain allowable stresses for unstiffened webs in Specification 20 is the factor of safety on ultimate strength, n_u. Shear buckling of unstiffened beam webs can cause collapse of the beam. Stiffened panels, however, can sustain loads much higher than the web buckling load, and the principal reason for guarding against shear buckling of such panels is to avoid the unsightly appearance of a wrinkled sheet at operating loads. For this reason, the factor of safety on the appearance of buckling, n_a, was used to establish allowable stresses in Specification 21. As in the case of the other specifications based on flat plate buckling, allowable stresses for the plates with the smaller h/t ratios are reduced if welding is used.

The required moment of inertia for transverse stiffeners to resist shear buckling of webs is:

$$\frac{s}{h} \leq 0.4 \qquad I_s = \frac{n_a V h^2}{22,400}\left(\frac{s}{h}\right) \tag{7a}$$

$$\frac{s}{h} > 0.4 \qquad I_s = \frac{n_a V h^2}{140,000}\left(\frac{h}{s}\right) \tag{7b}$$

where s = spacing of transverse stiffeners (clear distance between stiffeners for stiffeners composed of a pair of members, one on each side of the web; center-to-center distance between stiffeners composed of a member on one side of the web only), in.

h = clear height of web, in.

I_s = moment of inertia of transverse stiffener to resist shear buckling,* in.⁴

n_a = factor of safety on appearance of buckling

V = shear force on web at stiffener location, kips

Transverse stiffeners on webs at points of bearing should have a moment of inertia not less than

$$I_b = I_s + \frac{n_u P h^2}{\pi^2 E} \tag{8}$$

where I_b = required moment of inertia of bearing stiffener,* in.⁴

n_u = factor of safety on ultimate strength

P = local load concentration on bearing stiffener, kips

E = compressive modulus of elasticity, ksi

Longitudinal stiffeners are sometimes placed on thin-web girders to increase the resistance of the web to buckling under the influence of bending stresses. For greatest efficiency, such a stiffener should be located with the centroid 0.4 of the distance from the toe of the compression flange to the neutral axis of the girder. The moment of inertia should not be less than

$$I_h = 2\alpha f_f t h^3 \left[\left(1 + 6\frac{A_h}{ht}\right)\left(\frac{s}{h}\right)^2 + 0.4 \right] 10^{-6} \tag{9}$$

where I_h = moment of inertia of horizontal stiffener,* in.⁴

α = a factor equal to unity for a stiffener consisting of equal members on both sides of the web and equal to 3.5 for a stiffener consisting of a member on one side only

f_f = compressive stress at toe of girder flange, ksi

t = thickness of web, in.

A_h = gross area of cross section of horizontal stiffener, sq in.

---

* For a stiffener composed of members of equal size on both sides of the web, the moment of inertia is taken about the center line of the web. For a stiffener composed of a member on one side only, the moment of inertia is taken about the face of the web in contact with the stiffener.

Example No. 9—Shear in Beam Web

Can the girder of Examples 2, 7 and 8 support a shear load of 30 kips without intermediate stiffeners?

The section that controls the design is a horizontal section through the web within 1.0 in. of the weld at either flange. The allowable stress at a welded vertical splice would be the same.

$$\frac{h}{t} = \frac{48}{3/8} = 128$$

Since values of S_1 and S_2 are essentially the same for bridge structures as for building structures, they may be taken from Table 1, 5456-H321. Specification 20 (welded), gives $S_2 = 86$. Since $h/t > S_2$, the allowable stress is (from Table 4, Specification 20, and Tables 6 and 9):

$$\frac{\pi^2 E}{n_u(1.25h/t)^2} = \frac{\pi^2 \times 10,400}{2.2(1.25 \times 128)^2}$$

$$= 1.82 \text{ ksi}$$

The actual stress is $\dfrac{V}{A} = \dfrac{30}{48 \times 3/8} = 1.67$ ksi.

This means that the girder can support the given load without intermediate stiffeners.

SHEAR IN CONNECTIONS (Specifications 22 and 23)

As indicated by Table 5, allowable shear stresses on rivets, bolts and fillet welds are determined from the ultimate shear strength by applying a safety factor 20 per cent higher than the factor of safety generally applied to ultimate strength, n_u [1, 2].

The allowable shear stress in bolts is applied to the gross cross-sectional area of the bolt if there are no threads in the shear planes. Where threads extend into the shear planes, the allowable shear stress is applied to the root area of the bolt.

The effective diameter of rivets to be used in computing the shear area should be taken as the hole diameter, except that the effective diameter should not exceed the nominal diameter of the rivets by more than 4 per cent for cold-driven rivets or 7 per cent for hot-driven rivets.

If the filler metal used in fillet welds has the same strength as the parent metal, the shear strength of a fillet weld is controlled by the strength of the fillet. Where the filler metal is appreciably stronger than the parent metal, however, the shear strength of a fillet weld may be controlled by the strength of the parent metal adjacent to the fillet. For this reason, both the filler metal and parent metal strengths must be checked in determining an allowable shear stress as indicated in Table 5.

COMBINED COMPRESSION AND BENDING

Allowable stresses for members loaded in combined compression and bending can be determined with the aid of the following inter-action formulas, which apply either to bending introduced by initial eccentricity or crookedness or to bending introduced by lateral load. Combinations of stress such that the left-hand sides of the equations are less than unity are permissible.

Bending moment at center > 0.9 of maximum bending moment in span:

$$\frac{f_a}{F_a} + \frac{f_b}{F_b(1 - f_a/F_{ec})} \leq 1 \tag{10}$$

Bending moment at center < 0.5 of maximum bending moment in span:

$$\frac{f_a}{F_a} + \frac{f_b}{F_b} \leq 1 \tag{11}$$

Bending moment at center between 0.5 and 0.9 of maximum bend-ing moment in span:

$$\frac{f_a}{F_a} + \frac{f_b}{F_b[1 - (2M_c/M_m - 1)f_a/F_{ec}]} \leq 1 \tag{12}$$

where f_a = average compressive stress on cross section of member produced by axial compressive load, ksi

F_a = allowable compressive stress for member considered as an axially loaded column, ksi

f_b = maximum bending stress (compression) caused by transverse loads or end moments, ksi

F_b = allowable compressive stress for member considered as a beam, ksi

F_{ec} = $\pi^2 E/[n_u(L/r)^2]$, where L/r is slenderness ratio for mem-ber considered as a column tending to fail in the plane of the applied bending moments.

CRIPPLING STRENGTH OF THIN SECTIONS

The suggested allowable compressive stresses for flat-plate elements in Specifications 8, 9, 15 and 16 were established by applying the factor of safety on ultimate strength, n_u, to the local buckling strength. In some types of compression members, the local buckling stress is likely to be very close to the ultimate strength. This includes single angles, double angles, tees, cruciform sections, and outstanding flanges stiffened by lips or bulbs designed in accordance with Eq 14 or 15. The allowable stresses in such members cannot be permitted to exceed the values given in Table 1.

In other types of members, local buckling of thin elements does not necessarily bring about collapse. Examples are flat sections supported by webs on both sides, or outstanding flanges of beams. In such cases an element that has reached the local buckling stress may continue to carry load until failure eventually takes place by "crippling." The allowable stresses for these elements may be permitted to exceed the values given by Specifications 8, 9, 15 or 16, as discussed in the following paragraphs.

For flat plates supported on the two unloaded edges, as in Specifications 9 and 16, Table 1, conservative values of allowable stress, F_{cc}, based on crippling, can be determined from Eq 13a or 13b:

For all alloys except those that are artificially aged (All tempers except those beginning with -T5, -T6, -T7, -T8 or -T9):

$$\text{When } \frac{b}{t} \leq 0.35\frac{B_p}{D_p}, \qquad F_{cc} = F_1$$

$$\text{When } \frac{b}{t} > 0.35\frac{B_p}{D_p}, \qquad F_{cc} = \frac{1.25}{n_u}\sqrt{B_pE}\left(\frac{t}{b}\right) \tag{13a}$$

For artificially aged alloys (temper designations beginning with -T5, -T6, -T7, -T8 or -T9):

$$\text{When } \frac{b}{t} \leq 0.21\frac{B_p}{D_p}, \qquad F_{cc} = F_1$$

$$\text{When } \frac{b}{t} > 0.21\frac{B_p}{D_p}, \qquad F_{cc} = \frac{1.4}{n_u}\sqrt{B_pE}\left(\frac{t}{b}\right) \tag{13b}$$

F_1 is the allowable stress from Specification 9 or 16 (or Specification 8 or 15 in the case of outstanding flanges). Values of B_p, D_p

and E for various alloys are listed in Table 9. For the alloys covered in Table 1, limiting values of b/t and the corresponding expressions for F_{cc} for building structures are given in Table 11.

Eqs 13a and 13b may also be used to find allowable stresses based on crippling for flat-plate elements supported on only one unloaded edge, such as the flanges of H-sections, by substituting an equivalent width, b_e, for b in the formulas. Stress values that are consistent with Specifications 8 and 15 in Table 1 are obtained by letting b_e equal $3.1 \times b$ for components of columns and $2.8 \times b$ for components of beams, where the component is under uniform compression. The quantity b in the foregoing expressions is the clear width of the outstanding flange.

The allowable load based on crippling for a structural member is the sum of the allowable loads for the individual elements of the member.

If it is necessary to insure against a buckled appearance at design loads, the allowable stress should not exceed $(n_u/n_a) = 1.62$ times the allowable stress from Specification 8, 9, 15 or 16.

If a flat-plate element is a part of a column whose strength is controlled by overall column buckling, the allowable stress must not exceed the value given by Specification 7 in Table 1, as well as the stress from Eq 13a or 13b. Local buckling of flat-plate elements of a column causes a reduction in stiffness which may precipitate column failure before the crippling stress is reached. To take this into account, if the stress in a column is permitted to exceed the stress F_1 given by Specification 8, 9, 15 or 16, the slenderness ratio L/r should be multiplied by the ratio f_a/F_1, where f_a is the average stress on the column caused by the design load. This increased slenderness ratio, $(L/r)(f_a/F_1)$, should be used in place of L/r in checking the allowable stress in Specification 7.

Single-web beams with thin flanges are usually restrained against lateral buckling. If not, and if the stress is permitted to exceed the allowable value in Specification 15 or 16, the effect of local buckling on overall buckling can be checked in the same way as for a column. That is, the quantity $(L_b/r_y)(f_b/F_1)$ is substituted for L_b/r_y in Specification 11, where f_b is stress in the compression flange caused by the design load.

The provisions of this section differ somewhat from the specifications published by ASCE [1, 2], but agree satisfactorily with test results reported in Refs 6, 7 and 8.

STIFFENERS FOR FLAT PLATES IN COMPRESSION

It is possible to increase the allowable stress on outstanding flanges by reinforcing the free edge of the flange with a lip or bulb. The extrusion process permits such stiffening devices to be used readily on extruded shapes. It is also common to stiffen the free edges of formed sheet products by bending the edge to form a lip.

It is usually advantageous to make the stiffening lip large enough so that the compressive buckling stress of the stiffened flange is equal to that of a plate simply supported on both unloaded edges. If the thickness of the stiffening lip is the same as that of the supported flange, as in the case of formed-sheet construction, the clear width of the stiffening lip required for this purpose is given by the following formula:

$$b_L = \frac{b}{3} \text{ or } 8t, \text{ whichever is smaller} \tag{14}$$

where b_L = clear width of lip, in.
b = clear width of flange, in.
t = thickness of flange, in.

A more general formula, which does not require that the thickness of the stiffening lip be the same as that of the flange, is the following:

$$r_L = \frac{b}{5.2} \text{ or } 4.6t, \text{ whichever is smaller} \tag{15}$$

where r_L = radius of gyration of lip or bulb about face of flange from which lip projects, in.

If Eq 15 is used, the local buckling strength of the lip itself should also be checked.

Where plates are supported on two edges, such as the compression flange of a box beam, it may be advantageous to add intermediate longitudinal stiffeners to increase the allowable stress. Such stiffeners can be treated as columns and the allowable compressive stresses determined from Specification 7.

In computing the radius of gyration of a longitudinal stiffener for use in the column formulas, the stiffeners should be considered to consist of the stiffening member itself plus the width of attached sheet equal to the spacing between the stiffeners. The effective length of the stiffener may generally be taken to be the distance between points at which the stiffener is supported against movement in the direction normal to the plane of the plate.

In the case of long panels with relatively few stiffeners, the effective slenderness ratio may be less than that described above because of the restraining effect of the plate. The reduced effective slenderness ratio for such stiffeners is given by the equation below. This reduced effective slenderness ratio should be used whenever its value is less than the actual value of L/r for the stiffener.

$$\lambda_s = \frac{4N}{\sqrt{3}}\left(\frac{w}{t}\right)\sqrt{\frac{1 + A_s/(wt)}{1 + \sqrt{1 + 32I_e/(3t^3w)}}} \tag{16}$$

where λ_s = equivalent slenderness ratio for stiffener

N = total number of panels into which the longitudinal stiffeners divide the plate

w = stiffener spacing, in.

t = thickness of plate, in.

I_e = moment of inertia of plate-stiffener combination (using an effective width of plate equal to w), in.⁴

A_s = area of stiffener (not including any of the plate), in.²

The above formula does not appear in ASCE Papers 3341 and 3342 [1, 2], but can be derived from the information given in [9].

Example No. 10 — Compression in Longitudinal Stiffener

The extruded 6061-T6 beam shown in the sketch is subjected to bending forces that put compression in the top side. Check whether the beam can carry a bending moment of 100 in.-kips using allowable stresses for building structures.

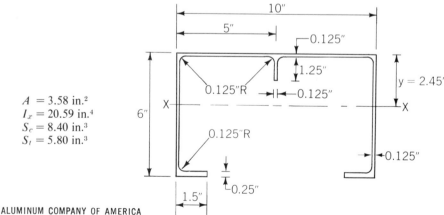

$A = 3.58$ in.²
$I_x = 20.59$ in.⁴
$S_c = 8.40$ in.³
$S_t = 5.80$ in.³

Allowable Tensile Stress

From Table 1, 6061-T6, Specification 1 (nonwelded), the allowable tensile stress is 19 ksi. The actual stress is

$$\frac{M}{S_t} = \frac{100}{5.80} = 17.2 \text{ ksi}$$

The tensile stress is satisfactory.

Allowable Compressive Stress

   Thin-Plate Elements

$$\frac{b}{t} = \frac{4.81}{0.125} = 38.5$$

From Table 1, 6061-T6, Specification 16 (nonwelded), the allowable stress is

$$\frac{19{,}200}{(b/t)^2} = \frac{19{,}200}{(38.5)^2} = 13.0 \text{ ksi}$$

   Stiffener-Plate Combination

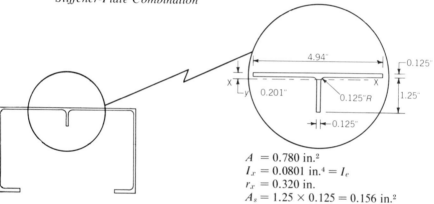

$A = 0.780$ in.^{2}
$I_x = 0.0801$ in.$^4 = I_e$
$r_x = 0.320$ in.
$A_s = 1.25 \times 0.125 = 0.156$ in.^{2}

From Eq 16

$$\lambda_s = \frac{4 \times 2}{\sqrt{3}}\left(\frac{4.94}{0.125}\right)\sqrt{\frac{1 + 0.156/(4.94 \times 0.125)}{1 + \sqrt{1 + \frac{32 \times 0.0801}{3(0.125)^3 \times 4.94}}}}$$

$$= 63.2$$

(The column strength of the stiffener is governed by λ_s unless the actual L/r for the stiffener is less than λ_s. For this example, λ_s governs as long as the unsupported length L exceeds $\lambda_s r_x = 63.2 \times 0.320 = 20$ in.)

From Table 1, 6061-T6, Specification 7 (nonwelded) the allowable stress is

$$20.4 - 0.135 \times 63.2 = 11.9 \text{ ksi}$$

The actual stress is

$$\frac{M}{S_c} = \frac{100}{8.40} = 11.9 \text{ ksi}$$

The member is satisfactory.

References

[1] Task Committee on Lightweight Alloys, "Suggested Specifications for Structures of Aluminum Alloys 6061-T6 and 6062-T6," *Paper No. 3341, Proceedings of the ASCE, Journal of the Structural Division,* December 1962, p. 1.

[2] Task Committee on Lightweight Alloys, "Suggested Specifications for Structures of Aluminum Alloy 6063-T5 and 6063-T6," *Paper No. 3342, Proceedings of the ASCE, Journal of the Structural Division,* December 1962, p. 47.

[3] J. W. Clark and R. L. Rolf, "Design of Aluminum Tubular Members," *Paper No. 4184, Proceedings of the ASCE, Journal of the Structural Division,* December 1964, p. 259.

[4] "Qualification Standard for Welding Procedures, Welders and Welding Operators," *ASME Boiler and Pressure Vessel Code,* Section IX, 1962, Par. QN-6, p. 18.

[5] H. N. Hill, J. W. Clark and R. J. Brungraber, "Design of Welded Aluminum Structures," *Transactions of the ASCE,* Vol. 127, Part II, 1962, p. 102.

[6] George Gerard, *Handbook of Structural Stability,* Part IV — "Failure of Plates and Composite Elements," Technical Note No. 3784, National Advisory Committee for Aeronautics, August 1957.

[7] W. F. Conley, L. A. Becker and R. B. Allnutt, *Buckling and Ultimate Strength of Plating Loaded in Edge Compression,* Progress Report 2 — "Unstiffened Panels," Report 1682. Department of the Navy, David Taylor Model Basin, May 1963.

[8] P. P. Bijlaard and G. P. Fisher, "Column Strength of H-Sections and Square Tubes in Postbuckling Range of Component Plates," Technical Note 2994, National Advisory Committee for Aeronautics, August 1953.

[9] Paul Seide and Manuel Stein, "Compressive Buckling of Simply Supported Plates with Longitudinal Stiffeners," Technical Note No. 1825, National Advisory Committee for Aeronautics, March 1949.

PART II TABLES

Notation

a_1 = shorter dimension of rectangular shear panel, in.

a_2 = longer dimension of rectangular shear panel, in.

a_e = $a_1/\sqrt{1 + 0.7\,(a_1/a_2)^2}$

A = net area of cross section of a tension member or tension flange of a beam, or gross area of cross section of a compression member or compression flange of a beam, sq in. (A beam flange is considered to consist of that portion of the member farther than $2c/3$ from the neutral axis, where c is the distance from the neutral axis to the extreme fiber.)

A_h = gross area of cross section of horizontal stiffener, sq in.

A_s = area of stiffener (not including any of the plate), in.^{2}

A_w = area within area A that lies within 1.0 in. of a weld, sq in.

b = clear width of outstanding flange or of flat plate supported on both unloaded edges, in.

b_L = clear width of lip, in.

B = coefficient in inelastic buckling formula, depending upon the stress-strain characteristics of the material, the type of member and the loading conditions, ksi. B_b, B_c, B_p, B_s, B_t, B_{tb} are values of B given by equations in Table 8.

c = distance from neutral axis to extreme fiber, in.

C = value of slenderness ratio or equivalent slenderness ratio at intersection of elastic and inelastic buckling curves. C_b, C_c, C_p, C_s, C_t, C_{tb} are values of C given by equations in Table 8.

d = depth of beam, in.

d_1 = distance from toe of compression flange to neutral axis, in.

D = coefficient in inelastic buckling formula, depending upon the stress-strain characteristics of the material, the type of member and the loading conditions, ksi. D_b, D_c, D_p, D_s, D_t, D_{tb} are values of D given by equations in Table 8.

E = compressive modulus of elasticity, ksi

f_a = average compressive stress on cross section of member produced by axial compressive load, ksi

f_b = maximum bending stress (compression) caused by transverse loads or end moments, ksi

f_c = compressive stress on flat plate, based on design loads and gross area, ksi

f_f = compressive stress at toe of girder flange, ksi

F_a = allowable compressive stress for member considered as an axially loaded column, ksi

F_b = allowable compressive stress for member considered as a beam, ksi

F_{bu} = bearing ultimate strength, ksi

F_{buw} = bearing ultimate strength within 1.0 in. of a weld, ksi

F_{by} = bearing yield strength, ksi

F_{byw} = bearing yield strength within 1.0 in. of a weld, ksi

F_c = allowable compressive or shear stress for slenderness less than S_1, ksi

F_{cc} = allowable compressive stress based on crippling strength of thin, flat sections, ksi

F_{cr} = buckling stress, ksi

F_{cy} = compressive yield strength, ksi

F_{cyw} = compressive yield strength across a butt weld (0.2 per cent offset in 10-in. gage length), ksi

F_e = allowable compressive or shear stress for slenderness greater than S_2 (value of F_e is controlled by elastic buckling), ksi

F_{ec} = $\pi^2 E/[n_u(L/r)^2]$, where L/r is slenderness ratio for member considered as a column tending to fail in the plane of the applied bending moments, ksi

F_n = allowable stress for cross section if there were no welds present, ksi

F_{pw} = allowable stress on cross section, part of whose area lies within 1.0 in. of a weld, ksi

F_{su} = shear ultimate strength, ksi

F_{suw} = shear ultimate strength within 1.0 in. of a weld, ksi

F_{sy} = shear yield strength, ksi

F_{syw} = shear yield strength within 1.0 in. of a weld, ksi

F_{tu} = tensile ultimate strength, ksi

F_{tuw} = tensile ultimate strength across a butt weld, ksi

F_{ty} = tensile yield strength, ksi

F_{tyw} = tensile yield strength across a butt weld (0.2 per cent offset in 10-in. gage length), ksi

F_w = allowable stress for cross section if entire area were within 1.0 in. of a weld, ksi

F_y = either F_{ty} or F_{cy}, whichever is smaller, ksi

F_1 = allowable stress on flat plate, based on Specification 8, 9, 15 or 16, ksi

g = spacing of rivet or bolt holes perpendicular to direction of load, in.

h = clear height of shear web, in.

I = moment of inertia of a beam, in.^{4}

I_b = required moment of inertia of bearing stiffener,* in.^{4}

I_e = moment of inertia of plate-stiffener combination, in.^{4}

I_h = moment of inertia of horizontal stiffener,[1] in.^{4}

I_s = moment of inertia of transverse stiffener to resist shear buckling,* in.^{4}

I_x = moment of inertia of a beam about axis perpendicular to web, in.^{4}

I_y = moment of inertia of a beam about axis parallel to web, in.^{4}

J = torsion constant of a beam, in.^{4}

k_b = coefficient depending on type of loading on a beam

k_c = coefficient given in Table 7

k_t = coefficient given in Table 7

L = length of compression member between points of lateral support, or twice the length of a cantilever column (except where analysis shows that a shorter length can be used), in.

L_b = length of beam between points at which the compression flange is supported against lateral movement, or length of cantilever beam from free end to point at which the compression flange is supported against lateral movement, in.

L_h = total length of portion of column lying within 1.0 in. of a weld (excluding welds at ends of columns that are supported at both ends), in.

L_w = increased length to be substituted in column formula to determine allowable stress for welded column, in.

M = bending moment, in.-kips

M_c = bending moment at center of span resulting from applied bending loads, in.-kips

M_m = maximum bending moment in span resulting from applied bending loads, in.-kips

---

* For a stiffener composed of members of equal size on both sides of the web, the moment of inertia is taken about the center line of the web. For a stiffener composed of a member on one side only, the moment of inertia is taken about the face of the web in contact with the stiffener.

$\left.\begin{matrix} M_1 \\ M_2 \end{matrix}\right\}$ = bending moments at two ends of a beam, in.-kips

n_a = factor of safety on appearance of buckling

n_u = factor of safety on ultimate strength

n_y = factor of safety on yielding

N = total number of panels into which the longitudinal stiffeners divide the plate

P = local load concentration on bearing stiffener, kips

r = least radius of gyration of a column, in.

r_L = radius of gyration of lip or bulb about face of flange from which lip projects, in.

r_y = radius of gyration of a beam (about axis parallel to web), in. (For beams that are unsymmetrical about the horizontal axis, r_y should be calculated as though both flanges were the same as the compression flange.)

R = outside radius of round tube or maximum outside radius for an oval tube, in.

R_b = outside radius of a round tube in bending or outside radius at the location of the critical compressive stress for an oval tube in bending, in.

s = spacing of transverse stiffeners (clear distance between stiffeners for stiffeners composed of a pair of members, one on each side of the web, center-to-center distance between stiffeners composed of a member on one side of the web only), in.; also spacing of rivet or bolt holes parallel to direction of load, in.

S_c = section modulus of a beam, compression side, in.^{3}

S_t = section modulus of a beam, tension side, in.^{3}

$\left.\begin{matrix} S_1 \\ S_2 \\ S_3 \end{matrix}\right\}$ = limiting slenderness values (see Table 4)

t = thickness of flange, plate, web or tube, in. (For tapered flanges, t is the average thickness.)

V = shear force on web at stiffener location, kips

w = spacing of longitudinal stiffeners, in.; also uniform load, psi

α = a factor equal to unity for a stiffener consisting of equal members on both sides of the web and equal to 3.5 for a stiffener consisting of a member on one side only

λ = slenderness ratio or equivalent slenderness ratio

λ_s = equivalent slenderness ratio for stiffener

Introduction to Table 1

The allowable stresses in Table 1 are suggested for application to building structures, since they are based on factors of safety recommended for the building field by the ASCE Task Committee on Lightweight Alloys. These factor-of-safety values are listed in the last column of Table 6. The allowable stresses in Table 1 can be used, of course, in designing any other structure for which similar factors of safety are ordinarily used.

Two sets of suggested allowable stresses are presented in each of the specifications in Table 1 (except in the case of alloy 2014-T6, which is not generally welded). The first set applies to all nonwelded structures, and to welded structures at locations outside the heat-affected zone. The second set of suggested allowable stresses, designated by shading, applies to regions within the heat-affected zone, which for design purposes is considered to extend for a distance of 1.0 in. on either side of the center line of a butt weld or the root of a fillet weld.

Where the term "flat plate" is used in Table 1, it refers to any flat element, regardless of whether the element is fabricated from plate (thickness of 0.250 in. or greater) or sheet (thickness less than 0.250 in.), or is part of an extrusion.

The allowable stresses in Table 1 for alloys 6061-T6, 6063-T5 and 6063-T6, were taken directly from ASCE Papers 3341 and 3342. The following notes apply to these tables:

① These allowable stresses apply to all material welded with 5356 or 5556 filler alloy and to material 3/8 in. or less in thickness welded with 4043 or 5554 filler alloy. For thicker material welded with 4043 or 5554 filler alloy, these allowable stresses should be reduced by multiplying them by 0.8. Allowable stresses not marked with a superscript apply to material welded with either 4043, 5356, 5554 or 5556 filler alloy. These recommendations are similar to those found in ASCE Paper 3341 [1], except that filler alloy 5554 has been added.

② These slenderness limits apply to all material welded with 5356 or 5556 filler alloy and to material 3/8 in. or less in thickness welded with 4043 or 5554 filler alloy. For thicker material welded with 4043 or 5554 filler alloy, these slenderness limits must be adjusted to correspond to the reduced values of maximum allowable stresses indicated in Note ① above.

TABLE 1—SUGGESTED ALLOWABLE STRESSES

(SEE INTRODUCTION TO TABLE 1, p. 41)

1100-H14 — Sheet and Plate, Rolled Rod and Bar, Drawn Tube
ANOCLAD TYPE 11-H14 — Sheet

In each stress column, the two values given correspond to **1100-H14** and **ANOCLAD TYPE 11-H14** respectively (shaded values are for ANOCLAD TYPE 11-H14).

Type of Stress	Type of Member or Component	Spec. No.	Allowable Stress, ksi (Slenderness ≤ S_1)	Slenderness Limit, S_1	Allowable Stress, ksi (Slenderness Between S_1 and S_2)	Slenderness Limit, S_2	Allowable Stress, ksi (Slenderness ≥ S_2)
TENSION, axial, net section	Any tension member	1	8 / 2.7				
TENSION IN BEAMS, extreme fiber, net section	Structural shapes, rectangular tubes, built-up members bent about X-axis	2	8 / 2.7				
	Round or oval tubes	3	10 / 3.2				
	Rectangular bars, plates, outstanding flanges of shapes bent about Y-axis	4	11 / 3.5				
BEARING	On rivets and bolts	5	12.5 / 4.8				
	On milled surfaces and pins	6	8.5 / 3.2				
COMPRESSION IN COLUMNS, axial, gross section	Columns (also see Specs. 8 to 10)	7	7 / 2.7	$\frac{L}{r}=12$ / ---	$7.4-0.034\frac{L}{r}$ / 2.7	$\frac{L}{r}=144$ / $\frac{L}{r}=137$	$\frac{51,000}{(L/r)^2}$ / $\frac{51,000}{(L/r)^2}$
	Components of columns (also see Spec. 7): Outstanding flanges and legs	8	7 / 2.7	$\frac{b}{t}=7.4$ / ---	$8.7-0.23\frac{b}{t}$ / 2.7	$\frac{b}{t}=26$ / $\frac{b}{t}=27$	$\frac{1,940}{(b/t)^2}$ / $\frac{1,940}{(b/t)^2}$
	Flat plates with both edges supported	9	7 / 2.7	$\frac{b}{t}=24$ / ---	$8.7-0.072\frac{b}{t}$ / 2.7	$\frac{b}{t}=82$ / $\frac{b}{t}=84$	$\frac{19,200}{(b/t)^2}$ / $\frac{19,200}{(b/t)^2}$
	Curved plates supported on both edges, walls of round or oval tubes	10	7 / 2.7	$\frac{R}{t}=35$ / $\frac{R}{t}=2.5$	$8.6-0.27\sqrt{\frac{R}{t}}$ / $2.8-0.063\sqrt{\frac{R}{t}}$	$\frac{R}{t}=460$ / $\frac{R}{t}=1160$	$\frac{3,200}{\frac{R}{t}\left(1+\frac{\sqrt{R/t}}{35}\right)}$ / $\frac{3,200}{\frac{R}{t}\left(1+\frac{\sqrt{R/t}}{35}\right)}$
COMPRESSION IN BEAMS, extreme fiber, gross section	Single-web beams bent about X-axis. Extreme fibers of beams (also see Specs. 15 to 19)	11	7 / 2.7	$\frac{L_b}{r_y}=14$ / $\frac{L_b}{r_y}=162$	$7.4-0.029\frac{L_b}{r_y}$ / $7.4-0.029\frac{L_b}{r_y}$	$\frac{L_b}{r_y}=173$ / $\frac{L_b}{r_y}=173$	$\frac{74,000}{(L_b/r_y)^2}$ / $\frac{74,000}{(L_b/r_y)^2}$
	Round or oval tubes	12	9 / 3.2	$\frac{R_b}{t}=36$ / $\frac{R_b}{t}=55$	$12.9-0.65\sqrt{\frac{R_b}{t}}$ / $4.3-0.148\sqrt{\frac{R_b}{t}}$	$\frac{R_b}{t}=133$ / $\frac{R_b}{t}=280$	Same as Specification No. 10 (See p. 21)

Table — DESIGN STRESSES FOR ALUMINUM

Category	No.	Section	value	lower limit	formula	upper limit	allowable stress
COMPRESSION IN BEAMS, extreme fiber, gross section	13	Solid rectangular beams bent about X-axis	10	$\frac{a}{t}\sqrt{\frac{L_b}{d}}=10$	$11.6-0.155\,\frac{a}{t}\sqrt{\frac{L_b}{d}}$	$\frac{a}{t}\sqrt{\frac{L_b}{d}}=50$	$\frac{20,000}{(d/t)^2(L_b/d)}$
		(shaded)	3.5	3.5	3.5	$\frac{d}{t}\sqrt{\frac{L_b}{d}}=53$	$\frac{9,700}{(d/t)^2(L_b/d)}$
Extreme fibers of beams (also see Specs. 15 to 19)	14	Rectangular tubes and box sections	7	$\frac{L_bS_c}{I_y}=53$	$7.4-0.055\sqrt{\frac{L_bS_c}{I_y}}$	$\frac{L_bS_c}{I_y}=8100$	$\frac{20,000}{(L_bS_c/I_y)}$
		(shaded)	2.7	$\frac{L_bS_c}{I_y}=7300$	$7.4-0.055\sqrt{\frac{L_bS_c}{I_y}}$	$\frac{L_bS_c}{I_y}=8100$	$\frac{20,000}{(L_bS_c/I_y)}$
COMPRESSION IN BEAMS, component under uniform compression (also see Specs. 11 to 14)	15	Outstanding flanges	7	$\frac{b}{t}=8.6$	$8.7-0.198\,\frac{b}{t}$	$\frac{b}{t}=30$	$\frac{2,500}{(b/t)^2}$
		(shaded)	2.7	---	2.7	$\frac{b}{t}=30$	$\frac{2,500}{(b/t)^2}$
	16	Flat plates with both edges supported	7	$\frac{b}{t}=24$	$8.7-0.072\,\frac{b}{t}$	$\frac{b}{t}=82$	$\frac{19,200}{(b/t)^2}$
		(shaded)	2.7	---	2.7	$\frac{b}{t}=84$	$\frac{19,200}{(b/t)^2}$
	17	Flat plates with compression edge free, tension edge supported	10	$\frac{b}{t}=6.7$	$11.6-0.24\,\frac{b}{t}$	$\frac{b}{t}=33$	$\frac{4,200}{(b/t)^2}$
		(shaded)	3.5	---	3.5	$\frac{b}{t}=35$	$\frac{4,200}{(b/t)^2}$
COMPRESSION IN BEAMS, component under bending in its own plane (also see Specs. 11 to 14)	18	Flat plates with both edges supported	7	---	7	$\frac{h}{t}=181$	$\frac{230,000}{(h/t)^2}$
		(shaded)	2.7	---	2.7	$\frac{h}{t}=290$	$\frac{230,000}{(h/t)^2}$
	19	Flat plates with horizontal stiffener, both edges supported	7	$\frac{h}{t}=370$	$18.8-0.032\,\frac{h}{t}$	$\frac{h}{t}=400$	$\frac{990,000}{(h/t)^2}$
		(shaded)	2.7	---	2.7	$\frac{h}{t}=610$	$\frac{990,000}{(h/t)^2}$
SHEAR IN WEBS, gross section	20	Unstiffened flat webs	4.8	$\frac{h}{t}=22$	$5.4-0.027\,\frac{h}{t}$	$\frac{h}{t}=134$	$\frac{33,000}{(h/t)^2}$
		(shaded)	1.5	---	1.5	$\frac{h}{t}=148$	$\frac{33,000}{(h/t)^2}$
	21	Stiffened flat webs	4.8	$\frac{a_e}{t}=91$	$8.8-0.044\,\frac{a_e}{t}$	$\frac{a_e}{t}=134$	$\frac{53,000}{(a_e/t)^2}$
		(shaded)	1.5	---	1.5	$\frac{a_e}{t}=188$	$\frac{53,000}{(a_e/t)^2}$

$$a_e = a_1/\sqrt{1+0.7\,(a_1/a_2)^2}$$

NONSHADED BARS apply to nonwelded members and to welded members at locations farther than 1.0 in. from a weld.

SHADED BARS apply within 1.0 in. of a weld.

TABLE 1–SUGGESTED ALLOWABLE STRESSES

Material: **2014-T6, -T651** — Sheet and Plate, Extrusions, Rolled Rod and Bar, Drawn Tube; **ALCLAD 2014-T6, -T651** — Sheet and Plate (applies to the slenderness columns).

Type of Stress	Type of Member or Component	Allowable Stress, ksi	Spec. No.	Allowable Stress, ksi, Slenderness $\leq S_1$	Slenderness Limit, S_1	Allowable Stress, ksi, Slenderness Between S_1 and S_2	Slenderness Limit, S_2	Allowable Stress, ksi, Slenderness $\geq S_2$
TENSION, axial, net section	Any tension member	25	1					
TENSION IN BEAMS, extreme fiber, net section	Structural shapes, rectangular tubes, built-up members bent about X-axis	25	2					
	Round or oval tubes	31	3					
	Rectangular bars, plates, outstanding flanges of shapes bent about Y-axis	35	4					
BEARING	On rivets and bolts	47	5					
	On milled surfaces and pins	31	6					
COMPRESSION IN COLUMNS, axial, gross section	Columns (also see Specs. 8 to 10)		7	30	$\dfrac{L}{r}=10$	$32.6-0.25\dfrac{L}{r}$	$\dfrac{L}{r}=54$	$\dfrac{55{,}000}{(L/r)^2}$
	Components of columns (also see Spec. 7): Outstanding flanges and legs		8	30	$\dfrac{b}{t}=4.8$	$37.6-1.58\dfrac{b}{t}$	$\dfrac{b}{t}=9.7$	$\dfrac{2{,}100}{(b/t)^2}$
	Flat plates with both edges supported		9	30	$\dfrac{b}{t}=15$	$37.6-0.50\dfrac{b}{t}$	$\dfrac{b}{t}=31$	$\dfrac{21{,}000}{(b/t)^2}$
	Curved plates supported on both edges, walls of round or oval tubes		10	30	$\dfrac{R}{t}=14$	$35.4-1.46\sqrt{\dfrac{R}{t}}$	$\dfrac{R}{t}=100$	$\dfrac{3400}{\dfrac{R}{t}\left(1+\sqrt{\dfrac{R/t}{35}}\,\right)^2}$
COMPRESSION IN BEAMS, extreme fiber, gross section	Single-web beams bent about Y-axis		11	30	$\dfrac{L_b}{r_y}=12$	$32.6-0.21\dfrac{L_b}{r_y}$	$\dfrac{L_b}{r_y}=65$	$\dfrac{79{,}000}{(L_b/r_y)^2}$
	Round or oval tubes		12	39	$\dfrac{R_b}{t}=9.2$	$51.1-4.0\sqrt{\dfrac{R_b}{t}}$	$\dfrac{R_b}{t}=39$	Same as Specification No. 10 (See p. 21)

			No.				
COMPRESSION IN BEAMS, extreme fiber, gross section	Extreme fibers of beams (also see Specs. 15 to 19)	Solid rectangular beams bent about X-axis	13	43	$\frac{d}{t}\sqrt{\frac{L_b}{d}}=8.5$	$56.6-1.60\frac{d}{t}\sqrt{\frac{L_b}{d}}$	$\frac{d}{t}\sqrt{\frac{L_b}{d}}=23$	$\frac{10,400}{(d/t)^2(L_b/d)}$
		Rectangular tubes and box sections	14	30	$\frac{L_bS_c}{I_y}=42$	$32.6-0.40\sqrt{\frac{L_bS_c}{I_y}}$	$\frac{L_bS_c}{I_y}=1140$	$\frac{22,000}{(L_bS_c/I_y)}$
	Components of beams, component under uniform compression (also see Specs. 11 to 14)	Outstanding flanges	15	30	$\frac{b}{t}=5.5$	$37.6-1.39\frac{b}{t}$	$\frac{b}{t}=11$	$\frac{2,700}{(b/t)^2}$
		Flat plates with both edges supported	16	30	$\frac{b}{t}=15$	$37.6-0.50\frac{b}{t}$	$\frac{b}{t}=31$	$\frac{21,000}{(b/t)^2}$
		Flat plates with compression edge free, tension edge supported	17	43	$\frac{b}{t}=5.7$	$56.6-2.4\frac{b}{t}$	$\frac{b}{t}=15$	$\frac{4,500}{(b/t)^2}$
	Components of beams, component under bending in its own plane (also see Specs. 11 to 14)	Flat plates with both edges supported	18	30	- - -	30	$\frac{h}{t}=91$	$\frac{250,000}{(h/t)^2}$
		Flat plates with horizontal stiffener, both edges supported	19	30	- - -	30	$\frac{h}{t}=189$	$\frac{1,070,000}{(h/t)^2}$
SHEAR IN WEBS, gross section	Unstiffened flat webs		20	18	$\frac{h}{t}=20$	$21.3-0.164\frac{h}{t}$	$\frac{h}{t}=53$	$\frac{35,000}{(h/t)^2}$
	Stiffened flat webs	$a_e = a_1/\sqrt{\sqrt{1+0.7(a_1/a_2)^2}}$	21	18	- - -	18	$\frac{a_e}{t}=56$	$\frac{57,000}{(a_e/t)^2}$

① Alloy 2014 is not generally welded. Data in this table apply to nonwelded members.

TABLE 1–SUGGESTED ALLOWABLE STRESSES

TABLE 1–SUGGESTED ALLOWABLE STRESSES *(SEE INTRODUCTION TO TABLE 1, p. 41)*

3003-H14 — Sheet and Plate, Rolled Rod and Bar, Drawn Tube

ANOCLAD TYPES 12-H14, 20-H14, 30-H14 AND 40-H14 — Sheet

Values given as **3003-H14 / ANOCLAD** where two values appear.

Type of Stress	Type of Member or Component	Spec. No.	Allowable Stress, ksi	Allowable Stress, ksi, Slenderness $\le S_1$	Slenderness Limit, S_1	Allowable Stress, ksi, Slenderness Between S_1 and S_2	Slenderness Limit, S_2	Allowable Stress, ksi, Slenderness $\ge S_2$
TENSION, axial, net section	Any tension member	1	10.5 / 4.2					
TENSION IN BEAMS, extreme fiber, net section	Structural shapes, rectangular tubes, built-up members bent about X-axis	2	10.5 / 4.2					
	Round or oval tubes	3	12 / 5					
	Rectangular bars, plates, outstanding flanges of shapes bent about Y-axis	4	13.5 / 5.5					
BEARING	On rivets and bolts	5	15 / 7.5					
	On milled surfaces and pins	6	10 / 4.8					
COMPRESSION IN COLUMNS, axial, gross section	Columns (also see Specs. 8 to 10)	7		7.5 / 4.2	$\frac{L}{r}=6$ / $\frac{L}{r}=103$	$8.1-0.038\frac{L}{r}$	$\frac{L}{r}=138$	$\dfrac{51{,}000}{(L/r)^2}$
	Outstanding flanges and legs	8		7.5 / 4.2	$\frac{b}{t}=7.6$ / $\frac{b}{t}=21$	$9.4-0.25\frac{b}{t}$	$\frac{b}{t}=25$	$\dfrac{1{,}940}{(b/t)^2}$
	Components of columns (also see Spec. 7) — Flat plates with both edges supported	9		7.5 / 4.2	$\frac{b}{t}=24$ / $\frac{b}{t}=65$	$9.4-0.080\frac{b}{t}$	$\frac{b}{t}=78$	$\dfrac{19{,}200}{(b/t)^2}$
	Curved plates supported on both edges, walls of round or oval tubes	10		7.5 / 4.2	$\frac{R}{t}=36$ / $\frac{R}{t}=6.7$	$9.3-0.30\sqrt{\frac{R}{t}}$ / $4.5-0.116\sqrt{\frac{R}{t}}$	$\frac{R}{t}=420$ / $\frac{R}{t}=810$	$\dfrac{3{,}200}{\frac{R}{t}\left(1+\frac{\sqrt{R/t}}{35}\right)^2}$
COMPRESSION IN BEAMS, extreme fiber, gross section	Single-web beams bent about X-axis (also see Specs. 15 to 19)	11		7.5 / 4.2	$\frac{L_b}{r_y}=19$ / $\frac{L_b}{r_y}=122$	$8.1-0.032\frac{L_b}{r_y}$	$\frac{L_b}{r_y}=166$	$\dfrac{74{,}000}{(L_b/r_y)^2}$
	Round or oval tubes	12		10 / 5	$\frac{R_b}{t}=29$ / $\frac{R_b}{t}=44$	$13.9-0.72\sqrt{\frac{R_b}{t}}$ / $6.8-0.27\sqrt{\frac{R_b}{t}}$	$\frac{R_b}{t}=127$ / $\frac{R_b}{t}=205$	Same as Specification No. 10

DESIGN STRESSES FOR ALUMINUM

Section	Case	Spec.	Bar	Value	First limit	Formula	Second limit	Beyond second limit
COMPRESSION IN BEAMS, extreme fiber, gross section	**Extreme fibers of beams** (also see Specs. 15 to 19) — Solid rectangular beams bent about X-axis	13	nonshaded	11	$\frac{d}{t}\sqrt{L_b/d}=9.2$	$12.6-0.173\frac{d}{t}\sqrt{L_b/d}$	$\frac{d}{t}\sqrt{L_b/d}=48$	$\frac{9,700}{(d/t)^2(L_b/d)}$
		13	**shaded**	**5.5**	$\frac{d}{t}\sqrt{L_b/d}=41$	$12.6-0.173\frac{d}{t}\sqrt{L_b/d}$	$\frac{d}{t}\sqrt{L_b/d}=48$	$\frac{9,700}{(d/t)^2(L_b/d)}$
	Rectangular tubes and box sections	14	nonshaded	7.5	$\frac{L_bS_c}{I_y}=94$	$8.1-0.062\sqrt{\frac{L_bS_c}{I_y}}$	$\frac{L_bS_c}{I_y}=7440$	$\frac{20,000}{(L_bS_c/I_y)}$
		14	**shaded**	**4.2**	$\frac{L_bS_c}{I_y}=3960$	$8.1-0.062\sqrt{\frac{L_bS_c}{I_y}}$	$\frac{L_bS_c}{I_y}=7440$	$\frac{20,000}{(L_bS_c/I_y)}$
	Components of beams, component under uniform compression (also see Specs. 11 to 14) — Outstanding flanges	15	nonshaded	7.5	$\frac{b}{t}=8.6$	$9.4-0.22\frac{b}{t}$	$\frac{b}{t}=28$	$\frac{2,500}{(b/t)^2}$
		15	**shaded**	**4.2**	$\frac{b}{t}=24$	$9.4-0.22\frac{b}{t}$	$\frac{b}{t}=28$	$\frac{2,500}{(b/t)^2}$
	Flat plates with both edges supported	16	nonshaded	7.5	$\frac{b}{t}=24$	$9.4-0.080\frac{b}{t}$	$\frac{b}{t}=78$	$\frac{19,200}{(b/t)^2}$
		16	**shaded**	**4.2**	$\frac{b}{t}=65$	$9.4-0.080\frac{b}{t}$	$\frac{b}{t}=78$	$\frac{19,200}{(b/t)^2}$
	Components of beams, component under bending in its own plane (also see Specs. 11 to 14) — Flat plates with compression edge free, tension edge supported	17	nonshaded	11	$\frac{b}{t}=6.2$	$12.6-0.26\frac{b}{t}$	$\frac{b}{t}=32$	$\frac{4,200}{(b/t)^2}$
		17	**shaded**	**5.5**	$\frac{b}{t}=27$	$12.6-0.26\frac{b}{t}$	$\frac{b}{t}=32$	$\frac{4,200}{(b/t)^2}$
	Flat plates with both edges supported	18	nonshaded	7.5	$\frac{h}{t}=175$	$20.4-0.074\frac{h}{t}$	$\frac{h}{t}=185$	$\frac{230,000}{(h/t)^2}$
		18	**shaded**	**4.2**	— — —	**4.2**	$\frac{h}{t}=234$	$\frac{230,000}{(h/t)^2}$
	Flat plates with horizontal stiffener, both edges supported	19	nonshaded	7.5	$\frac{h}{t}=360$	$20.4-0.036\frac{h}{t}$	$\frac{h}{t}=380$	$\frac{990,000}{(h/t)^2}$
		19	**shaded**	**4.2**	— — —	**4.2**	$\frac{h}{t}=490$	$\frac{990,000}{(h/t)^2}$
SHEAR IN WEBS, gross section	Unstiffened flat webs	20	nonshaded	6	$\frac{h}{t}=24$	$6.9-0.038\frac{h}{t}$	$\frac{h}{t}=119$	$\frac{33,000}{(h/t)^2}$
		20	**shaded**	**2.4**	— — —	**2.4**	$\frac{h}{t}=117$	$\frac{33,000}{(h/t)^2}$
	Stiffened flat webs	21	nonshaded	6	$\frac{a_e}{t}=84$	$11.3-0.063\frac{a_e}{t}$	$\frac{a_e}{t}=119$	$\frac{53,000}{(a_e/t)^2}$
		21	**shaded**	**2.4**	— — —	**2.4**	$\frac{a_e}{t}=149$	$\frac{53,000}{(a_e/t)^2}$

Sketch annotations include (Spec 17) "Compression Flange"; (Spec 19) "Compression Flange", "Neutral Axis"; (Spec 21):

$$a_e = a_1 / \sqrt{1 + 0.7\,(a_1 / a_2)^2}$$

NONSHADED BARS apply to nonwelded members and to welded members at locations farther than 1.0 in. from a weld

SHADED BARS apply within 1.0 in. of a weld

TABLE 1—SUGGESTED ALLOWABLE STRESSES *(SEE INTRODUCTION TO TABLE 1, p. 41)*

3003-H16
Sheet and Plate
Rolled Rod and Bar
Drawn Tube

In the table below, each cell gives the non-shaded value / shaded value as printed.

Type of Stress	Type of Member or Component	Spec. No.	Allowable Stress, ksi (Slenderness $\le S_1$)	Slenderness Limit, S_1	Allowable Stress, ksi, Slenderness Between S_1 and S_2	Slenderness Limit, S_2	Allowable Stress, ksi, Slenderness $\ge S_2$
TENSION, axial, net section	Any tension member	1	12.5 / 4.2				
TENSION IN BEAMS, extreme fiber, net section	Structural shapes, rectangular tubes, built-up members bent about X-axis	2	12.5 / 4.2				
	Round or oval tubes	3	15 / 5				
	Rectangular bars, plates, outstanding flanges of shapes bent about Y-axis	4	17 / 5.5				
BEARING	On rivets and bolts	5	19 / 7.5				
	On milled surfaces and pins	6	12.5 / 4.8				
COMPRESSION IN COLUMNS, axial, gross section	Columns (also see Specs. 8 to 10)	7	10 / 4.2	$\frac{L}{r}=8.8$ / $\frac{L}{r}=111$	$10.5-0.057\frac{L}{r}$ / $10.5-0.057\frac{L}{r}$	$\frac{L}{r}=121$ / $\frac{L}{r}=121$	$\dfrac{51{,}000}{(L/r)^2}$ / $\dfrac{51{,}000}{(L/r)^2}$
	Components of columns (also see Spec. 7) — Outstanding flanges and legs	8	10 / 4.2	$\frac{b}{t}=6.3$ / —	$12.4-0.38\frac{b}{t}$ / 4.2	$\frac{b}{t}=22$ / $\frac{b}{t}=21$	$\dfrac{1{,}940}{(b/t)^2}$ / $\dfrac{1{,}940}{(b/t)^2}$
	Flat plates with both edges supported	9	10 / 4.2	$\frac{b}{t}=20$ / —	$12.4-0.121\frac{b}{t}$ / 4.2	$\frac{b}{t}=68$ / $\frac{b}{t}=68$	$\dfrac{19{,}200}{(b/t)^2}$ / $\dfrac{19{,}200}{(b/t)^2}$
	Curved plates supported on both edges, walls of round or oval tubes	10	10 / 4.2	$\frac{R}{t}=24$ / $\frac{R}{t}=6.7$	$12.1-0.43\sqrt{\frac{R}{t}}$ / $4.5-0.116\sqrt{\frac{R}{t}}$	$\frac{R}{t}=330$ / $\frac{R}{t}=810$	$\dfrac{3{,}200}{\frac{R}{t}\left(1+\frac{\sqrt{R/t}}{35}\right)^2}$ / $\dfrac{3{,}200}{\frac{R}{t}\left(1+\frac{\sqrt{R/t}}{35}\right)^2}$
COMPRESSION IN BEAMS, extreme fiber, gross section	Extreme fibers of beams (also see Specs. 15 to 19) — Single-web beams bent about X-axis	11	10 / 4.2	$\frac{L_b}{r_y}=10$ / $\frac{L_b}{r_y}=131$	$10.5-0.048\frac{L_b}{r_y}$ / $10.5-0.048\frac{L_b}{r_y}$	$\frac{L_b}{r_y}=145$ / $\frac{L_b}{r_y}=145$	$\dfrac{74{,}000}{(L_b/r_y)^2}$ / $\dfrac{74{,}000}{(L_b/r_y)^2}$
	Round or oval tubes	12	13 / 5	$\frac{R_b}{t}=25$ / $\frac{R_b}{t}=44$	$18.1-1.02\sqrt{\frac{R_b}{t}}$ / $6.8-0.27\sqrt{\frac{R_b}{t}}$	$\frac{R_b}{t}=106$ / $\frac{R_b}{t}=205$	Same as Specification No. 10 (See p. 21)

Design stresses table (aluminum). The table is read with two sub-rows per numbered specification: the first (nonshaded) and the second (shaded, applying within 1.0 in. of a weld).

Section	Description	No.	Bar					
COMPRESSION IN BEAMS, extreme fiber, gross section	Extreme fibers of beams (also see Specs. 15 to 19) — Solid rectangular beams bent about X-axis	13	nonshaded	14	$\frac{d}{t}\sqrt{L_b/d}=9.6$	$16.5-0.26\frac{d}{t}\sqrt{L_b/d}$	$\frac{d}{t}\sqrt{L_b/d}=42$	$\dfrac{9{,}100}{(d/t)^2(L_b/d)}$
			shaded	5.5	— — —	5.5	$\frac{d}{t}\sqrt{L_b/d}=42$	$\dfrac{9{,}700}{(d/t)^2(L_b/d)}$
	Rectangular tubes and box sections	14	nonshaded	10	$\frac{L_bS_c}{I_y}=30$	$10.5-0.092\sqrt{\frac{L_bS_c}{I_y}}$	$\frac{L_bS_c}{I_y}=5720$	$\dfrac{20{,}000}{(L_bS_c/I_y)}$
			shaded	4.2	$\frac{L_bS_c}{I_y}=4690$	$10.5-0.092\sqrt{\frac{L_bS_c}{I_y}}$	$\frac{L_bS_c}{I_y}=5720$	$\dfrac{20{,}000}{(L_bS_c/I_y)}$
Components of beams, component under uniform compression (also see Specs. 11 to 14)	Outstanding flanges	15	nonshaded	10	$\frac{b}{t}=7.3$	$12.4-0.33\frac{b}{t}$	$\frac{b}{t}=25$	$\dfrac{2{,}500}{(b/t)^2}$
			shaded	4.2	— — —	4.2	$\frac{b}{t}=24$	$\dfrac{2{,}500}{(b/t)^2}$
	Flat plates with both edges supported	16	nonshaded	10	$\frac{b}{t}=20$	$12.4-0.121\frac{b}{t}$	$\frac{b}{t}=68$	$\dfrac{19{,}200}{(b/t)^2}$
			shaded	4.2	— — —	4.2	$\frac{b}{t}=68$	$\dfrac{19{,}200}{(b/t)^2}$
	Flat plates with compression edge free, tension edge supported	17	nonshaded	14	$\frac{b}{t}=6.3$	$16.5-0.40\frac{b}{t}$	$\frac{b}{t}=28$	$\dfrac{4{,}200}{(b/t)^2}$
			shaded	5.5	— — —	5.5	$\frac{b}{t}=28$	$\dfrac{4{,}200}{(b/t)^2}$
Components of beams, component under bending in its own plane (also see Specs. 11 to 14)	Flat plates with both edges supported	18	nonshaded	10	$\frac{h}{t}=152$	$26.8-0.111\frac{h}{t}$	$\frac{h}{t}=162$	$\dfrac{230{,}000}{(h/t)^2}$
			shaded	4.2	— — —	4.2	$\frac{h}{t}=234$	$\dfrac{230{,}000}{(h/t)^2}$
	Flat plates with horizontal stiffener, both edges supported	19	nonshaded	10	$\frac{h}{t}=310$	$26.8-0.054\frac{h}{t}$	$\frac{h}{t}=330$	$\dfrac{990{,}000}{(h/t)^2}$
			shaded	4.2	— — —	4.2	$\frac{h}{t}=490$	$\dfrac{990{,}000}{(h/t)^2}$
SHEAR IN WEBS, gross section	Unstiffened flat webs	20	nonshaded	7	$\frac{h}{t}=27$	$8.4-0.052\frac{h}{t}$	$\frac{h}{t}=108$	$\dfrac{33{,}000}{(h/t)^2}$
			shaded	2.4	— — —	2.4	$\frac{h}{t}=117$	$\dfrac{33{,}000}{(h/t)^2}$
	Stiffened flat webs	21	nonshaded	7	$\frac{a_e}{t}=80$	$13.7-0.084\frac{a_e}{t}$	$\frac{a_e}{t}=108$	$\dfrac{53{,}000}{(a_e/t)^2}$
			shaded	2.4	— — —	2.4	$\frac{a_e}{t}=149$	$\dfrac{53{,}000}{(a_e/t)^2}$

$$a_e = a_1/\sqrt{1+0.7(a_1/a_2)^2}$$

NONSHADED BARS apply to nonwelded members and to welded members at locations farther than 1.0 in. from a weld.

SHADED BARS apply within 1.0 in. of a weld.

TABLE 1—SUGGESTED ALLOWABLE STRESSES

TABLE 1—SUGGESTED ALLOWABLE STRESSES (SEE INTRODUCTION TO TABLE 1, p. 41)

ALCLAD 3004-H16 Sheet

Type of Stress	Type of Member or Component	Spec. No.	Allowable Stress, ksi	Allowable Stress, ksi, Slenderness ≤ S_1	Slenderness Limit, S_1	Allowable Stress, ksi, Slenderness Between S_1 and S_2	Slenderness Limit, S_2	Allowable Stress, ksi, Slenderness ≥ S_2
TENSION, axial, net section	Any tension member	1	18					
TENSION IN BEAMS, extreme fiber, net section	Structural shapes, rectangular tubes, built-up members bent about X-axis	2	18					
	Round or oval tubes	3	21					
	Rectangular bars, plates, outstanding flanges of shapes bent about Y-axis	4	24					
BEARING	On rivets and bolts	5	27					
	On milled surfaces and pins	6	18					
COMPRESSION IN COLUMNS, axial, gross section	Columns (also see Specs. 8 to 10)	7		14.5	$\frac{L}{r}=9.6$	$15.5-0.104\frac{L}{r}$	$\frac{L}{r}=100$	$\dfrac{51,000}{(L/r)^2}$
				6.5	$\frac{L}{r}=87$	$15.5-0.104\frac{L}{r}$	$\frac{L}{r}=100$	$\dfrac{51,000}{(L/r)^2}$
	Outstanding flanges and legs	8		14.5	$\frac{b}{t}=5.7$	$18.5-0.70\frac{b}{t}$	$\frac{b}{t}=18$	$\dfrac{1,940}{(b/t)^2}$
				6.5	— — —	6.5	$\frac{b}{t}=17$	$\dfrac{1,940}{(b/t)^2}$
Components of columns (also see Spec. 7)	Flat plates with both edges supported	9		14.5	$\frac{b}{t}=18$	$18.5-0.22\frac{b}{t}$	$\frac{b}{t}=56$	$\dfrac{19,200}{(b/t)^2}$
				6.5	— — —	6.5	$\frac{b}{t}=54$	$\dfrac{19,200}{(b/t)^2}$
	Curved plates supported on both edges, walls of round or oval tubes	10		14.5	$\frac{R}{t}=20$	$17.7-0.72\sqrt{\frac{R}{t}}$	$\frac{R}{t}=229$	$\dfrac{3,200}{\frac{R}{t}\left(1+\frac{\sqrt{R/t}^2}{35}\right)}$
				6.5	$\frac{R}{t}=10$	$7.2-0.22\sqrt{\frac{R}{t}}$	$\frac{R}{t}=510$	$\dfrac{3,200}{\frac{R}{t}\left(1+\frac{\sqrt{R/t}^2}{35}\right)}$
COMPRESSION IN BEAMS, extreme fiber, gross section	Single-web beams bent about X-axis (Extreme fibers of beams, also see Specs. 15 to 19)	11		14.5	$\frac{L_b}{r_y}=12$	$15.5-0.086\frac{L_b}{r_y}$	$\frac{L_b}{r_y}=120$	$\dfrac{74,000}{(L_b/r_y)^2}$
				6.5	$\frac{L_b}{r_y}=105$	$15.5-0.086\frac{L_b}{r_y}$	$\frac{L_b}{r_y}=120$	$\dfrac{74,000}{(L_b/r_y)^2}$
	Round or oval tubes	12		18	$\frac{R_b}{t}=26$	$26.6-1.70\sqrt{\frac{R_b}{t}}$	$\frac{R_b}{t}=82$	Same as Specification No. 10 (See p. 21)
				8	$\frac{R_b}{t}=30$	$10.8-0.51\sqrt{\frac{R_b}{t}}$	$\frac{R_b}{t}=150$	

COMPRESSION IN BEAMS, extreme fiber, gross section

Spec.	Description	Bar	Value	Lower limit	Straight-line formula	Upper limit	Curve formula
13	Extreme fibers of beams (also see Specs. 15 to 19) — Solid rectangular beams bent about X-axis	nonshaded	20	$\dfrac{d}{t}\sqrt{\dfrac{L_b}{d}} = 9.8$	$24.7 - 0.48\,\dfrac{d}{t}\sqrt{\dfrac{L_b}{d}}$	$\dfrac{d}{t}\sqrt{\dfrac{L_b}{d}} = 34$	$\dfrac{9{,}700}{(d/t)^2(L_b/d)}$
		shaded	8.5	---	8.5	$\dfrac{d}{t}\sqrt{\dfrac{L_b}{d}} = 34$	$\dfrac{9{,}700}{(d/t)^2(L_b/d)}$
14	Rectangular tubes and box sections	nonshaded	14.5	$\dfrac{L_b S_c}{I_y} = 36$	$15.5 - 0.166\sqrt{\dfrac{L_b S_c}{I_y}}$	$\dfrac{L_b S_c}{I_y} = 3910$	$\dfrac{20{,}000}{(L_b S_c/I_y)}$
		shaded	6.5	$\dfrac{L_b S_c}{I_y} = 2940$	$15.5 - 0.166\sqrt{\dfrac{L_b S_c}{I_y}}$	$\dfrac{L_b S_c}{I_y} = 3910$	$\dfrac{20{,}000}{(L_b S_c/I_y)}$
15	Components of beams, component under uniform compression (also see Specs. 11 to 14) — Outstanding flanges	nonshaded	14.5	$\dfrac{b}{t} = 6.6$	$18.5 - 0.61\,\dfrac{b}{t}$	$\dfrac{b}{t} = 20$	$\dfrac{2{,}500}{(b/t)^2}$
		shaded	6.5	---	6.5	$\dfrac{b}{t} = 20$	$\dfrac{2{,}500}{(b/t)^2}$
16	Flat plates with both edges supported	nonshaded	14.5	$\dfrac{b}{t} = 18$	$18.5 - 0.22\,\dfrac{b}{t}$	$\dfrac{b}{t} = 56$	$\dfrac{19{,}200}{(b/t)^2}$
		shaded	6.5	---	6.5	$\dfrac{b}{t} = 54$	$\dfrac{19{,}200}{(b/t)^2}$
17	Components of beams, component under bending in its own plane (also see Specs. 11 to 14) — Flat plates with compression edge free, tension edge supported	nonshaded	20	$\dfrac{b}{t} = 6.4$	$24.7 - 0.73\,\dfrac{b}{t}$	$\dfrac{b}{t} = 23$	$\dfrac{4{,}200}{(b/t)^2}$
		shaded	8.5	---	8.5	$\dfrac{b}{t} = 22$	$\dfrac{4{,}200}{(b/t)^2}$
18	Flat plates with both edges supported	nonshaded	14.5	---	14.5	$\dfrac{h}{t} = 126$	$\dfrac{230{,}000}{(h/t)^2}$
		shaded	6.5	---	6.5	$\dfrac{h}{t} = 188$	$\dfrac{230{,}000}{(h/t)^2}$
19	Flat plates with horizontal stiffener, both edges supported	nonshaded	14.5	---	14.5	$\dfrac{h}{t} = 260$	$\dfrac{990{,}000}{(h/t)^2}$
		shaded	6.5	---	6.5	$\dfrac{h}{t} = 390$	$\dfrac{990{,}000}{(h/t)^2}$

SHEAR IN WEBS, gross section

Spec.	Description	Bar	Value	Lower limit	Straight-line formula	Upper limit	Curve formula
20	Unstiffened flat webs	nonshaded	10.5	$\dfrac{h}{t} = 21$	$12.4 - 0.092\,\dfrac{h}{t}$	$\dfrac{h}{t} = 90$	$\dfrac{33{,}000}{(h/t)^2}$
		shaded	3.9	---	3.9	$\dfrac{h}{t} = 92$	$\dfrac{33{,}000}{(h/t)^2}$
21	Stiffened flat webs	nonshaded	10.5	$\dfrac{a_e}{t} = 64$	$20.1 - 0.150\,\dfrac{a_e}{t}$	$\dfrac{a_e}{t} = 90$	$\dfrac{53{,}000}{(a_e/t)^2}$
		shaded	3.9	---	3.9	$\dfrac{a_e}{t} = 117$	$\dfrac{53{,}000}{(a_e/t)^2}$

$$a_e = a_1 / \sqrt{1 + 0.7\,(a_1/a_2)^2}$$

NONSHADED BARS — apply to nonwelded members and to welded members at locations farther than 1.0 in. from a weld.

SHADED BARS — apply within 1.0 in. of a weld.

TABLE 1 — SUGGESTED ALLOWABLE STRESSES (SEE INTRODUCTION TO TABLE 1, p. 41)

5052-H34
Sheet and Plate
Rolled Rod and Bar
Drawn Tube

Type of Stress	Type of Member or Component	Spec. No.	Allowable Stress, ksi, Slenderness ≤ S₁	Slenderness Limit, S₁	Allowable Stress, ksi, Slenderness Between S₁ and S₂	Slenderness Limit, S₂	Allowable Stress, ksi, Slenderness ≥ S₂
TENSION, axial, net section	Any tension member	1	16				
			8				
TENSION IN BEAMS, extreme fiber, net section	Structural shapes, rectangular tubes, built-up members bent about X-axis	2	16				
			8				
	Round or oval tubes	3	18				
			9				
	Rectangular bars, plates, outstanding flanges of shapes bent about Y-axis	4	20				
			10				
BEARING	On rivets and bolts	5	27				
			11.5				
	On milled surfaces and pins	6	18				
			7.5				
COMPRESSION IN COLUMNS, axial, gross section	Columns (also see Specs. 8 to 10)	7	13	$\frac{L}{r}=13$	$14.2-0.091\frac{L}{r}$	$\frac{L}{r}=104$	$\frac{52{,}000}{(L/r)^2}$
			8	$\frac{L}{r}=68$	$14.2-0.091\frac{L}{r}$	$\frac{L}{r}=104$	$\frac{52{,}000}{(L/r)^2}$
	Components of columns (also see Spec. 7) — Outstanding flanges and legs	8	13	$\frac{b}{t}=6.6$	$17.0-0.61\frac{b}{t}$	$\frac{b}{t}=19$	$\frac{1{,}960}{(b/t)^2}$
			8	$\frac{b}{t}=15$	$17.0-0.61\frac{b}{t}$	$\frac{b}{t}=19$	$\frac{1{,}960}{(b/t)^2}$
	Flat plates with both edges supported	9	13	$\frac{b}{t}=21$	$17.0-0.193\frac{b}{t}$	$\frac{b}{t}=59$	$\frac{19{,}400}{(b/t)^2}$
			8	$\frac{b}{t}=47$	$17.0-0.193\frac{b}{t}$	$\frac{b}{t}=59$	$\frac{19{,}400}{(b/t)^2}$
	Curved plates supported on both edges, walls of round or oval tubes	10	13	$\frac{R}{t}=27$	$16.3-0.64\sqrt{\frac{R}{t}}$	$\frac{R}{t}=250$	$\frac{3{,}200}{\frac{R}{t}\left(1+\frac{\sqrt{R/t}}{35}\right)}$
			8	$\frac{R}{t}=4.9$	$8.6-0.27\sqrt{\frac{R}{t}}$	$\frac{R}{t}=460$	$\frac{3{,}200}{\frac{R}{t}\left(1+\frac{\sqrt{R/t}}{35}\right)}$
COMPRESSION IN BEAMS, extreme fiber, gross section	Extreme fibers of beams (also see Specs. 15 to 19) — Single-web beams bent about X-axis	11	13	$\frac{L_b}{r_y}=16$	$14.2-0.076\frac{L_b}{r_y}$	$\frac{L_b}{r_y}=125$	$\frac{74{,}000}{(L_b/r_y)^2}$
			8	$\frac{L_b}{r_y}=82$	$14.2-0.076\frac{L_b}{r_y}$	$\frac{L_b}{r_y}=125$	$\frac{74{,}000}{(L_b/r_y)^2}$
	Round or oval tubes	12	17	$\frac{R_b}{t}=24$	$24.5-1.52\sqrt{\frac{R_b}{t}}$	$\frac{R_b}{t}=88$	Same as Specification No. 10 (See p. 21)
			9	$\frac{R_b}{t}=37$	$12.9-0.64\sqrt{\frac{R_b}{t}}$	$\frac{R_b}{t}=134$	

Design stresses for aluminum — compression in beams and shear in webs.

Category	Description	Diagram	No.	Allowable stress (const.)	Slenderness limit S_1	Intermediate formula	Slenderness limit S_2	Large-slenderness formula
COMPRESSION IN BEAMS, extreme fiber, gross section	Solid rectangular beams bent about X-axis		13	19 / **10**	$\frac{d}{t}\sqrt{\frac{L_b}{d}}=8.6$ / $\frac{d}{t}\sqrt{\frac{L_b}{d}}=\mathbf{30}$	$22.6-0.42\frac{d}{t}\sqrt{\frac{L_b}{d}}$ / $22.6-0.42\frac{d}{t}\sqrt{\frac{L_b}{d}}$	$\frac{d}{t}\sqrt{\frac{L_b}{d}}=36$ / $\frac{d}{t}\sqrt{\frac{L_b}{d}}=\mathbf{36}$	$\frac{9,800}{(d/t)^2(L_b/d)}$ / $\frac{\mathbf{9,800}}{\mathbf{(d/t)^2(L_b/d)}}$
	Rectangular tubes and box sections		14	13 / **8**	$\frac{L_bS_c}{I_y}=68$ / $\frac{L_bS_c}{I_y}=\mathbf{1830}$	$14.2-0.145\sqrt{\frac{L_bS_c}{I_y}}$ / $14.2-0.145\sqrt{\frac{L_bS_c}{I_y}}$	$\frac{L_bS_c}{I_y}=4220$ / $\frac{L_bS_c}{I_y}=\mathbf{4220}$	$\frac{20,000}{(L_bS_c/I_y)}$ / $\frac{\mathbf{20,000}}{\mathbf{(L_bS_c/I_y)}}$
COMPRESSION IN BEAMS, extreme fiber, gross section — Components of beams, component under uniform compression (also see Specs. 11 to 14)	Outstanding flanges		15	13 / **8**	$\frac{b}{t}=7.5$ / $\frac{b}{t}=\mathbf{17}$	$17.0-0.53\frac{b}{t}$ / $17.0-0.53\frac{b}{t}$	$\frac{b}{t}=21$ / $\frac{b}{t}=\mathbf{21}$	$\frac{2,500}{(b/t)^2}$ / $\frac{\mathbf{2,500}}{\mathbf{(b/t)^2}}$
	Flat plates with both edges supported		16	13 / **8**	$\frac{b}{t}=21$ / $\frac{b}{t}=\mathbf{47}$	$17.0-0.193\frac{b}{t}$ / $17.0-0.193\frac{b}{t}$	$\frac{b}{t}=59$ / $\frac{b}{t}=\mathbf{59}$	$\frac{19,400}{(b/t)^2}$ / $\frac{\mathbf{19,400}}{\mathbf{(b/t)^2}}$
	Flat plates with compression edge free, tension edge supported		17	19 / **10**	$\frac{b}{t}=5.6$ / $\frac{b}{t}=\mathbf{20}$	$22.6-0.64\frac{b}{t}$ / $22.6-0.64\frac{b}{t}$	$\frac{b}{t}=24$ / $\frac{b}{t}=\mathbf{24}$	$\frac{4,200}{(b/t)^2}$ / $\frac{\mathbf{4,200}}{\mathbf{(b/t)^2}}$
Components of beams, component under bending in its own plane (also see Specs. 11 to 14)	Flat plates with both edges supported		18	13 / **8**	--- / ---	13 / **8**	$\frac{h}{t}=133$ / $\frac{h}{t}=\mathbf{170}$	$\frac{230,000}{(h/t)^2}$ / $\frac{\mathbf{230,000}}{\mathbf{(h/t)^2}}$
	Flat plates with horizontal stiffener, both edges supported		19	13 / **8**	--- / ---	13 / **8**	$\frac{h}{t}=280$ / $\frac{h}{t}=\mathbf{350}$	$\frac{1,000,000}{(h/t)^2}$ / $\frac{\mathbf{1,000,000}}{\mathbf{(h/t)^2}}$
SHEAR IN WEBS, gross section	Unstiffened flat webs		20	9 / **4.5**	$\frac{h}{t}=24$ / $\frac{h}{t}=\mathbf{85}$	$10.8-0.074\frac{h}{t}$ / $10.8-0.074\frac{h}{t}$	$\frac{h}{t}=96$ / $\frac{h}{t}=\mathbf{96}$	$\frac{33,000}{(h/t)^2}$ / $\frac{\mathbf{33,000}}{\mathbf{(h/t)^2}}$
	Stiffened flat webs		21	9 / **4.5**	$\frac{a_e}{t}=70$ / ---	$17.5-0.121\frac{a_e}{t}$ / **4.5**	$\frac{a_e}{t}=96$ / $\frac{a_e}{t}=\mathbf{110}$	$\frac{54,000}{(a_e/t)^2}$ / $\frac{\mathbf{54,000}}{\mathbf{(a_e/t)^2}}$

$$a_e = a_1 / \sqrt{1 + 0.7\,(a_1/a_2)^2}$$

NONSHADED BARS apply to nonwelded members and to welded members at locations farther than 1.0 in. from a weld.

SHADED BARS apply within 1.0 in. of a weld.

TABLE 1–SUGGESTED ALLOWABLE STRESSES

(SEE INTRODUCTION TO TABLE 1, p. 41)

5083-H111 Extrusions

Type of Stress	Type of Member or Component	Spec. No.	Allowable Stress, ksi	Allowable Stress, ksi, Slenderness $\le S_1$	Slenderness Limit, S_1	Allowable Stress, ksi, Slenderness Between S_1 and S_2	Slenderness Limit, S_2	Allowable Stress, ksi, Slenderness $\ge S_2$
TENSION, axial, net section	Any tension member	1	14.5 / 12.5					
TENSION IN BEAMS, extreme fiber, net section	Structural shapes, rectangular tubes, built-up members bent about X-axis	2	14.5 / 12.5					
	Round or oval tubes	3	17 / 15					
	Rectangular bars, plates, outstanding flanges of shapes bent about Y-axis	4	19 / 17					
BEARING	On rivets and bolts	5	23 / 19					
	On milled surfaces and pins	6	15 / 13					
COMPRESSION IN COLUMNS, axial, gross section	Columns (also see Specs. 8 to 10)	7		11.5	$\dfrac{L}{r}=11$	$12.3-0.073\dfrac{L}{r}$	$\dfrac{L}{r}=113$	$\dfrac{53{,}000}{(L/r)^2}$
	Outstanding flanges and legs	8		11.5	$\dfrac{b}{t}=6.7$	$14.7-0.48\dfrac{b}{t}$	$\dfrac{b}{t}=20$	$\dfrac{2{,}000}{(b/t)^2}$
	Flat plates with both edges supported	9		11.5	$\dfrac{b}{t}=21$	$14.7-0.154\dfrac{b}{t}$	$\dfrac{b}{t}=64$	$\dfrac{19{,}800}{(b/t)^2}$
	Curved plates supported on both edges, walls of round or oval tubes	10		11.5	$\dfrac{R}{t}=26$	$14.2-0.53\sqrt{\dfrac{R}{t}}$	$\dfrac{R}{t}=290$	$\dfrac{3{,}300}{\dfrac{R}{t}\left(1+\dfrac{\sqrt{R/t}}{35}\right)}$
					$\dfrac{R}{t}=16$	$13.5-0.50\sqrt{\dfrac{R}{t}}$	$\dfrac{R}{t}=300$	$\dfrac{3{,}300}{\dfrac{R}{t}\left(1+\dfrac{\sqrt{R/t}}{35}\right)}$
COMPRESSION IN BEAMS, extreme fiber, gross section	Single-web beams bent about X-axis (also see Specs. 15 to 19)	11		11.5	$\dfrac{L_0}{r_y}=13$	$12.3-0.061\dfrac{L_0}{r_y}$	$\dfrac{L_0}{r_y}=136$	$\dfrac{76{,}000}{(L_0/r_y)^2}$
	Round or oval tubes	12		15	$\dfrac{R_b}{t}=25$	$21.3-1.25\sqrt{\dfrac{R_b}{t}}$	$\dfrac{R_b}{t}=97$	Same as Specification No. 10 (See p. 21)
				14	$\dfrac{R_b}{t}=28$	$20.2-1.17\sqrt{\dfrac{R_b}{t}}$	$\dfrac{R_b}{t}=101$	

Section	Member type	No.	Bar					
COMPRESSION IN BEAMS, extreme fiber, gross section	Extreme fibers of beams (also see Specs. 15 to 19): Solid rectangular beams bent about X-axis	13	Nonshaded	17	$\dfrac{d}{t}\sqrt{\dfrac{L_b}{d}} = 7.6$	$19.5 - 0.33\dfrac{d}{t}\sqrt{\dfrac{L_b}{d}}$	$\dfrac{d}{t}\sqrt{\dfrac{L_b}{d}} = 39$	$\dfrac{10,000}{(d/t)^2(L_b/d)}$
			Shaded	16	$\dfrac{d}{t}\sqrt{\dfrac{L_b}{d}} = 11$	$19.5 - 0.33\dfrac{d}{t}\sqrt{\dfrac{L_b}{d}}$	$\dfrac{d}{t}\sqrt{\dfrac{L_b}{d}} = 39$	$\dfrac{10,000}{(d/t)^2(L_b/d)}$
	Rectangular tubes and box sections	14	Nonshaded	11.5	$\dfrac{L_b S_c}{I_y} = 47$	$12.3 - 0.117\sqrt{\dfrac{L_b S_c}{I_y}}$	$\dfrac{L_b S_c}{I_y} = 4990$	$\dfrac{21,000}{(L_b)\sqrt{L_b S_c/I_y}}$
			Shaded	11.5	$\dfrac{L_b S_c}{I_y} = 47$	$12.3 - 0.117\sqrt{\dfrac{L_b S_c}{I_y}}$	$\dfrac{L_b S_c}{I_y} = 4990$	$\dfrac{21,000}{(L_b S_c/I_y)}$
	Components of beams, component under uniform compression (also see Specs. 11 to 14): Outstanding flanges	15	Nonshaded	11.5	$\dfrac{b}{t} = 7.6$	$14.7 - 0.42\dfrac{b}{t}$	$\dfrac{b}{t} = 23$	$\dfrac{2,600}{(b/t)^2}$
			Shaded	11.5	$\dfrac{b}{t} = 7.6$	$14.7 - 0.42\dfrac{b}{t}$	$\dfrac{b}{t} = 23$	$\dfrac{2,600}{(b/t)^2}$
	Flat plates with both edges supported	16	Nonshaded	11.5	$\dfrac{b}{t} = 21$	$14.7 - 0.154\dfrac{b}{t}$	$\dfrac{b}{t} = 64$	$\dfrac{19,800}{(b/t)^2}$
			Shaded	11.5	$\dfrac{b}{t} = 21$	$14.7 - 0.154\dfrac{b}{t}$	$\dfrac{b}{t} = 64$	$\dfrac{19,800}{(b/t)^2}$
	Components of beams, component under bending in its own plane (also see Specs. 11 to 14): Flat plates with compression edge free, tension edge supported	17	Nonshaded	17	$\dfrac{b}{t} = 4.9$	$19.5 - 0.51\dfrac{b}{t}$	$\dfrac{b}{t} = 26$	$\dfrac{4,300}{(b/t)^2}$
			Shaded	16	$\dfrac{b}{t} = 6.9$	$19.5 - 0.51\dfrac{b}{t}$	$\dfrac{b}{t} = 26$	$\dfrac{4,300}{(b/t)^2}$
	Flat plates with both edges supported	18	Nonshaded	11.5	— — —	11.5	$\dfrac{h}{t} = 144$	$\dfrac{240,000}{(h/t)^2}$
			Shaded	11.5	— — —	11.5	$\dfrac{h}{t} = 144$	$\dfrac{240,000}{(h/t)^2}$
	Flat plates with horizontal stiffener, both edges supported	19	Nonshaded	11.5	— — —	11.5	$\dfrac{h}{t} = 300$	$\dfrac{1,020,000}{(h/t)^2}$
			Shaded	11.5	— — —	11.5	$\dfrac{h}{t} = 300$	$\dfrac{1,020,000}{(h/t)^2}$
SHEAR IN WEBS, gross section	Unstiffened flat webs	20	Nonshaded	8.5	$\dfrac{h}{t} = 21$	$9.9 - 0.066\dfrac{h}{t}$	$\dfrac{h}{t} = 101$	$\dfrac{34,000}{(h/t)^2}$
			Shaded	7.5	$\dfrac{h}{t} = 36$	$9.9 - 0.066\dfrac{h}{t}$	$\dfrac{h}{t} = 101$	$\dfrac{34,000}{(h/t)^2}$
	Stiffened flat webs	21	Nonshaded	8.5	$\dfrac{a_e}{t} = 72$	$16.2 - 0.107\dfrac{a_e}{t}$	$\dfrac{a_e}{t} = 101$	$\dfrac{55,000}{(a_e/t)^2}$
			Shaded	7.5	$\dfrac{a_e}{t} = 81$	$16.2 - 0.107\dfrac{a_e}{t}$	$\dfrac{a_e}{t} = 101$	$\dfrac{55,000}{(a_e/t)^2}$

Diagram notes:

Row 19: Compression Flange, $0.4d_1$, d_1, Neutral Axis

Row 21: $a_e = a_1/\sqrt{1 + 0.7(a_1/a_2)^2}$

NONSHADED BARS apply to nonwelded members and to welded members at locations farther than 1.0 in. from a weld.

TABLE 1—SUGGESTED ALLOWABLE STRESSES

TABLE 1—SUGGESTED ALLOWABLE STRESSES (SEE INTRODUCTION TO TABLE 1, p. 41)

5083-H321 — Sheet and Plate (Thickness—0.188–1.500 in.)

Type of Stress	Type of Member or Component	Spec. No.	Allowable Stress, ksi, Slenderness ≤ S1	Slenderness Limit, S1	Allowable Stress, ksi, Slenderness Between S1 and S2	Slenderness Limit, S2	Allowable Stress, ksi, Slenderness ≥ S2
TENSION, axial, net section	Any tension member	1	19				
TENSION IN BEAMS, extreme fiber, net section	Structural shapes, rectangular tubes, built-up members bent about X-axis	2	19				
	Round or oval tubes	3	22				
	Rectangular bars, plates, outstanding flanges of shapes bent about Y-axis	4	24				
BEARING	On rivets and bolts	5	32				
	On milled surfaces and pins	6	21				
COMPRESSION IN COLUMNS, axial, gross section	Columns (also see Specs. 8 to 10)	7	14.5	$\frac{L}{r} = 9.8$	$15.5 - 0.102\frac{L}{r}$	$\frac{L}{r} = 101$	$\frac{53{,}000}{(L/r)^2}$
	Components of columns (also see Spec. 7) — Outstanding flanges and legs	8	14.5	$\frac{b}{t} = 5.8$	$18.5 - 0.69\frac{b}{t}$	$\frac{b}{t} = 18$	$\frac{2{,}000}{(b/t)^2}$
	Flat plates with both edges supported	9	14.5	$\frac{b}{t} = 18$	$18.5 - 0.22\frac{b}{t}$	$\frac{b}{t} = 56$	$\frac{19{,}800}{(b/t)^2}$
	Curved plates supported on both edges, walls of round or oval tubes	10	14.5	$\frac{R}{t} = 20$	$17.7 - 0.72\sqrt{\frac{R}{t}}$	$\frac{R}{t} = 235$	$\dfrac{3{,}300}{\frac{R}{t}\left(1 + \frac{\sqrt{R/t}}{35}\right)^2}$
		10	14.5	$\frac{R}{t} = 7.9$	$16.3 - 0.64\sqrt{\frac{R}{t}}$	$\frac{R}{t} = 250$	$\dfrac{3{,}300}{\frac{R}{t}\left(1 + \frac{\sqrt{R/t}}{35}\right)^2}$
COMPRESSION IN BEAMS, extreme fiber, gross section (also see Specs. 15 to 19)	Single-web beams bent about X-axis	11	14.5	$\frac{L_b}{r_y} = 12$	$15.5 - 0.085\frac{L_b}{r_y}$	$\frac{L_b}{r_y} = 121$	$\frac{76{,}000}{(L_b/r_y)^2}$
	Round or oval tubes	12	18	$\frac{R_b}{t} = 26$	$26.6 - 1.68\sqrt{\frac{R_b}{t}}$	$\frac{R_b}{t} = 84$	Same as Specification No. 10 (See p. 21)
		12	17	$\frac{R_b}{t} = 25$	$24.5 - 1.51\sqrt{\frac{R_b}{t}}$	$\frac{R_b}{t} = 89$	Same as Specification No. 10 (See p. 21)

Design stresses table for aluminum (Specifications 13–21).

Legend: **Shaded (bold) values** apply within 1.0 in. of a weld. Nonshaded values apply to nonwelded members and to welded members at locations farther than 1.0 in. from a weld.

Group	Description	No.	Value	Slenderness limit	Formula	Slenderness limit	Formula
COMPRESSION IN BEAMS, extreme fiber, gross section — Extreme fibers of beams (also see Specs. 15 to 19)	Solid rectangular beams bent about X-axis	13	20	$\frac{d}{t}\sqrt{\frac{L_b}{d}} = 10$	$24.7-0.47\frac{d}{t}\sqrt{\frac{L_b}{d}}$	$\frac{d}{t}\sqrt{\frac{L_b}{d}} = 35$	$\frac{10,000}{(d/t)^2(L_b/d)}$
			19	$\frac{d}{t}\sqrt{\frac{L_b}{d}} = 12$	$\mathbf{24.7-0.47\frac{d}{t}\sqrt{\frac{L_b}{d}}}$	$\frac{d}{t}\sqrt{\frac{L_b}{d}} = 35$	$\mathbf{\frac{10,000}{(d/t)^2(L_b/d)}}$
	Rectangular tubes and box sections	14	14.5	$\frac{L_b S_c}{I_y} = 38$	$15.5-0.163\sqrt{\frac{L_b S_c}{I_y}}$	$\frac{L_b S_c}{I_y} = 3980$	$\frac{21,000}{(L_b S_c/I_y)}$
			14.5	$\frac{L_b S_c}{I_y} = 38$	$\mathbf{15.5-0.163\sqrt{\frac{L_b S_c}{I_y}}}$	$\frac{L_b S_c}{I_y} = 3980$	$\mathbf{\frac{21,000}{(L_b S_c/I_y)}}$
Components of beams, component under uniform compression (also see Specs. 11 to 14)	Outstanding flanges	15	14.5	$\frac{b}{t} = 6.7$	$18.5-0.60\frac{b}{t}$	$\frac{b}{t} = 20$	$\frac{2,600}{(b/t)^2}$
			14.5	$\frac{b}{t} = 6.7$	$\mathbf{18.5-0.60\frac{b}{t}}$	$\frac{b}{t} = 20$	$\mathbf{\frac{2,600}{(b/t)^2}}$
	Flat plates with both edges supported	16	14.5	$\frac{b}{t} = 18$	$18.5-0.22\frac{b}{t}$	$\frac{b}{t} = 56$	$\frac{19,800}{(b/t)^2}$
			14.5	$\frac{b}{t} = 18$	$\mathbf{18.5-0.22\frac{b}{t}}$	$\frac{b}{t} = 56$	$\mathbf{\frac{19,800}{(b/t)^2}}$
Components of beams, component under bending in its own plane (also see Specs. 11 to 14)	Flat plates with compression edge free, tension edge supported	17	20	$\frac{b}{t} = 6.5$	$24.7-0.72\frac{b}{t}$	$\frac{b}{t} = 23$	$\frac{4,300}{(b/t)^2}$
			19	$\frac{b}{t} = 7.9$	$\mathbf{24.7-0.72\frac{b}{t}}$	$\frac{b}{t} = 23$	$\mathbf{\frac{4,300}{(b/t)^2}}$
	Flat plates with both edges supported	18	14.5	$- - -$	14.5	$\frac{h}{t} = 129$	$\frac{240,000}{(h/t)^2}$
			14.5	$- - -$	$\mathbf{14.5}$	$\frac{h}{t} = 129$	$\mathbf{\frac{240,000}{(h/t)^2}}$
	Flat plates with horizontal stiffener, both edges supported	19	14.5	$\frac{h}{t} = 260$	$40.0-0.097\frac{h}{t}$	$\frac{h}{t} = 280$	$\frac{1,020,000}{(h/t)^2}$
			14.5	$\frac{h}{t} = 260$	$\mathbf{40.0-0.097\frac{h}{t}}$	$\frac{h}{t} = 280$	$\mathbf{\frac{1,020,000}{(h/t)^2}}$
SHEAR IN WEBS, gross section	Unstiffened flat webs	20	11	$\frac{h}{t} = 21$	$13.1-0.100\frac{h}{t}$	$\frac{h}{t} = 88$	$\frac{34,000}{(h/t)^2}$
			8.5	$\frac{h}{t} = 46$	$\mathbf{13.1-0.100\frac{h}{t}}$	$\frac{h}{t} = 88$	$\mathbf{\frac{34,000}{(h/t)^2}}$
	Stiffened flat webs	21	11	$\frac{a_e}{t} = 63$	$21.3-0.163\frac{a_e}{t}$	$\frac{a_e}{t} = 88$	$\frac{55,000}{(a_e/t)^2}$
			8.5	$\frac{a_e}{t} = 79$	$\mathbf{21.3-0.163\frac{a_e}{t}}$	$\frac{a_e}{t} = 88$	$\mathbf{\frac{55,000}{(a_e/t)^2}}$

For stiffened flat webs (Spec. 21):
$$a_e = a_1 / \sqrt{1 + 0.7\,(a_1 / a_2)^2}$$

NONSHADED BARS apply to nonwelded members and to welded members at locations farther than 1.0 in. from a weld. SHADED BARS apply within 1.0 in. of a weld.

TABLE 1—SUGGESTED ALLOWABLE STRESSES

(SEE INTRODUCTION TO TABLE 1, p. 41)

5086-H111 Extrusions

Each "Allowable Stress / Slenderness Limit" group below shows two printed columns; the shaded column (listed first) is **5086-H111**, the second is the adjacent (general) column.

Type of Stress	Type of Member or Component	Spec. No.	Allowable Stress, ksi, Slenderness ≤ S_1 (5086-H111)	Allowable Stress, ksi, Slenderness ≤ S_1 (gen.)	Slenderness Limit, S_1 (5086-H111)	Slenderness Limit, S_1 (gen.)	Allowable Stress, ksi, Slenderness Between S_1 and S_2 (5086-H111)	Allowable Stress, ksi, Slenderness Between S_1 and S_2 (gen.)	Slenderness Limit, S_2 (5086-H111)	Slenderness Limit, S_2 (gen.)	Allowable Stress, ksi, Slenderness ≥ S_2 (5086-H111)	Allowable Stress, ksi, Slenderness ≥ S_2 (gen.)
TENSION, axial, net section	Any tension member	1	11	12.5								
TENSION IN BEAMS, extreme fiber, net section	Structural shapes, rectangular tubes, built-up members bent about X-axis	2	11	12.5								
	Round or oval tubes	3	13	15								
	Rectangular bars, plates, outstanding flanges of shapes bent about Y-axis	4	14	17								
BEARING	On rivets and bolts	5	17	21								
	On milled surfaces and pins	6	11.5	13.5								
COMPRESSION IN COLUMNS, axial, gross section	Columns (also see Specs. 8 to 10)	7	10	10	$\frac{L}{r}=8.8$	$\frac{L}{r}=8.8$	$10.5-0.057\frac{L}{r}$	$10.5-0.057\frac{L}{r}$	$\frac{L}{r}=123$	$\frac{L}{r}=123$	$\dfrac{53,000}{(L/r)^2}$	$\dfrac{53,000}{(L/r)^2}$
	Outstanding flanges and legs	8	10	10	$\frac{b}{t}=6.3$	$\frac{b}{t}=6.3$	$12.4-0.38\frac{b}{t}$	$12.4-0.38\frac{b}{t}$	$\frac{b}{t}=22$	$\frac{b}{t}=22$	$\dfrac{2,000}{(b/t)^2}$	$\dfrac{2,000}{(b/t)^2}$
Components of columns (also see Spec. 7)	Flat plates with both edges supported	9	10	10	$\frac{b}{t}=20$	$\frac{b}{t}=20$	$12.4-0.120\frac{b}{t}$	$12.4-0.120\frac{b}{t}$	$\frac{b}{t}=69$	$\frac{b}{t}=69$	$\dfrac{19,800}{(b/t)^2}$	$\dfrac{19,800}{(b/t)^2}$
	Curved plates supported on both edges, walls of round or oval tubes	10	10	10	$\frac{R}{t}=12$	$\frac{R}{t}=24$	$11.4-0.40\sqrt{\frac{R}{t}}$	$12.1-0.43\sqrt{\frac{R}{t}}$	$\frac{R}{t}=350$	$\frac{R}{t}=340$	$\dfrac{3,300}{\frac{R}{t}\left(1+\frac{\sqrt{R/t}}{35}\right)^2}$	$\dfrac{3,300}{\frac{R}{t}\left(1+\frac{\sqrt{R/t}}{35}\right)^2}$
COMPRESSION IN BEAMS, extreme fiber, gross section	Single-web beams bent about X-axis (also see Specs. 15 to 19)	11	10	10	$\frac{L_o}{r_y}=11$	$\frac{L_o}{r_y}=11$	$10.5-0.047\frac{L_o}{r_y}$	$10.5-0.047\frac{L_o}{r_y}$	$\frac{L_o}{r_y}=148$	$\frac{L_o}{r_y}=148$	$\dfrac{76,000}{(L_o/r_y)^2}$	$\dfrac{76,000}{(L_o/r_y)^2}$
	Round or oval tubes	12	12	13	$\frac{R_b}{t}=29$	$\frac{R_b}{t}=25$	$17.0-0.93\sqrt{\frac{R_b}{t}}$	$18.1-1.01\sqrt{\frac{R_b}{t}}$	$\frac{R_b}{t}=113$	$\frac{R_b}{t}=108$	Same as Specification No. 10 (See p. 21)	Same as Specification No. 10 (See p. 21)

Category	Section	Diagram	No.					
COMPRESSION IN BEAMS, extreme fiber, gross section	Extreme fibers of beams (also see Specs. 15 to 19) — Solid rectangular beams bent about X-axis		13	14	$\frac{a}{t}\sqrt{\frac{L_b}{d}} = 9.6$	$16.5 - 0.26\frac{a}{t}\sqrt{\frac{L_b}{d}}$	$\frac{a}{t}\sqrt{\frac{L_b}{d}} = 43$	$\frac{10,000}{(d/t)^2(L_b/d)}$
				13.5	$\frac{d}{t}\sqrt{\frac{L_b}{d}} = 12$	$16.5 - 0.26\frac{d}{t}\sqrt{\frac{L_b}{d}}$	$\frac{d}{t}\sqrt{\frac{L_b}{d}} = 43$	$\frac{10,000}{(d/t)^2(L_b/d)}$
	Rectangular tubes and box sections		14	10	$\frac{L_b S_c}{I_y} = 30$	$10.5 - 0.091\sqrt{\frac{L_b S_c}{I_y}}$	$\frac{L_b S_c}{I_y} = 5910$	$\frac{21,000}{(L_b S_c/I_y)}$
				10	$\frac{L_b S_c}{I_y} = 30$	$10.5 - 0.091\sqrt{\frac{L_b S_c}{I_y}}$	$\frac{L_b S_c}{I_y} = 5910$	$\frac{21,000}{(L_b S_c/I_y)}$
	Components of beams, component under uniform compression (also see Specs. 11 to 14) — Outstanding flanges		15	10	$\frac{b}{t} = 7.3$	$12.4 - 0.33\frac{b}{t}$	$\frac{b}{t} = 25$	$\frac{2,600}{(b/t)^2}$
				10	$\frac{b}{t} = 7.3$	$12.4 - 0.33\frac{b}{t}$	$\frac{b}{t} = 25$	$\frac{2,600}{(b/t)^2}$
	Flat plates with both edges supported		16	10	$\frac{b}{t} = 20$	$12.4 - 0.120\frac{b}{t}$	$\frac{b}{t} = 69$	$\frac{19,800}{(b/t)^2}$
				10	$\frac{b}{t} = 20$	$12.4 - 0.120\frac{b}{t}$	$\frac{b}{t} = 69$	$\frac{19,800}{(b/t)^2}$
	Components of beams, component in bending in its own plane (also see Specs. 11 to 14) — Flat plates with compression edge free, tension edge supported		17	14	$\frac{b}{t} = 6.4$	$16.5 - 0.39\frac{b}{t}$	$\frac{b}{t} = 28$	$\frac{4,300}{(b/t)^2}$
				13.5	$\frac{b}{t} = 7.7$	$16.5 - 0.39\frac{b}{t}$	$\frac{b}{t} = 28$	$\frac{4,300}{(b/t)^2}$
	Flat plates with both edges supported		18	10	$\frac{h}{t} = 153$	$26.8 - 0.110\frac{h}{t}$	$\frac{h}{t} = 163$	$\frac{240,000}{(h/t)^2}$
				10	$\frac{h}{t} = 153$	$26.8 - 0.110\frac{h}{t}$	$\frac{h}{t} = 163$	$\frac{240,000}{(h/t)^2}$
	Flat plates with horizontal stiffener, both edges supported		19	10	$\frac{h}{t} = 320$	$26.8 - 0.053\frac{h}{t}$	$\frac{h}{t} = 340$	$\frac{1,020,000}{(h/t)^2}$
				10	$\frac{h}{t} = 320$	$26.8 - 0.053\frac{h}{t}$	$\frac{h}{t} = 340$	$\frac{1,020,000}{(h/t)^2}$
SHEAR IN WEBS, gross section	Unstiffened flat webs		20	7.5	$\frac{h}{t} = 18$	$8.4 - 0.051\frac{h}{t}$	$\frac{h}{t} = 110$	$\frac{34,000}{(h/t)^2}$
				6	$\frac{h}{t} = 47$	$8.4 - 0.051\frac{h}{t}$	$\frac{h}{t} = 110$	$\frac{34,000}{(h/t)^2}$
	Stiffened flat webs		21	7.5	$\frac{a_e}{t} = 75$	$13.7 - 0.083\frac{a_e}{t}$	$\frac{a_e}{t} = 110$	$\frac{55,000}{(a_e/t)^2}$
				6	$\frac{a_e}{t} = 93$	$13.7 - 0.083\frac{a_e}{t}$	$\frac{a_e}{t} = 110$	$\frac{55,000}{(a_e/t)^2}$

$$a_e = a_1 / \sqrt{1 + 0.7(a_1/a_2)^2}$$

NONSHADED BARS apply to nonwelded members and to welded members at locations farther than 1.0 in. from a weld.

SHADED BARS apply within 1.0 in. of a weld.

TABLE 1–SUGGESTED ALLOWABLE STRESSES

(SEE INTRODUCTION TO TABLE 1, p. 41)

5086-H34
Sheet and Plate, Drawn Tube

Type of Stress	Type of Member or Component	Spec. No.	Allowable Stress, ksi, Slenderness ≤ S_1	Slenderness Limit, S_1	Allowable Stress, ksi, Slenderness Between S_1 and S_2	Slenderness Limit, S_2	Allowable Stress, ksi, Slenderness ≥ S_2
TENSION, axial, net section	Any tension member	1	21				
TENSION IN BEAMS, extreme fiber, net section	Structural shapes, rectangular tubes, built-up members bent about X-axis	2	21				
	Round or oval tubes	3	24				
	Rectangular bars, plates, outstanding flanges of shapes bent about Y-axis	4	27				
BEARING	On rivets and bolts	5	35				
	On milled surfaces and pins	6	23				
COMPRESSION IN COLUMNS, axial, gross section	Columns (also see Specs. 8 to 10)	7	18	$\frac{L}{r}=9.1$	$19.3-0.143\frac{L}{r}$	$\frac{L}{r}=90$	$\dfrac{53{,}000}{(L/r)^2}$
			11.5	$\frac{L}{r}=55$	$19.3-0.143\frac{L}{r}$	$\frac{L}{r}=90$	$\dfrac{53{,}000}{(L/r)^2}$
Components of columns (also see Spec. 7)	Outstanding flanges and legs	8	18	$\frac{b}{t}=5.5$	$23.3-0.97\frac{b}{t}$	$\frac{b}{t}=16$	$\dfrac{2{,}000}{(b/t)^2}$
			11.5	$\frac{b}{t}=12$	$23.3-0.97\frac{b}{t}$	$\frac{b}{t}=16$	$\dfrac{2{,}000}{(b/t)^2}$
	Flat plates with both edges supported	9	18	$\frac{b}{t}=17$	$23.3-0.31\frac{b}{t}$	$\frac{b}{t}=50$	$\dfrac{19{,}800}{(b/t)^2}$
			11.5	$\frac{b}{t}=38$	$23.3-0.31\frac{b}{t}$	$\frac{b}{t}=50$	$\dfrac{19{,}800}{(b/t)^2}$
	Curved plates supported on both edges, walls of round or oval tubes	10	18	$\frac{R}{t}=18$	$22.1-0.96\sqrt{\frac{R}{t}}$	$\frac{R}{t}=192$	$\dfrac{3{,}300}{\frac{R}{t}\left(1+\frac{\sqrt{R/t}}{35}\right)}$
			11.5	$\frac{R}{t}=8$	$12.8-0.46\sqrt{\frac{R}{t}}$	$\frac{R}{t}=320$	$\dfrac{3{,}300}{\frac{R}{t}\left(1+\frac{\sqrt{R/t}}{35}\right)}$
COMPRESSION IN BEAMS, extreme fiber, gross section	Single-web beams bent about X-axis (also see Specs. 15 to 19)	11	18	$\frac{L_b}{r_y}=11$	$19.3-0.119\frac{L_b}{r_y}$	$\frac{L_b}{r_y}=108$	$\dfrac{76{,}000}{(L_b/r_y)^2}$
			11.5	$\frac{L_b}{r_y}=66$	$19.3-0.119\frac{L_b}{r_y}$	$\frac{L_b}{r_y}=108$	$\dfrac{76{,}000}{(L_b/r_y)^2}$
	Round or oval tubes	12	23	$\frac{R_b}{t}=19$	$33.1-2.3\sqrt{\frac{R_b}{t}}$	$\frac{R_b}{t}=73$	Same as Specification No. 10
			13.5	$\frac{R_b}{t}=27$	$19.2-1.09\sqrt{\frac{R_b}{t}}$	$\frac{R_b}{t}=104$	

Design stresses for aluminum — specifications 13–21.

Category	Description	No.	Bar	Value	Limit (slenderness)	Straight-line formula	Limit (slenderness)	Formula
COMPRESSION IN BEAMS, extreme fiber, gross section	Extreme fibers of beams (also see Specs. 15 to 19) — Solid rectangular beams bent about X-axis	13	nonshaded	25	$\frac{r}{d}\sqrt{\frac{L_b}{d}} = 9$	$31.0-0.6\frac{r}{t}\sqrt{\frac{L_b}{d}}$	$\frac{r}{t}\sqrt{\frac{L_b}{d}} = 31$	$(d/t)^2(L_b/d)$
			shaded	15	$\frac{r}{d}\sqrt{\frac{L_b}{d}} = 24$	$31.0-0.67\frac{d}{t}\sqrt{\frac{L_b}{d}}$	$\frac{d}{t}\sqrt{\frac{L_b}{d}} = 31$	$\dfrac{10,000}{(d/t)^2(L_b/d)}$
	Rectangular tubes and box sections	14	nonshaded	18	$\frac{L_bS_c}{I_y} = 32$	$19.3-0.23\sqrt{\frac{L_bS_c}{I_y}}$	$\frac{L_bS_c}{I_y} = 3160$	$\dfrac{21,000}{(L_bS_c/I_y)}$
			shaded	11.5	$\frac{L_bS_c}{I_y} = 1150$	$19.3-0.23\sqrt{\frac{L_bS_c}{I_y}}$	$\frac{L_bS_c}{I_y} = 3160$	$\dfrac{21,000}{(L_bS_c/I_y)}$
	Components of beams, component under uniform compression (also see Specs. 11 to 14) — Outstanding flanges	15	nonshaded	18	$\frac{b}{t} = 6.2$	$23.3-0.85\frac{b}{t}$	$\frac{b}{t} = 18$	$\dfrac{2,600}{(b/t)^2}$
			shaded	11.5	$\frac{b}{t} = 14$	$23.3-0.85\frac{b}{t}$	$\frac{b}{t} = 18$	$\dfrac{2,600}{(b/t)^2}$
	Flat plates with both edges supported	16	nonshaded	18	$\frac{b}{t} = 17$	$23.3-0.31\frac{b}{t}$	$\frac{b}{t} = 50$	$\dfrac{19,800}{(b/t)^2}$
			shaded	11.5	$\frac{b}{t} = 38$	$23.3-0.31\frac{b}{t}$	$\frac{b}{t} = 50$	$\dfrac{19,800}{(b/t)^2}$
	Components of beams, component under bending in its own plane (also see Specs. 11 to 14) — Flat plates with compression edge free, tension edge supported	17	nonshaded	25	$\frac{b}{t} = 5.9$	$31.0-1.01\frac{b}{t}$	$\frac{b}{t} = 20$	$\dfrac{4,300}{(b/t)^2}$
			shaded	15	$\frac{b}{t} = 16$	$31.0-1.01\frac{b}{t}$	$\frac{b}{t} = 20$	$\dfrac{4,300}{(b/t)^2}$
	Flat plates with both edges supported	18	nonshaded	18	— —	18	$\frac{h}{t} = 115$	$\dfrac{240,000}{(h/t)^2}$
			shaded	11.5	— —	11.5	$\frac{h}{t} = 144$	$\dfrac{240,000}{(h/t)^2}$
	Flat plates with horizontal stiffener, both edges supported	19	nonshaded	18	— — —	18	$\frac{h}{t} = 238$	$\dfrac{1,020,000}{(h/t)^2}$
			shaded	11.5	— — —	11.5	$\frac{h}{t} = 300$	$\dfrac{1,020,000}{(h/t)^2}$
SHEAR IN WEBS, gross section	Unstiffened flat webs	20	nonshaded	12	$\frac{h}{t} = 24$	$14.8-0.119\frac{h}{t}$	$\frac{h}{t} = 83$	$\dfrac{34,000}{(h/t)^2}$
			shaded	6.5	$\frac{h}{t} = 70$	$14.8-0.119\frac{h}{t}$	$\frac{h}{t} = 83$	$\dfrac{34,000}{(h/t)^2}$
	Stiffened flat webs	21	nonshaded	12	$\frac{a_e}{t} = 62$	$24.0-0.193\frac{a_e}{t}$	$\frac{a_e}{t} = 83$	$\dfrac{55,000}{(a_e/t)^2}$
			shaded	6.5	— —	6.5	$\frac{a_e}{t} = 92$	$\dfrac{55,000}{(a_e/t)^2}$

For Spec. 21 (stiffened flat webs):

$$a_e = a_1 / \sqrt{1 + 0.7\,(a_1/a_2)^2}$$

NONSHADED BARS apply to nonwelded members and to welded members at locations farther than 1.0 in. from a weld.

SHADED BARS apply within 1.0 in. of a weld.

TABLE 1—SUGGESTED ALLOWABLE STRESSES *(SEE INTRODUCTION TO TABLE 1, p. 41)*

5454-H111 Extrusions

Where two values are shown in a cell, the first is the plain (upper) value and the second is the bold/shaded (lower) value as printed.

Type of Stress	Type of Member or Component	Spec. No.	Allowable Stress, ksi, Slenderness $\le S_1$	Slenderness Limit, S_1	Allowable Stress, ksi, Slenderness Between S_1 and S_2	Slenderness Limit, S_2	Allowable Stress, ksi, Slenderness $\ge S_2$
TENSION, axial, net section	Any tension member	1	11.5 / 9.5				
TENSION IN BEAMS, extreme fiber, net section	Structural shapes, rectangular tubes, built-up members bent about X-axis	2	11.5 / 9.5				
	Round or oval tubes	3	13.5 / 11.5				
	Rectangular bars, plates, outstanding flanges of shapes bent about Y-axis	4	15 / 12.5				
BEARING	On rivets and bolts	5	18 / 14.5				
	On milled surfaces and pins	6	12 / 9.5				
COMPRESSION IN COLUMNS, axial, gross section	Columns (also see Specs. 8 to 10)	7	9	$\dfrac{L}{r}=4.3$	$9.2-0.047\dfrac{L}{r}$	$\dfrac{L}{r}=131$	$\dfrac{53{,}000}{(L/r)^2}$
	Components of columns (also see Spec. 7) — Outstanding flanges and legs	8	9	$\dfrac{b}{t}=6.1$	$10.9-0.31\dfrac{b}{t}$	$\dfrac{b}{t}=23$	$\dfrac{2{,}000}{(b/t)^2}$
	Flat plates with both edges supported	9	9	$\dfrac{b}{t}=19$	$10.9-0.099\dfrac{b}{t}$	$\dfrac{b}{t}=74$	$\dfrac{19{,}800}{(b/t)^2}$
	Curved plates supported on both edges, walls of round or oval tubes	10	9	$\dfrac{R}{t}=22$ / $\dfrac{R}{t}=7.4$	$10.7-0.36\sqrt{\dfrac{R}{t}}$ / $9.9-0.33\sqrt{\dfrac{R}{t}}$	$\dfrac{R}{t}=380$ / $\dfrac{R}{t}=410$	$\dfrac{3{,}300}{\dfrac{R}{t}\left(1+\dfrac{\sqrt{R/t}}{35}\right)}$
COMPRESSION IN BEAMS, extreme fiber, gross section	Single-web beams bent about X-axis (Extreme fibers of beams, also see Specs. 15 to 19)	11	9	$\dfrac{L_b}{r_y}=5.1$	$9.2-0.039\dfrac{L_b}{r_y}$	$\dfrac{L_b}{r_y}=157$	$\dfrac{76{,}000}{(L_b/r_y)^2}$
	Round or oval tubes	12	11.5 / 10.5	$\dfrac{R_b}{t}=28$ / $\dfrac{R_b}{t}=33$	$16.0-0.85\sqrt{\dfrac{R_b}{t}}$ / $15.0-0.78\sqrt{\dfrac{R_b}{t}}$	$\dfrac{R_b}{t}=118$ / $\dfrac{R_b}{t}=123$	$\dfrac{76{,}000}{(L_b/r_b)^2}$; Same as Specification No. 10 (See p. 71)

Table — Design stresses for aluminum (continued). Items 13–21.

Legend: NONSHADED BARS = nonwelded members (and welded members farther than 1.0 in. from a weld). SHADED BARS = within 1.0 in. of a weld.

Group	Type of member	No.	(coef.)	Slenderness limit (low)	Allowable stress	Slenderness limit (high)	Allowable stress
COMPRESSION IN BEAMS, extreme fiber, gross section — Extreme fibers of beams (also see Specs. 15 to 19)	Solid rectangular beams bent about X-axis	13	12.5	$\frac{d}{t}\sqrt{\frac{L_b}{d}}=9.5$	$14.5-0.21\frac{d}{t}\sqrt{\frac{L_b}{d}}$	$\frac{d}{t}\sqrt{\frac{L_b}{d}}=45$	$\dfrac{10{,}000}{(d/t)^2(L_b/d)}$
			12	$\frac{d}{t}\sqrt{\frac{L_b}{d}}=12$	$14.5-0.21\frac{d}{t}\sqrt{\frac{L_b}{d}}$	$\frac{d}{t}\sqrt{\frac{L_b}{d}}=45$	$\dfrac{10{,}000}{(d/t)^2(L_b/d)}$
	Rectangular tubes and box sections	14	9	$\frac{L_bS_c}{I_y}=7.1$	$9.2-0.075\sqrt{\frac{L_bS_c}{I_y}}$	$\frac{L_bS_c}{I_y}=6700$	$\dfrac{21{,}000}{(L_bS_c/I_y)}$
			9	$\frac{L_bS_c}{I_y}=7.1$	$9.2-0.075\sqrt{\frac{L_bS_c}{I_y}}$	$\frac{L_bS_c}{I_y}=6700$	$\dfrac{21{,}000}{(L_bS_c/I_y)}$
Components of beams, component under uniform compression (also see Specs. 11 to 14)	Outstanding flanges	15	9	$\frac{b}{t}=7$	$10.9-0.27\frac{b}{t}$	$\frac{b}{t}=27$	$\dfrac{2{,}600}{(b/t)^2}$
			9	$\frac{b}{t}=7$	$10.9-0.27\frac{b}{t}$	$\frac{b}{t}=27$	$\dfrac{2{,}600}{(b/t)^2}$
	Flat plates with both edges supported	16	9	$\frac{b}{t}=19$	$10.9-0.099\frac{b}{t}$	$\frac{b}{t}=74$	$\dfrac{19{,}800}{(b/t)^2}$
			9	$\frac{b}{t}=19$	$10.9-0.099\frac{b}{t}$	$\frac{b}{t}=74$	$\dfrac{19{,}800}{(b/t)^2}$
	Flat plates with compression edge free, tension edge supported	17	12.5	$\frac{b}{t}=6.3$	$14.5-0.32\frac{b}{t}$	$\frac{b}{t}=30$	$\dfrac{4{,}300}{(b/t)^2}$
			12	$\frac{b}{t}=7.8$	$14.5-0.32\frac{b}{t}$	$\frac{b}{t}=30$	$\dfrac{4{,}300}{(b/t)^2}$
Components of beams, component under bending in its own plane (also see Specs. 11 to 14)	Flat plates with both edges supported	18	9	$\frac{h}{t}=162$	$23.5-0.090\frac{h}{t}$	$\frac{h}{t}=175$	$\dfrac{240{,}000}{(h/t)^2}$
			9	$\frac{h}{t}=162$	$23.5-0.090\frac{h}{t}$	$\frac{h}{t}=175$	$\dfrac{240{,}000}{(h/t)^2}$
	Flat plates with horizontal stiffener, both edges supported	19	9	$\frac{h}{t}=330$	$23.5-0.044\frac{h}{t}$	$\frac{h}{t}=360$	$\dfrac{1{,}020{,}000}{(h/t)^2}$
			9	$\frac{h}{t}=330$	$23.5-0.044\frac{h}{t}$	$\frac{h}{t}=360$	$\dfrac{1{,}020{,}000}{(h/t)^2}$
SHEAR IN WEBS, gross section	Unstiffened flat webs	20	6.5	$\frac{h}{t}=25$	$7.6-0.044\frac{h}{t}$	$\frac{h}{t}=115$	$\dfrac{34{,}000}{(h/t)^2}$
			6	$\frac{h}{t}=36$	$7.6-0.044\frac{h}{t}$	$\frac{h}{t}=115$	$\dfrac{34{,}000}{(h/t)^2}$
	Stiffened flat webs	21	6.5	$\frac{a_e}{t}=82$	$12.4-0.072\frac{a_e}{t}$	$\frac{a_e}{t}=115$	$\dfrac{55{,}000}{(a_e/t)^2}$
			6	$\frac{a_e}{t}=89$	$12.4-0.072\frac{a_e}{t}$	$\frac{a_e}{t}=115$	$\dfrac{55{,}000}{(a_e/t)^2}$

$$a_e = a_1 / \sqrt{1 + 0.7\,(a_1/a_2)^2}$$

NONSHADED BARS apply to nonwelded members and to welded members at locations farther than 1.0 in. from a weld.

SHADED BARS apply within 1.0 in. of a weld.

TABLE 1—SUGGESTED ALLOWABLE STRESSES *(SEE INTRODUCTION TO TABLE 1, p. 41)*

5454-H34
Sheet and Plate
Drawn Tube

Type of Stress	Type of Member or Component	Spec. No.	Allowable Stress, ksi, Slenderness ≤ S₁	Slenderness Limit, S₁	Allowable Stress, ksi, Slenderness Between S₁ and S₂	Slenderness Limit, S₂	Allowable Stress, ksi, Slenderness ≥ S₂
TENSION, axial, net section	Any tension member	1	18				
TENSION IN BEAMS, extreme fiber, net section	Structural shapes, rectangular tubes, built-up members bent about X-axis	2	18				
	Round or oval tubes	3	21				
	Rectangular bars, plates, outstanding flanges of shapes bent about Y-axis	4	23				
BEARING	On rivets and bolts	5	30				
	On milled surfaces and pins	6	20				
COMPRESSION IN COLUMNS, axial, gross section	Columns (also see Specs. 8 to 10)	7	15 9.5	$\frac{L}{r}=10$ $\frac{L}{r}=61$	$16.1-0.109\frac{L}{r}$	$\frac{L}{r}=99$	$\dfrac{53,000}{(L/r)^2}$
	Components of columns (also see Spec. 7): Outstanding flanges and legs	8	15 9.5	$\frac{b}{t}=5.9$ $\frac{b}{t}=13$	$19.3-0.73\frac{b}{t}$	$\frac{b}{t}=18$	$\dfrac{2,000}{(b/t)^2}$
	Flat plates with both edges supported	9	15 9.5	$\frac{b}{t}=19$ $\frac{b}{t}=43$	$19.3-0.23\frac{b}{t}$	$\frac{b}{t}=56$	$\dfrac{19,800}{(b/t)^2}$
	Curved plates supported on both edges, walls of round or oval tubes	10	15 9.5	$\frac{R}{t}=22$ $\frac{R}{t}=11$	$18.5-0.75\sqrt{\frac{R}{t}}$ $10.7-0.36\sqrt{\frac{R}{t}}$	$\frac{R}{t}=226$ $\frac{R}{t}=380$	$\dfrac{3,300}{\frac{R}{t}\left(1+\frac{\sqrt{R/t}}{35}\right)^2}$
COMPRESSION IN BEAMS, extreme fiber, gross section	Extreme fibers of beams (also see Specs. 15 to 19): Single-web beams bent about X-axis	11	15 9.5	$\frac{L_b}{r_y}=12$ $\frac{L_b}{r_y}=73$	$16.1-0.09\frac{L_b}{r_y}$ $16.1-0.091\frac{L_b}{r_y}$	$\frac{L_b}{r_y}=119$	$\dfrac{76,000}{(L_b/r_y)^2}$
	Round or oval tubes	12	19 11.5	$\frac{R_b}{t}=24$ $\frac{R_b}{t}=28$	$27.7-1.78\sqrt{\frac{R_b}{t}}$ $16.0-0.85\sqrt{\frac{R_b}{t}}$	$\frac{R_b}{t}=82$ $\frac{R_b}{t}=118$	Same as Specification No. 10

	Description	No.	Value	Value (shaded)	Limit	Formula	Limit	Final formula
COMPRESSION IN BEAMS, extreme fiber, gross section	Solid rectangular beams bent about X-axis	13	21	**12.5**	$\dfrac{\sqrt{d}}{t}=9.4$ $\dfrac{d}{t}\sqrt{\dfrac{L_b}{d}}=26$	$25.7-0.50\dfrac{d}{t}\sqrt{\dfrac{L_b}{d}}$ $25.7-0.50\dfrac{d}{t}\sqrt{\dfrac{L_b}{d}}$	$\dfrac{\sqrt{d}}{t}\sqrt{\dfrac{d}{}}=34$ $\dfrac{d}{t}\sqrt{\dfrac{L_b}{d}}=34$	$\overline{(d/t)^2(L_b/d)}$ $\dfrac{10{,}000}{(d/t)^2(L_b/d)}$
	Rectangular tubes and box sections	14	15 **9.5**		$\dfrac{L_bS_c}{I_y}=40$ $\dfrac{L_bS_c}{I_y}=1440$	$16.1-0.174\sqrt{\dfrac{L_bS_c}{I_y}}$ $16.1-0.174\sqrt{\dfrac{L_bS_c}{I_y}}$	$\dfrac{L_bS_c}{I_y}=3830$ $\dfrac{L_bS_c}{I_y}=3830$	$\dfrac{21{,}000}{(L_bS_c/I_y)}$ $\dfrac{21{,}000}{(L_bS_c/I_y)}$
Components of beams, component under uniform compression (also see Specs. 11 to 14)	Outstanding flanges	15	15 **9.5**		$\dfrac{b}{t}=6.7$ $\dfrac{b}{t}=15$	$19.3-0.64\dfrac{b}{t}$ $19.3-0.64\dfrac{b}{t}$	$\dfrac{b}{t}=20$ $\dfrac{b}{t}=20$	$\dfrac{2{,}600}{(b/t)^2}$ $\dfrac{2{,}600}{(b/t)^2}$
	Flat plates with both edges supported	16	15 **9.5**		$\dfrac{b}{t}=19$ $\dfrac{b}{t}=43$	$19.3-0.23\dfrac{b}{t}$ $19.3-0.23\dfrac{b}{t}$	$\dfrac{b}{t}=56$ $\dfrac{b}{t}=56$	$\dfrac{19{,}800}{(b/t)^2}$ $\dfrac{19{,}800}{(b/t)^2}$
	Flat plates with compression edge free, tension edge supported	17	21 **12.5**		$\dfrac{b}{t}=6.2$ $\dfrac{b}{t}=17$	$25.7-0.76\dfrac{b}{t}$ $25.7-0.76\dfrac{b}{t}$	$\dfrac{b}{t}=22$ $\dfrac{b}{t}=22$	$\dfrac{4{,}300}{(b/t)^2}$ $\dfrac{4{,}300}{(b/t)^2}$
Components of beams, component under bending in its own plane (also see Specs. 11 to 14)	Flat plates with both edges supported	18	15 **9.5**		– – – –	15 9.5	$\dfrac{h}{t}=126$ $\dfrac{h}{t}=159$	$\dfrac{240{,}000}{(h/t)^2}$ $\dfrac{240{,}000}{(h/t)^2}$
	Flat plates with horizontal stiffener, both edges supported	19	15 **9.5**		– – – –	15 9.5	$\dfrac{h}{t}=260$ $\dfrac{h}{t}=330$	$\dfrac{1{,}020{,}000}{(h/t)^2}$ $\dfrac{1{,}020{,}000}{(h/t)^2}$
SHEAR IN WEBS, gross section	Unstiffened flat webs	20	10.5 **6**		$\dfrac{h}{t}=21$ $\dfrac{h}{t}=70$	$12.4-0.091\dfrac{h}{t}$ $12.4-0.091\dfrac{h}{t}$	$\dfrac{h}{t}=90$ $\dfrac{h}{t}=90$	$\dfrac{34{,}000}{(h/t)^2}$ $\dfrac{34{,}000}{(h/t)^2}$
	Stiffened flat webs	21	10.5 **6**		$\dfrac{a_e}{t}=65$ – –	$20.1-0.148\dfrac{a_e}{t}$ 6	$\dfrac{a_e}{t}=90$ $\dfrac{a_e}{t}=96$	$\dfrac{55{,}000}{(a_e/t)^2}$ $\dfrac{55{,}000}{(a_e/t)^2}$

$$a_e = a_1\,/\,\sqrt{1+0.7\,(a_1/a_2)^2}$$

Extreme fibers of beams (also see Specs. 15 to 19)

Compression Flange

Neutral Axis

NONSHADED BARS apply to nonwelded members and to welded members at locations farther than 1.0 in. from a weld.   SHADED BARS apply within 1.0 in. of a weld.

TABLE 1–SUGGESTED ALLOWABLE STRESSES

TABLE 1—SUGGESTED ALLOWABLE STRESSES *(SEE INTRODUCTION TO TABLE 1, p. 41)*

5456-H111 Extrusions

In the paired entries below, the first number (plain) and the second number (shaded, under the *5456-H111 Extrusions* heading) are given as printed.

Type of Stress	Type of Member or Component	Spec. No.	Allowable Stress, ksi	Allowable Stress, ksi, Slenderness $\le S_1$	Slenderness Limit, S_1	Allowable Stress, ksi, Slenderness Between S_1 and S_2	Slenderness Limit, S_2	Allowable Stress, ksi, Slenderness $\ge S_2$
TENSION, axial, net section	Any tension member	1	16 / 14.5					
TENSION IN BEAMS, extreme fiber, net section	Structural shapes, rectangular tubes, built-up members bent about X-axis	2	16 / 14.5					
	Round or oval tubes	3	18 / 17					
	Rectangular bars, plates, outstanding flanges of shapes bent about Y-axis	4	20 / 19					
BEARING	On rivets and bolts	5	25 / 23					
	On milled surfaces and pins	6	17 / 15					
COMPRESSION IN COLUMNS, axial, gross section	Columns (also see Specs. 8 to 10)	7		12	$\dfrac{L}{r}=13$	$13.0-0.078\dfrac{L}{r}$	$\dfrac{L}{r}=110$	$\dfrac{53{,}000}{(L/r)^2}$
	Outstanding flanges and legs	8		12	$\dfrac{b}{t}=6.5$	$15.4-0.52\dfrac{b}{t}$	$\dfrac{b}{t}=20$	$\dfrac{2{,}000}{(b/t)^2}$
	Flat plates with both edges supported	9		12	$\dfrac{b}{t}=20$	$15.4-0.166\dfrac{b}{t}$	$\dfrac{b}{t}=62$	$\dfrac{19{,}800}{(b/t)^2}$
	Curved plates supported on both edges, walls of round or oval tubes	10		12	$\dfrac{R}{t}=26$	$14.9-0.57\sqrt{\dfrac{R}{t}}$	$\dfrac{R}{t}=280$	$\dfrac{3{,}300}{\dfrac{R}{t}\left(1+\dfrac{\sqrt{R/t}}{35}\right)^2}$
COMPRESSION IN BEAMS, extreme fiber, gross section	Single-web beams bent about X-axis	11		12	$\dfrac{L_b}{r_y}=15$	$13.0-0.065\dfrac{L_b}{r_y}$	$\dfrac{L_b}{r_y}=132$	$\dfrac{76{,}000}{(L_b/r_y)^2}$
	Round or oval tubes	12		16	$\dfrac{R_b}{t}=23$	$22.4-1.33\sqrt{\dfrac{R_b}{t}}$	$\dfrac{R_b}{t}=94$	Same as Specification No. 10

Note (specs 8, 9, 10): Components of columns (also see Spec. 7).

Note (spec 11, 12): Extreme fibers of beams (also see Specs. 15 to 19).

Category	Description	Diagram	Spec									
Extreme fibers of beams (also see Specs. 15 to 19)	Solid rectangular beams bent about X-axis		**13**	17	$\dfrac{a}{t}\sqrt{\dfrac{L_b}{d}}=9.7$	$20.5-0.36\dfrac{a}{t}\sqrt{\dfrac{L_b}{d}}$	$\dfrac{a}{t}\sqrt{\dfrac{L_b}{d}}=38$	$\dfrac{(d/t)^2(L_b/d)}{10,000}$				
				17	$\dfrac{d}{t}\sqrt{\dfrac{L_b}{d}}=9.7$	$20.5-0.36\dfrac{d}{t}\sqrt{\dfrac{L_b}{d}}$	$\dfrac{d}{t}\sqrt{\dfrac{L_b}{d}}=38$	$\dfrac{10,000}{(d/t)^2(L_b/d)}$				
	Rectangular tubes and box sections		**14**	12	$\dfrac{L_bS_c}{I_y}=64$	$13.0-0.125\sqrt{\dfrac{L_bS_c}{I_y}}$	$\dfrac{L_bS_c}{I_y}=4730$	$\dfrac{21,000}{(L_bS_c/I_y)}$				
				12	$\dfrac{L_bS_c}{I_y}=64$	$13.0-0.125\sqrt{\dfrac{L_bS_c}{I_y}}$	$\dfrac{L_bS_c}{I_y}=4730$	$\dfrac{21,000}{(L_bS_c/I_y)}$				
COMPRESSION IN BEAMS, extreme fiber, gross section. Components of beams, component under uniform compression (also see Specs. 11 to 14)	Outstanding flanges		**15**	12	$\dfrac{b}{t}=7.4$	$15.4-0.46\dfrac{b}{t}$	$\dfrac{b}{t}=22$	$\dfrac{2,600}{(b/t)^2}$				
				12	$\dfrac{b}{t}=7.4$	$15.4-0.46\dfrac{b}{t}$	$\dfrac{b}{t}=22$	$\dfrac{2,600}{(b/t)^2}$				
	Flat plates with both edges supported		**16**	12	$\dfrac{b}{t}=20$	$15.4-0.166\dfrac{b}{t}$	$\dfrac{b}{t}=62$	$\dfrac{19,800}{(b/t)^2}$				
				12	$\dfrac{b}{t}=20$	$15.4-0.166\dfrac{b}{t}$	$\dfrac{b}{t}=62$	$\dfrac{19,800}{(b/t)^2}$				
Components of beams, component under bending in its own plane (also see Specs. 11 to 14)	Flat plates with compression edge free, tension edge supported		**17**	17	$\dfrac{b}{t}=6.4$	$20.5-0.55\dfrac{b}{t}$	$\dfrac{b}{t}=25$	$\dfrac{4,300}{(b/t)^2}$				
				17	$\dfrac{b}{t}=6.4$	$20.5-0.55\dfrac{b}{t}$	$\dfrac{b}{t}=25$	$\dfrac{4,300}{(b/t)^2}$				
	Flat plates with both edges supported		**18**	12	– – –	12	$\dfrac{h}{t}=141$	$\dfrac{240,000}{(h/t)^2}$				
				12	– – –	12	$\dfrac{h}{t}=141$	$\dfrac{240,000}{(h/t)^2}$				
	Flat plates with horizontal stiffener, both edges supported		**19**	12	– – –	12	$\dfrac{h}{t}=290$	$\dfrac{1,020,000}{(h/t)^2}$				
				12	– – –	12	$\dfrac{h}{t}=290$	$\dfrac{1,020,000}{(h/t)^2}$				
SHEAR IN WEBS, gross section	Unstiffened flat webs		**20**	9	$\dfrac{h}{t}=24$	$10.8-0.074\dfrac{h}{t}$	$\dfrac{h}{t}=97$	$\dfrac{34,000}{(h/t)^2}$				
				8.5	$\dfrac{h}{t}=31$	$10.8-0.074\dfrac{h}{t}$	$\dfrac{h}{t}=97$	$\dfrac{34,000}{(h/t)^2}$				
	Stiffened flat webs		**21**	9	$\dfrac{a_e}{t}=71$	$17.5-0.120\dfrac{a_e}{t}$	$\dfrac{a_e}{t}=97$	$\dfrac{55,000}{(a_e/t)^2}$				
				8.5	$\dfrac{a_e}{t}=75$	$17.5-0.120\dfrac{a_e}{t}$	$\dfrac{a_e}{t}=97$	$\dfrac{55,000}{(a_e/t)^2}$				

$$a_e = a_1 / \sqrt{1 + 0.7\,(a_1 / a_2)^2}$$

NONSHADED BARS apply to nonwelded members and to welded members at locations farther than 1.0 in. from a weld.   SHADED BARS apply within 1.0 in. of a weld.

TABLE 1–SUGGESTED ALLOWABLE STRESSES

(SEE INTRODUCTION TO TABLE 1, p. 41)

5456-H321
Sheet and Plate
(Thickness—0.188-1.250 in.)

Type of Stress	Type of Member or Component	Spec. No.	Allowable Stress, ksi, Slenderness ≤ S_1	Slenderness Limit, S_1	Allowable Stress, ksi, Slenderness Between S_1 and S_2	Slenderness Limit, S_2	Allowable Stress, ksi, Slenderness ≥ S_2
TENSION, axial, net section	Any tension member	1	20				16
TENSION IN BEAMS, extreme fiber, net section	Structural shapes, rectangular tubes, built-up members bent about X-axis	2	20				16
	Round or oval tubes	3	23				18
	Rectangular bars, plates, outstanding flanges of shapes bent about Y-axis	4	26				20
BEARING	On rivets and bolts	5	34				23
	On milled surfaces and pins	6	23				15
COMPRESSION IN COLUMNS, axial, gross section	Columns (also see Specs. 8 to 10)	7	15	$\frac{L}{r}=10$	$16.1-0.109\frac{L}{r}$	$\frac{L}{r}=99$	$\frac{53{,}000}{(L/r)^2}$
			14.5	$\frac{L}{r}=15$	$16.1-0.109\frac{L}{r}$	$\frac{L}{r}=99$	$\frac{53{,}000}{(L/r)^2}$
	Components of columns (also see Spec. 7) — Outstanding flanges and legs	8	15	$\frac{b}{t}=5.9$	$19.3-0.73\frac{b}{t}$	$\frac{b}{t}=18$	$\frac{2{,}000}{(b/t)^2}$
			14.5	$\frac{b}{t}=6.6$	$19.3-0.73\frac{b}{t}$	$\frac{b}{t}=18$	$\frac{2{,}000}{(b/t)^2}$
	Flat plates with both edges supported	9	15	$\frac{b}{t}=19$	$19.3-0.23\frac{b}{t}$	$\frac{b}{t}=56$	$\frac{19{,}800}{(b/t)^2}$
			14.5	$\frac{b}{t}=21$	$19.3-0.23\frac{b}{t}$	$\frac{b}{t}=56$	$\frac{19{,}800}{(b/t)^2}$
	Curved plates supported on both edges, walls of round or oval tubes	10	15	$\frac{R}{t}=22$	$18.5-0.75\sqrt{\frac{R}{t}}$	$\frac{R}{t}=226$	$\frac{3{,}300}{\frac{R}{t}\left(1+\frac{\sqrt{R/t}}{35}\right)^2}$
			14.5	$\frac{R}{t}=7.9$	$16.3-0.64\sqrt{\frac{R}{t}}$	$\frac{R}{t}=250$	$\frac{3{,}300}{\frac{R}{t}\left(1+\frac{\sqrt{R/t}}{35}\right)^2}$
COMPRESSION IN BEAMS, extreme fiber, gross section	Extreme fibers of beams (also see Specs. 15 to 19) — Single-web beams bent about X-axis	11	15	$\frac{L_b}{r_y}=12$	$16.1-0.091\frac{L_b}{r_y}$	$\frac{L_b}{r_y}=119$	$\frac{76{,}000}{(L_b/r_y)^2}$
			14.5	$\frac{L_b}{r_y}=18$	$16.1-0.091\frac{L_b}{r_y}$	$\frac{L_b}{r_y}=119$	$\frac{76{,}000}{(L_b/r_y)^2}$
	Round or oval tubes	12	19	$\frac{R_b}{t}=24$	$27.7-1.78\sqrt{\frac{R_b}{t}}$	$\frac{R_b}{t}=82$	Same as Specification No. 10 (See p. 21)
			17	$\frac{R_b}{t}=25$	$24.5-1.51\sqrt{\frac{R_b}{t}}$	$\frac{R_b}{t}=89$	

Design Stresses for Aluminum

COMPRESSION IN BEAMS, extreme fiber, gross section

Extreme fibers of beams (also see Specs. 15 to 19)

Spec.	Member	Allowable stress	S_1 limit	Intermediate formula	S_2 limit	Beyond S_2
13	Solid rectangular beams bent about X-axis	21	$\frac{d}{t}\sqrt{\frac{L_b}{d}}=9.4$	$25.7-0.50\frac{d}{t}\sqrt{\frac{L_b}{d}}$	$\frac{d}{t}\sqrt{\frac{L_b}{d}}=34$	$\frac{10,000}{(d/t)^2(L_b/d)}$
13		**19**	$\mathbf{=13}$	$\mathbf{25.7-0.50\frac{d}{t}\sqrt{\frac{L_b}{d}}}$	$\mathbf{=34}$	$\mathbf{\frac{10,000}{(d/t)^2(L_b/d)}}$
14	Rectangular tubes and box sections	15	$\frac{L_bS_c}{I_y}=40$	$16.1-0.174\sqrt{\frac{L_bS_c}{I_y}}$	$\frac{L_bS_c}{I_y}=3830$	$\frac{21,000}{L_bS_c/I_y}$
14		**14.5**	$\mathbf{=85}$	$\mathbf{16.1-0.174\sqrt{\frac{L_bS_c}{I_y}}}$	$\mathbf{=3830}$	$\mathbf{\frac{21,000}{L_bS_c/I_y}}$

Components of beams, component under uniform compression (also see Specs. 11 to 14)

Spec.	Member	Allowable stress	S_1 limit	Intermediate formula	S_2 limit	Beyond S_2
15	Outstanding flanges	15	$\frac{b}{t}=6.7$	$19.3-0.64\frac{b}{t}$	$\frac{b}{t}=20$	$\frac{2,600}{(b/t)^2}$
15		**14.5**	$\mathbf{=7.5}$	$\mathbf{19.3-0.64\frac{b}{t}}$	$\mathbf{=20}$	$\mathbf{\frac{2,600}{(b/t)^2}}$
16	Flat plates with both edges supported	15	$\frac{b}{t}=19$	$19.3-0.23\frac{b}{t}$	$\frac{b}{t}=56$	$\frac{19,800}{(b/t)^2}$
16		**14.5**	$\mathbf{=21}$	$\mathbf{19.3-0.23\frac{b}{t}}$	$\mathbf{=56}$	$\mathbf{\frac{19,800}{(b/t)^2}}$

Components of beams, component under bending in its own plane (also see Specs. 11 to 14)

Spec.	Member	Allowable stress	S_1 limit	Intermediate formula	S_2 limit	Beyond S_2
17	Flat plates with compression edge free, tension edge supported	21	$\frac{b}{t}=6.2$	$25.7-0.76\frac{b}{t}$	$\frac{b}{t}=22$	$\frac{4,300}{(b/t)^2}$
17		**19**	$\mathbf{=8.8}$	$\mathbf{25.7-0.76\frac{b}{t}}$	$\mathbf{=22}$	$\mathbf{\frac{4,300}{(b/t)^2}}$
18	Flat plates with both edges supported	15	$---$	15	$\frac{h}{t}=126$	$\frac{240,000}{(h/t)^2}$
18		**14.5**	$---$	$\mathbf{14.5}$	$\mathbf{=129}$	$\mathbf{\frac{240,000}{(h/t)^2}}$
19	Flat plates with horizontal stiffener, both edges supported	15	$---$	15	$\frac{h}{t}=260$	$\frac{1,020,000}{(h/t)^2}$
19		**14.5**	$---$	$\mathbf{14.5}$	$\mathbf{=270}$	$\mathbf{\frac{1,020,000}{(h/t)^2}}$

SHEAR IN WEBS, gross section

Spec.	Member	Allowable stress	S_1 limit	Intermediate formula	S_2 limit	Beyond S_2
20	Unstiffened flat webs	11.5	$\frac{h}{t}=22$	$13.9-0.109\frac{h}{t}$	$\frac{h}{t}=86$	$\frac{34,000}{(h/t)^2}$
20		**9**	$\mathbf{=45}$	$\mathbf{13.9-0.109\frac{h}{t}}$	$\mathbf{=86}$	$\mathbf{\frac{34,000}{(h/t)^2}}$
21	Stiffened flat webs	11.5	$\frac{a_e}{t}=63$	$22.7-0.177\frac{a_e}{t}$	$\frac{a_e}{t}=86$	$\frac{55,000}{(a_e/t)^2}$
21		**9**	$\mathbf{=77}$	$\mathbf{22.7-0.177\frac{a_e}{t}}$	$\mathbf{=86}$	$\mathbf{\frac{55,000}{(a_e/t)^2}}$

$$a_e = a_1 / \sqrt{1+0.7(a_1/a_2)^2}$$

NONSHADED BARS apply to nonwelded members and to welded members at locations farther than 1.0 in. from a weld.

SHADED BARS apply within 1.0 in. of a weld.

TABLE 1—SUGGESTED ALLOWABLE STRESSES *(SEE INTRODUCTION TO TABLE 1, p. 41)*

5456-H343 Sheet

Tension and Bearing

Type of Stress	Type of Member or Component	Spec. No.	Allowable Stress, ksi
TENSION, axial, net section	Any tension member	1	25 / 16
TENSION IN BEAMS, extreme fiber, net section	Structural shapes, rectangular tubes, built-up members bent about X-axis	2	25 / 16
	Round or oval tubes	3	29 / 18
	Rectangular bars, plates, outstanding flanges of shapes bent about Y-axis	4	32 / 20
BEARING	On rivets and bolts	5	42 / 23
	On milled surfaces and pins	6	28 / 15

Compression

Type of Stress	Type of Member or Component	Spec. No.	Allowable Stress, ksi, Slenderness ≤ S₁	Slenderness Limit, S₁	Allowable Stress, ksi, Slenderness Between S₁ and S₂	Slenderness Limit, S₂	Allowable Stress, ksi, Slenderness ≥ S₂
COMPRESSION IN COLUMNS, axial, gross section	Columns (also see Specs. 8 to 10)	7	21	$\frac{L}{r}=15$	$23.9-0.196\frac{L}{r}$	$\frac{L}{r}=81$	$\dfrac{53{,}000}{(L/r)^2}$
			16	$\frac{L}{r}=40$	$23.9-0.196\frac{L}{r}$	$\frac{L}{r}=81$	$\dfrac{53{,}000}{(L/r)^2}$
	Outstanding flanges and legs	8	21	$\frac{b}{t}=5.9$	$28.9-1.34\frac{b}{t}$	$\frac{b}{t}=14$	$\dfrac{2{,}000}{(b/t)^2}$
			16	$\frac{b}{t}=9.6$	$28.9-1.34\frac{b}{t}$	$\frac{b}{t}=14$	$\dfrac{2{,}000}{(b/t)^2}$
Components of columns (also see Spec. 7)	Flat plates with both edges supported	9	21	$\frac{b}{t}=18$	$28.9-0.43\frac{b}{t}$	$\frac{b}{t}=45$	$\dfrac{19{,}800}{(b/t)^2}$
			16	$\frac{b}{t}=30$	$28.9-0.43\frac{b}{t}$	$\frac{b}{t}=45$	$\dfrac{19{,}800}{(b/t)^2}$
	Curved plates supported on both edges, walls of round or oval tubes	10	21	$\frac{R}{t}=24$	$27.2-1.26\sqrt{\frac{R}{t}}$	$\frac{R}{t}=157$	$\dfrac{3{,}300}{\frac{R}{t}\left(1+\frac{\sqrt{R/t}}{35}\right)}$
			16	$\frac{R}{t}=5.6$	$17.7-0.72\sqrt{\frac{R}{t}}$	$\frac{R}{t}=235$	$\dfrac{3{,}300}{\frac{R}{t}\left(1+\frac{\sqrt{R/t}}{35}\right)}$
COMPRESSION IN BEAMS, extreme fiber, gross section	Single-web beams bent about X-axis. Extreme fibers of beams (also see Specs. 15 to 19)	11	21	$\frac{L_b}{r_y}=18$	$23.9-0.164\frac{L_b}{r_y}$	$\frac{L_b}{r_y}=97$	$\dfrac{76{,}000}{(L_b/r_y)^2}$
			16	$\frac{L_b}{r_y}=48$	$23.9-0.164\frac{L_b}{r_y}$	$\frac{L_b}{r_y}=97$	$\dfrac{76{,}000}{(L_b/r_y)^2}$
	Round or oval tubes	12	28	$\frac{R_b}{t}=18$	$40.8-3.0\sqrt{\frac{R_b}{t}}$	$\frac{R_b}{t}=63$	Same as Specification No. 10
			18	$\frac{R_b}{t}=26$	$26.6-1.68\sqrt{\frac{R_b}{t}}$	$\frac{R_b}{t}=84$	(See p. 21)

ALUMINUM COMPANY OF AMERICA

COMPRESSION IN BEAMS, extreme fiber, gross section

Member	Bar	Spec. No.	F (ksi)	Slenderness limit	F (intermediate)	Slenderness limit	F (large slenderness)
Extreme fibers of beams (also see Specs. 15 to 19) — Solid rectangular beams bent about X-axis	nonshaded	13	31	$\frac{d}{t}\sqrt{\frac{L_b}{d}}=8.3$	$38.6-0.92\frac{d}{t}\sqrt{\frac{L_b}{d}}$	$\frac{d}{t}\sqrt{\frac{L_b}{d}}=28$	$\frac{10,000}{(d/t)^2(L_b/d)}$
	shaded		20	$\frac{d}{t}\sqrt{\frac{L_b}{d}}=20$	$38.6-0.92\frac{d}{t}\sqrt{\frac{L_b}{d}}$	$\frac{d}{t}\sqrt{\frac{L_b}{d}}=28$	$\frac{10,000}{(d/t)^2(L_b/d)}$
Rectangular tubes and box sections	nonshaded	14	21	$\frac{L_bS_c}{I_y}=88$	$23.9-0.31\sqrt{\frac{L_bS_c}{I_y}}$	$\frac{L_bS_c}{I_y}=2560$	$\frac{21,000}{(L_bS_c/I_y)}$
	shaded		16	$\frac{L_bS_c}{I_y}=650$	$23.9-0.31\sqrt{\frac{L_bS_c}{I_y}}$	$\frac{L_bS_c}{I_y}=2560$	$\frac{21,000}{(L_bS_c/I_y)}$
Components of beams, component under uniform compression (also see Specs. 11 to 14) — Outstanding flanges	nonshaded	15	21	$\frac{b}{t}=6.8$	$28.9-1.17\frac{b}{t}$	$\frac{b}{t}=16$	$\frac{2,600}{(b/t)^2}$
	shaded		16	$\frac{b}{t}=11$	$28.9-1.17\frac{b}{t}$	$\frac{b}{t}=16$	$\frac{2,600}{(b/t)^2}$
Flat plates with both edges supported	nonshaded	16	21	$\frac{b}{t}=18$	$28.9-0.43\frac{b}{t}$	$\frac{b}{t}=45$	$\frac{19,800}{(b/t)^2}$
	shaded		16	$\frac{b}{t}=30$	$28.9-0.43\frac{b}{t}$	$\frac{b}{t}=45$	$\frac{19,800}{(b/t)^2}$
Components of beams, component under bending in its own plane (also see Specs. 11 to 14) — Flat plates with compression edge free, tension edge supported	nonshaded	17	31	$\frac{b}{t}=5.4$	$38.6-1.41\frac{b}{t}$	$\frac{b}{t}=18$	$\frac{4,300}{(b/t)^2}$
	shaded		20	$\frac{b}{t}=13$	$38.6-1.41\frac{b}{t}$	$\frac{b}{t}=18$	$\frac{4,300}{(b/t)^2}$
Flat plates with both edges supported	nonshaded	18	21	---	21	$\frac{h}{t}=107$	$\frac{240,000}{(h/t)^2}$
	shaded		16	---	16	$\frac{h}{t}=122$	$\frac{240,000}{(h/t)^2}$
Flat plates with horizontal stiffener, both edges supported	nonshaded	19	21	---	21	$\frac{h}{t}=220$	$\frac{1,020,000}{(h/t)^2}$
	shaded		16	---	16	$\frac{h}{t}=250$	$\frac{1,020,000}{(h/t)^2}$

SHEAR IN WEBS, gross section

Member	Bar	Spec. No.	F (ksi)	Slenderness limit	F (intermediate)	Slenderness limit	F (large slenderness)
Unstiffened flat webs	nonshaded	20	14.5	$\frac{h}{t}=23$	$18.1-0.160\frac{h}{t}$	$\frac{h}{t}=75$	$\frac{34,000}{(h/t)^2}$
	shaded		9	$\frac{h}{t}=57$	$18.1-0.160\frac{h}{t}$	$\frac{h}{t}=75$	$\frac{34,000}{(h/t)^2}$
Stiffened flat webs	nonshaded	21	14.5	$\frac{a_e}{t}=57$	$29.3-0.26\frac{a_e}{t}$	$\frac{a_e}{t}=75$	$\frac{55,000}{(a_e/t)^2}$
	shaded		9	---	9	$\frac{a_e}{t}=78$	$\frac{55,000}{(a_e/t)^2}$

$$a_e = a_1/\sqrt{1+0.7(a_1/a_2)^2}$$

NONSHADED BARS apply to nonwelded members and to welded members at locations farther than 1.0 in. from a weld.

SHADED BARS apply within 1.0 in. of a weld.

TABLE 1—SUGGESTED ALLOWABLE STRESSES

TABLE 1—SUGGESTED ALLOWABLE STRESSES (*SEE INTRODUCTION TO TABLE 1, p. 41*)

6061-T6, -T651, -T6510, -T6511
Extrusions, Sheet and Plate, Standard Structural Shapes, Rolled Rod and Bar, Drawn Tube, Pipe

Type of Stress	Type of Member or Component	Spec. No.	Allowable Stress, ksi, Slenderness ≤ S_1	Slenderness Limit, S_1	Allowable Stress, ksi, Slenderness Between S_1 and S_2	Slenderness Limit, S_2	Allowable Stress, ksi, Slenderness ≥ S_2
TENSION, axial, net section	Any tension member	1	19				
			11[1]				
TENSION IN BEAMS, extreme fiber, net section	Structural shapes, rectangular tubes, built-up members bent about X-axis	2	19				
			11[1]				
	Round or oval tubes	3	24				
			13[1]				
	Rectangular bars, plates, outstanding flanges of shapes bent about Y-axis	4	26				
			13[1]				
BEARING	On rivets and bolts	5	34				
			18[1]				
	On milled surfaces and pins	6	23				
			12[1]				
COMPRESSION IN COLUMNS, axial, gross section	Columns (also see Specs. 8 to 10)	7	19	$\frac{L}{r}=10$	$20.4-0.135\frac{L}{r}$	$\frac{L}{r}=67$	$\frac{51,000}{(L/r)^2}$
			11[1]	– – –	11[1]	$\frac{L}{r}=68$[2]	$\frac{51,000}{(L/r)^2}$
	Components of columns (also see Spec. 7): Outstanding flanges and legs	8	19	$\frac{b}{t}=5.5$	$23.7-0.86\frac{b}{t}$	$\frac{b}{t}=12$	$\frac{1,940}{(b/t)^2}$
			11[1]	$\frac{b}{t}=4.9$[2]	$\frac{24.4}{\sqrt{b/t}}$	$\frac{b}{t}=19$	$\frac{1,940}{(b/t)^2}$
	Flat plates with both edges supported	9	19	$\frac{b}{t}=17$	$23.7-0.27\frac{b}{t}$	$\frac{b}{t}=38$	$\frac{19,200}{(b/t)^2}$
			11[1]	– – –	11[1]	$\frac{b}{t}=44$[2]	$\frac{19,200}{(b/t)^2}$
	Curved plates supported on both edges, walls of round or oval tubes	10	19	$\frac{R}{t}=22$	$22.6-0.76\sqrt{\frac{R}{t}}$	$\frac{R}{t}=125$	– – –
			11[1]	$\frac{R}{t}=14$[2]	$\frac{21.3}{(R/t)^{1/4}}$	$\frac{R}{t}=200$	– – –
COMPRESSION IN BEAMS, extreme fiber, gross section	Single-web beams bent about X-axis (Extreme fibers of beams, also see Specs. 15 to 19)	11	19	$\frac{L_b}{r_y}=12$	$20.4-0.113\frac{L_b}{r_y}$	$\frac{L_b}{r_y}=81$	$\frac{74,000}{(L_b/r_y)^2}$
			11[1]	– – –	11[1]	$\frac{L_b}{r_y}=82$[2]	$\frac{74,000}{(L_b/r_y)^2}$
	Round or oval tubes	12	24	$\frac{R_b}{t}=19$	$28.2-0.22\frac{R_b}{t}$	$\frac{R_b}{t}=60$	– – –
			13[1]	$\frac{R_b}{t}=13$[2]	$\frac{24.7}{(R_b/t)^{1/4}}$	$\frac{R_b}{t}=135$	– – –

Section	Element	No.					
COMPRESSION IN BEAMS, extreme fiber, gross section	**Extreme fibers of beams** (also see Specs. 15 to 19) — Solid rectangular beams bent about X-axis	**13**	26	$\frac{d}{t}\sqrt{\frac{L_b}{d}}=11$	$34.9-0.80\frac{d}{t}\sqrt{\frac{L_b}{d}}$	$\frac{d}{t}\sqrt{\frac{L_b}{d}}=29$	$\dfrac{9{,}900}{(d/t)^2(L_b/d)}$
	(shaded)		13[1]	$\frac{d}{t}\sqrt{\frac{L_b}{d}}=11$[2]	$\dfrac{42.3}{[(d/t)^2(L_b/d)]^{1/4}}$	$\frac{d}{t}\sqrt{\frac{L_b}{d}}=38$	$\dfrac{9{,}900}{(d/t)^2(L_b/d)}$
	Rectangular tubes and box sections	**14**	19	$\frac{L_bS_c}{I_y}=40$	$20.4-0.22\sqrt{\frac{L_bS_c}{I_y}}$	$\frac{L_bS_c}{I_y}=1810$	$\dfrac{20{,}000}{(L_bS_c/I_y)}$
	(shaded)		11[1]	— — —	11[1]	$\frac{L_bS_c}{I_y}=1820$[2]	$\dfrac{20{,}000}{(L_bS_c/I_y)}$
	Components of beams, component under uniform compression (also see Specs. 11 to 14) — Outstanding flanges	**15**	19	$\frac{b}{t}=6.2$	$23.7-0.76\frac{b}{t}$	$\frac{b}{t}=14$	$\dfrac{2{,}500}{(b/t)^2}$
	(shaded)		11[1]	$\frac{b}{t}=5.3$[2]	$\dfrac{25.4}{\sqrt{b/t}}$	$\frac{b}{t}=21$	$\dfrac{2{,}500}{(b/t)^2}$
	Flat plates with both edges supported	**16**	19	$\frac{b}{t}=17$	$23.7-0.27\frac{b}{t}$	$\frac{b}{t}=38$	$\dfrac{19{,}200}{(b/t)^2}$
	(shaded)		11[1]	— — —	11[1]	$\frac{b}{t}=44$[2]	$\dfrac{19{,}200}{(b/t)^2}$
	Components of beams, component under bending in its own plane (also see Specs. 11 to 14) — Flat plates with compression edge free, tension edge supported	**17**	26	$\frac{b}{t}=7.3$	$34.9-1.24\frac{b}{t}$	$\frac{b}{t}=19$	$\dfrac{4{,}200}{(b/t)^2}$
	(shaded)		13[1]	$\frac{b}{t}=6.8$[2]	$\dfrac{34.0}{\sqrt{b/t}}$	$\frac{b}{t}=25$	$\dfrac{4{,}200}{(b/t)^2}$
	Flat plates with both edges supported	**18**	19	— — —	19	$\frac{h}{t}=110$	$\dfrac{230{,}000}{(h/t)^2}$
	(shaded)		11[1]	— — —	11[1]	$\frac{h}{t}=144$[2]	$\dfrac{230{,}000}{(h/t)^2}$
	Flat plates with horizontal stiffener, both edges supported	**19**	19	— — —	19	$\frac{h}{t}=228$	$\dfrac{990{,}000}{(h/t)^2}$
	(shaded)		11[1]	— — —	11[1]	$\frac{h}{t}=300$[2]	$\dfrac{990{,}000}{(h/t)^2}$
SHEAR IN WEBS, gross section	Unstiffened flat webs	**20**	12	$\frac{h}{t}=18$	$13.7-0.092\frac{h}{t}$	$\frac{h}{t}=66$	$\dfrac{33{,}000}{(h/t)^2}$
	(shaded)		7[1]	— — —	7[1]	$\frac{h}{t}=69$[2]	$\dfrac{33{,}000}{(h/t)^2}$
	Stiffened flat webs — $a_e=a_1/\sqrt{1+0.7(a_1/a_2)^2}$	**21**	12	— — —	12	$\frac{a_e}{t}=66$	$\dfrac{53{,}000}{(a_e/t)^2}$
	(shaded)		7[1]	— — —	7[1]	$\frac{a_e}{t}=87$[2]	$\dfrac{53{,}000}{(a_e/t)^2}$

NONSHADED BARS apply to nonwelded members and to welded members at locations farther than 1.0 in. from a weld.

SHADED BARS apply within 1.0 in. of a weld.

TABLE 1—SUGGESTED ALLOWABLE STRESSES

TABLE 1—SUGGESTED ALLOWABLE STRESSES (SEE INTRODUCTION TO TABLE 1, p. 41)

Right-hand columns apply to two material groups:
- **ANOCLAD TYPES 5-T5, 10-T5 AND 11-T5 Extrusions** (white columns)
- **6063-T5 Extrusions, Pipe (Thickness up thru 0.500 in.)** (shaded columns)

Type of Stress	Type of Member or Component	Spec. No.	Alloy	Allowable Stress, ksi, Slenderness ≤ S_1	Slenderness Limit, S_1	Allowable Stress, ksi, Slenderness Between S_1 and S_2	Slenderness Limit, S_2	Allowable Stress, ksi, Slenderness ≥ S_2
TENSION, axial, net section	Any tension member	1	Anoclad	9.5				
			6063-T5	6.5				
TENSION IN BEAMS, extreme fiber, net section	Structural shapes, rectangular tubes, built-up members bent about X-axis	2	Anoclad	9.5				
			6063-T5	6.5				
	Round or oval tubes	3	Anoclad	11				
			6063-T5	7.5				
	Rectangular bars, plates, outstanding flanges of shapes bent about Y-axis	4	Anoclad	13.5				
			6063-T5	7.5				
BEARING	On rivets and bolts	5	Anoclad	15				
			6063-T5	10				
	On milled surfaces and pins	6	Anoclad	10				
			6063-T5	7				
COMPRESSION IN COLUMNS, axial, gross section	Columns (also see Specs. 8 to 10)	7	Anoclad	8.5	$\frac{L}{r}=13$	$9.0-0.039\frac{L}{r}$	$\frac{L}{r}=100$	$\frac{51{,}000}{(L/r)^2}$
			6063-T5	6.5	$\frac{L}{r}=64$	$9.0-0.039\frac{L}{r}$	$\frac{L}{r}=100$	$\frac{51{,}000}{(L/r)^2}$
	Components of columns (also see Spec. 7) — Outstanding flanges and legs	8	Anoclad	8.5	$\frac{b}{t}=6.8$	$10.2-0.25\frac{b}{t}$	$\frac{b}{t}=19$	$\frac{1{,}940}{(b/t)^2}$
			6063-T5	6.5	$\frac{b}{t}=4.4$	$\frac{13.6}{\sqrt{b/t}}$	$\frac{b}{t}=27$	$\frac{1{,}940}{(b/t)^2}$
	Flat plates with both edges supported	9	Anoclad	8.5	$\frac{b}{t}=22$	$10.2-0.079\frac{b}{t}$	$\frac{b}{t}=58$	$\frac{19{,}200}{(b/t)^2}$
			6063-T5	6.5	$\frac{b}{t}=47$	$10.2-0.079\frac{b}{t}$	$\frac{b}{t}=58$	$\frac{19{,}200}{(b/t)^2}$
	Curved plates supported on both edges, walls of round or oval tubes	10	Anoclad	8.5	$\frac{R}{t}=12$	$9.2-0.198\sqrt{\frac{R}{t}}$	$\frac{R}{t}=200$	– – –
			6063-T5	6.5	$\frac{R}{t}=12$	$\frac{12.0}{(R/t)^{1/4}}$		– – –
COMPRESSION IN BEAMS, extreme fiber, gross section	Single-web beams bent about X-axis	11	Anoclad	8.5	$\frac{L_b}{r_y}=16$	$9.0-0.032\frac{L_b}{r_y}$	$\frac{L_b}{r_y}=120$	$\frac{74{,}000}{(L_b/r_y)^2}$
			6063-T5	6.5	$\frac{L_b}{r_y}=78$	$9.0-0.032\frac{L_b}{r_y}$	$\frac{L_b}{r_y}=120$	$\frac{74{,}000}{(L_b/r_y)^2}$
	Round or oval tubes	12	Anoclad	11	$\frac{R_b}{t}=9.4$	$11.3-0.032\frac{R_b}{t}$	$\frac{R_b}{t}=140$	– – –
			6063-T5	7.5	$\frac{R_b}{t}=12$	$\frac{13.9}{(R_b/t)^{1/4}}$	$\frac{R_b}{t}=125$	– – –

Category	Member	No.	Bar	Value	Slenderness limit 1	Intermediate formula	Slenderness limit 2	Large-slenderness formula
Extreme fibers of beams (also see Specs. 15 to 19)	Solid rectangular beams bent about X-axis	13	nonshaded	13.5	$\dfrac{d}{t}\sqrt{\dfrac{L_b}{d}} = 8.8$	$15.6 - 0.24\dfrac{d}{t}\sqrt{\dfrac{L_b}{d}}$	$\dfrac{d}{t}\sqrt{\dfrac{L_b}{d}} = 44$	$\dfrac{9{,}900}{(d/t)^2(L_b/d)}$
			shaded	7.5	$\dfrac{d}{t}\sqrt{\dfrac{L_b}{d}} = 11$	$\dfrac{24.3}{[(d/t)^2(L_b/d)]^{1/4}}$	$\dfrac{d}{t}\sqrt{\dfrac{L_b}{d}} = 55$	$\dfrac{9{,}900}{(d/t)^2(L_b/d)}$
	Rectangular tubes and box sections	14	nonshaded	8.5	$\dfrac{L_bS_c}{I_y} = 65$	$9.0 - 0.062\sqrt{\dfrac{L_bS_c}{I_y}}$	$\dfrac{L_bS_c}{I_y} = 3920$	$\dfrac{20{,}000}{(L_bS_c/I_y)}$
			shaded	6.5	$\dfrac{L_bS_c}{I_y} = 1620$	$9.0 - 0.062\sqrt{\dfrac{L_bS_c}{I_y}}$	$\dfrac{L_bS_c}{I_y} = 3920$	$\dfrac{20{,}000}{(L_bS_c/I_y)}$
COMPRESSION IN BEAMS, extreme fiber, gross section — Components of beams, component under uniform compression (also see Specs. 11 to 14)	Outstanding flanges	15	nonshaded	8.5	$\dfrac{b}{t} = 7.7$	$10.2 - 0.22\dfrac{b}{t}$	$\dfrac{b}{t} = 22$	$\dfrac{2{,}500}{(b/t)^2}$
			shaded	6.5	$\dfrac{b}{t} = 4.8$	$\dfrac{14.2}{\sqrt{b/t}}$	$\dfrac{b}{t} = 31$	$\dfrac{2{,}500}{(b/t)^2}$
	Flat plates with both edges supported	16	nonshaded	8.5	$\dfrac{b}{t} = 22$	$10.2 - 0.079\dfrac{b}{t}$	$\dfrac{b}{t} = 58$	$\dfrac{19{,}200}{(b/t)^2}$
			shaded	6.5	$\dfrac{b}{t} = 47$	$10.2 - 0.079\dfrac{b}{t}$	$\dfrac{b}{t} = 58$	$\dfrac{19{,}200}{(b/t)^2}$
Components of beams, component under bending in its own plane (also see Specs. 11 to 14)	Flat plates with compression edge free, tension edge supported	17	nonshaded	13.5	$\dfrac{b}{t} = 5.7$	$15.6 - 0.37\dfrac{b}{t}$	$\dfrac{b}{t} = 28$	$\dfrac{4{,}200}{(b/t)^2}$
			shaded	7.5	$\dfrac{b}{t} = 6.9$	$\dfrac{19.6}{\sqrt{b/t}}$	$\dfrac{b}{t} = 36$	$\dfrac{4{,}200}{(b/t)^2}$
	Flat plates with both edges supported	18	nonshaded	8.5	---	8.5	$\dfrac{h}{t} = 164$	$\dfrac{230{,}000}{(h/t)^2}$
			shaded	6.5	---	6.5	$\dfrac{h}{t} = 188$	$\dfrac{230{,}000}{(h/t)^2}$
	Flat plates with horizontal stiffener, both edges supported	19	nonshaded	---	---	---	---	---
			shaded	---	---	---	---	---
SHEAR IN WEBS, gross section	Unstiffened flat webs	20	nonshaded	5.5	$\dfrac{h}{t} = 15$	$5.9 - 0.027\dfrac{h}{t}$	$\dfrac{h}{t} = 103$	$\dfrac{33{,}000}{(h/t)^2}$
			shaded	4	$\dfrac{h}{t} = 70$	$5.9 - 0.027\dfrac{h}{t}$	$\dfrac{h}{t} = 103$	$\dfrac{33{,}000}{(h/t)^2}$
	Stiffened flat webs	21	nonshaded	---	---	---	---	---
			shaded	---	---	---	---	---

$$a_e = a_1/\sqrt{1 + 0.7\,(a_1/a_2)^2}$$

NONSHADED BARS apply to nonwelded members and to welded members at locations farther than 1.0 in. from a weld.

SHADED BARS apply within 1.0 in. of a weld.

TABLE 1–SUGGESTED ALLOWABLE STRESSES

(SEE INTRODUCTION TO TABLE 1, p. 41)

6063-T6 Extrusions / Pipe

(Values shown as: Extrusions / Pipe [shaded])

Type of Stress	Type of Member or Component	Spec. No.	Allowable Stress, ksi	Allowable Stress, ksi, Slenderness ≤ S_1	Slenderness Limit, S_1	Allowable Stress, ksi, Slenderness Between S_1 and S_2	Slenderness Limit, S_2	Allowable Stress, ksi, Slenderness ≥ S_2
TENSION, axial, net section	Any tension member	1	15 / 6.5					
TENSION IN BEAMS, extreme fiber, net section	Structural shapes, rectangular tubes, built-up members bent about X-axis	2	15 / 6.5					
	Round or oval tubes	3	17 / 6.5					
	Rectangular bars, plates, outstanding flanges of shapes bent about Y-axis	4	19 / 7.5					
BEARING	On rivets and bolts	5	24 / 10					
	On milled surfaces and pins	6	16 / 7					
COMPRESSION IN COLUMNS, axial, gross section	Columns (also see Specs. 8 to 10)	7		13.5 / 6.5	$\frac{L}{r} = 11$ / ---	$14.4-0.080\frac{L}{r}$ / 6.5	$\frac{L}{r} = 80$ / $\frac{L}{r} = 88$	$\frac{51{,}000}{(L/r)^2}$ / $\frac{51{,}000}{(L/r)^2}$
	Components of columns (also see Spec. 7): Outstanding flanges and legs	8		13.5 / 6.5	$\frac{b}{t} = 6$ / $\frac{b}{t} = 4.4$	$16.5-0.50\frac{b}{t}$ / $\frac{13.6}{\sqrt{b/t}}$	$\frac{b}{t} = 15$ / $\frac{b}{t} = 27$	$\frac{1{,}940}{(b/t)^2}$ / $\frac{1{,}940}{(b/t)^2}$
	Flat plates with both edges supported	9		13.5 / 6.5	$\frac{b}{t} = 19$ / ---	$16.5-0.160\frac{b}{t}$ / 6.5	$\frac{b}{t} = 46$ / $\frac{b}{t} = 54$	$\frac{19{,}200}{(b/t)^2}$ / $\frac{19{,}200}{(b/t)^2}$
	Curved plates supported on both edges, walls of round or oval tubes	10		13.5 / 6.5	$\frac{R}{t} = 16$ / $\frac{R}{t} = 12$	$15.4-0.47\sqrt{\frac{R}{t}}$ / $\frac{12.0}{(R/t)^{1/4}}$	$\frac{R}{t} = 140$ / $\frac{R}{t} = 125$	--- / ---
COMPRESSION IN BEAMS, extreme fiber, gross section	Single-web beams bent about X-axis	11		13.5 / 6.5	$\frac{L_b}{r_y} = 14$ / ---	$14.4-0.066\frac{L_b}{r_y}$ / 6.5	$\frac{L_b}{r_y} = 96$ / $\frac{L_b}{r_y} = 107$	$\frac{74{,}000}{(L_b/r_y)^2}$ / $\frac{74{,}000}{(L_b/r_y)^2}$
	Round or oval tubes (also see Specs. 15 to 19)	12		17 / 7.5	$\frac{R_b}{t} = 16$ / $\frac{R_b}{t} = 12$	$18.0-0.064\frac{R_b}{t}$ / $\frac{13.9}{(R_b/t)^{1/4}}$	$\frac{R_b}{t} = 120$ / $\frac{R_b}{t} = 125$	--- / ---

Design stresses table for aluminum (compression in beams and shear in webs). Columns paired as nonshaded (apply to nonwelded members and to welded members farther than 1.0 in. from a weld) / shaded (apply within 1.0 in. of a weld).

Category	Member / component	No.	A (ns)	A (sh)	B (ns)	B (sh)	C (ns)	C (sh)	D (ns)	D (sh)	E (ns)	E (sh)
COMPRESSION IN BEAMS, extreme fiber, gross section — Extreme fibers of beams (also see Specs. 15 to 19)	Solid rectangular beams bent about X-axis	13	19	7.5	$\frac{d}{t}\sqrt{\frac{L_b}{d}}=12$	$\frac{d}{t}\sqrt{\frac{L_b}{d}}=11$	$24.8-0.48\,\frac{d}{t}\sqrt{\frac{L_b}{d}}$	$\dfrac{24.3}{[(d/t)^2(L_b/d)]^{1/4}}$	$\frac{d}{t}\sqrt{\frac{L_b}{d}}=33$	$\frac{d}{t}\sqrt{\frac{L_b}{d}}=55$	$\dfrac{9{,}900}{(d/t)^2(L_b/d)}$	$\dfrac{9{,}900}{(d/t)^2(L_b/d)}$
	Rectangular tubes and box sections	14	13.5	6.5	$\frac{L_bS_c}{I_y}=49$	— — —	$14.4-0.128\sqrt{\frac{L_bS_c}{I_y}}$	6.5	$\frac{L_bS_c}{I_y}=2510$	$\frac{L_bS_c}{I_y}=3080$	$\dfrac{20{,}000}{(L_bS_c/I_y)}$	$\dfrac{20{,}000}{(L_bS_c/I_y)}$
Components of beams, component under uniform compression (also see Specs. 11 to 14)	Outstanding flanges	15	13.5	6.5	$\frac{b}{t}=6.8$	$\frac{b}{t}=4.8$	$16.5-0.44\frac{b}{t}$	$\dfrac{14.2}{\sqrt{b/t}}$	$\frac{b}{t}=16$	$\frac{b}{t}=31$	$\dfrac{2{,}500}{(b/t)^2}$	$\dfrac{2{,}500}{(b/t)^2}$
	Flat plates with both edges supported	16	13.5	6.5	$\frac{b}{t}=19$	— — —	$16.5-0.160\frac{b}{t}$	6.5	$\frac{b}{t}=46$	$\frac{b}{t}=54$	$\dfrac{19{,}200}{(b/t)^2}$	$\dfrac{19{,}200}{(b/t)^2}$
Components of beams, component under bending in its own plane (also see Specs. 11 to 14)	Flat plates with compression edge free, tension edge supported	17	19	7.5	$\frac{b}{t}=7.6$	$\frac{b}{t}=6.9$	$24.8-0.74\frac{b}{t}$	$\dfrac{19.6}{\sqrt{b/t}}$	$\frac{b}{t}=22$	$\frac{b}{t}=36$	$\dfrac{4{,}200}{(b/t)^2}$	$\dfrac{4{,}200}{(b/t)^2}$
	Flat plates with both edges supported	18	13.5	6.5	— — —	— — —	13.5	6.5	$\frac{h}{t}=130$	$\frac{h}{t}=188$	$\dfrac{230{,}000}{(h/t)^2}$	$\dfrac{230{,}000}{(h/t)^2}$
	Flat plates with horizontal stiffener, both edges supported	19	— — —	— — —	— — —	— — —	— — —	— — —	— — —	— — —	— — —	— — —
SHEAR IN WEBS, gross section	Unstiffened flat webs	20	8.5	4	$\frac{h}{t}=19$	— — —	$9.5-0.054\frac{h}{t}$	4	$\frac{h}{t}=79$	$\frac{h}{t}=91$	$\dfrac{33{,}000}{(h/t)^2}$	$\dfrac{33{,}000}{(h/t)^2}$
	Stiffened flat webs	21	— — —	— — —	— — —	— — —	— — —	— — —	— — —	— — —	— — —	— — —

For stiffened flat webs (Spec. 21):

$$a_e = a_1 \big/ \sqrt{1 + 0.7\,(a_1/a_2)^2}$$

NONSHADED BARS apply to nonwelded members and to welded members at locations farther than 1.0 in. from a weld.

SHADED BARS apply within 1.0 in. of a weld.

TABLE 1—SUGGESTED ALLOWABLE STRESSES

(SEE INTRODUCTION TO TABLE 1, p. 41)

6070-T6 Extrusions

Type of Stress	Type of Member or Component	Spec. No.	Allowable Stress, ksi, Slenderness ≤ S_1	Slenderness Limit, S_1	Allowable Stress, ksi, Slenderness Between S_1 and S_2	Slenderness Limit, S_2	Allowable Stress, ksi, Slenderness ≥ S_2
TENSION, axial, net section	Any tension member	1	22 / 11.5				
TENSION IN BEAMS, extreme fiber, net section	Structural shapes, rectangular tubes, built-up members bent about X-axis	2	22 / 11.5				
	Round or oval tubes	3	28 / 14.5				
	Rectangular bars, plates, outstanding flanges of shapes bent about Y-axis	4	32 / 17				
BEARING	On rivets and bolts	5	39 / 18				
	On milled surfaces and pins	6	26 / 12				
COMPRESSION IN COLUMNS, axial, gross section	Columns (also see Specs. 8 to 10)	7	24 / 14.5	$\frac{L}{r}=13$ / ---	$26.4-0.188\frac{L}{r}$ / 14.5	$\frac{L}{r}=57$ / $\frac{L}{r}=59$	$\dfrac{51,000}{(L/r)^2}$ / $\dfrac{51,000}{(L/r)^2}$
	Components of columns (also see Spec. 7) — Outstanding flanges and legs	8	24 / 14.5	$\frac{b}{t}=5.3$ / ---	$30.3-1.19\frac{b}{t}$ / 14.5	$\frac{b}{t}=10$ / $\frac{b}{t}=12$	$\dfrac{1,940}{(b/t)^2}$ / $\dfrac{1,940}{(b/t)^2}$
	Flat plates with both edges supported	9	24 / 14.5	$\frac{b}{t}=17$ / ---	$30.3-0.38\frac{b}{t}$ / 14.5	$\frac{b}{t}=33$ / $\frac{b}{t}=36$	$\dfrac{19,200}{(b/t)^2}$ / $\dfrac{19,200}{(b/t)^2}$
	Curved plates supported on both edges, walls of round or oval tubes	10	24 / 14.5	$\frac{R}{t}=18$ / $\frac{R}{t}=7.7$	$28.8-1.13\sqrt{\frac{R}{t}}$ / $16.3-0.65\sqrt{\frac{R}{t}}$	$\frac{R}{t}=112$ / $\frac{R}{t}=247$	$\dfrac{3,200}{\frac{R}{t}\left(1+\frac{\sqrt{R/t}}{35}\right)}$ / $\dfrac{3,200}{\frac{R}{t}\left(1+\frac{\sqrt{R/t}}{35}\right)}$
COMPRESSION IN BEAMS, extreme fiber, gross section	Single-web beams bent about X-axis (also see Specs. 15 to 19)	11	24 / 14.5	$\frac{L_o}{r_y}=15$ / ---	$26.4-0.156\frac{L_o}{r_y}$ / 14.5	$\frac{L_o}{r_y}=68$ / $\frac{L_o}{r_y}=71$	$\dfrac{74,000}{(L_o/r_y)^2}$ / $\dfrac{74,000}{(L_o/r_y)^2}$
	Round or oval tubes	12	32 / 17	$\frac{R_b}{t}=12$ / $\frac{R_b}{t}=24$	$43.1-3.2\sqrt{\frac{R_b}{t}}$ / $24.5-1.52\sqrt{\frac{R_b}{t}}$	$\frac{R_b}{t}=47$ / $\frac{R_b}{t}=87$	Same as Specification No. 10 (See p. 21)

COMPRESSION IN BEAMS, extreme fiber, gross section							
Extreme fibers of beams (also see Specs. 15 to 19)	Solid rectangular beams bent about X-axis	**13**	35	$\dfrac{d}{t}\sqrt{\dfrac{L_b}{d}}=8.6$	$45.2-1.19\dfrac{d}{t}\sqrt{\dfrac{L_b}{d}}$	$\dfrac{d}{t}\sqrt{\dfrac{L_b}{d}}=25$	$\dfrac{9{,}700}{(d/t)^2(L_b/d)}$
			19	$\dfrac{d}{t}\sqrt{\dfrac{L_b}{d}}=22$	$45.2-1.19\dfrac{d}{t}\sqrt{\dfrac{L_b}{d}}$	$\dfrac{d}{t}\sqrt{\dfrac{L_b}{d}}=25$	$\dfrac{9{,}700}{(d/t)^2(L_b/d)}$
	Rectangular tubes and box sections	**14**	24	$\dfrac{L_bS_c}{I_y}=64$	$26.4-0.30\sqrt{\dfrac{L_bS_c}{I_y}}$	$\dfrac{L_bS_c}{I_y}=1270$	$\dfrac{20{,}000}{(L_bS_c/I_y)}$
			14.5	$---$	**14.5**	$\dfrac{L_bS_c}{I_y}=1380$	$\dfrac{20{,}000}{(L_bS_c/I_y)}$
Components of beams, component under uniform compression (also see Specs. 11 to 14)	Outstanding flanges	**15**	24	$\dfrac{b}{t}=6.1$	$30.3-1.04\dfrac{b}{t}$	$\dfrac{b}{t}=12$	$\dfrac{2{,}500}{(b/t)^2}$
			14.5	$---$	**14.5**	$\dfrac{b}{t}=13$	$\dfrac{2{,}500}{(b/t)^2}$
	Flat plates with both edges supported	**16**	24	$\dfrac{b}{t}=17$	$30.3-0.38\dfrac{b}{t}$	$\dfrac{b}{t}=33$	$\dfrac{19{,}200}{(b/t)^2}$
			14.5	$---$	**14.5**	$\dfrac{b}{t}=36$	$\dfrac{19{,}200}{(b/t)^2}$
Components of beams, component under bending in its own plane (also see Specs. 11 to 14)	Flat plates with compression edge free, tension edge supported	**17**	35	$\dfrac{b}{t}=5.6$	$45.2-1.81\dfrac{b}{t}$	$\dfrac{b}{t}=17$	$\dfrac{4{,}200}{(b/t)^2}$
			19	$\dfrac{b}{t}=14$	$45.2-1.81\dfrac{b}{t}$	$\dfrac{b}{t}=16$	$\dfrac{4{,}200}{(b/t)^2}$
	Flat plates with both edges supported	**18**	24	$---$	24	$\dfrac{h}{t}=98$	$\dfrac{230{,}000}{(h/t)^2}$
			14.5	$---$	**14.5**	$\dfrac{h}{t}=126$	$\dfrac{230{,}000}{(h/t)^2}$
	Flat plates with horizontal stiffener, both edges supported	**19**	24	$---$	24	$\dfrac{h}{t}=203$	$\dfrac{990{,}000}{(h/t)^2}$
			14.5	$---$	**14.5**	$\dfrac{h}{t}=260$	$\dfrac{990{,}000}{(h/t)^2}$
SHEAR IN WEBS, gross section	Unstiffened flat webs	**20**	15	$\dfrac{h}{t}=20$	$17.6-0.128\dfrac{h}{t}$	$\dfrac{h}{t}=56$	$\dfrac{33{,}000}{(h/t)^2}$
			8.5	$---$	**8.5**	$\dfrac{h}{t}=62$	$\dfrac{33{,}000}{(h/t)^2}$
	Stiffened flat webs	**21**	15	$---$	15	$\dfrac{a_r}{t}=59$	$\dfrac{53{,}000}{(a_r/t)^2}$
			8.5	$---$	**8.5**	$\dfrac{a_r}{t}=79$	$\dfrac{53{,}000}{(a_r/t)^2}$

$$a_e = a_1/\sqrt{1+0.7(a_1/a_2)^2}$$

NONSHADED BARS apply to nonwelded members and to welded members at locations farther than 1.0 in. from a weld.

SHADED BARS apply within 1.0 in. of a weld.

TABLE 2—SUGGESTED ALLOWABLE STRESSES FOR RIVETS AND BOLTS①
Specification 22

Designation Before Driving	Driving Procedure	Designation After Driving	Minimum Shear Strength, ksi	ALLOWABLE STRESS, ksi	
				Shear on Effective Area②	Tension on Root Area
RIVETS					
1100-H14	Cold, as received	**1100-F**	9.5③	4	—
2017-T4	Cold, as received	**2017-T3**	34③	14.5	—
2017-T4	Cold, immediately after quenching	**2017-T31**	30③	13	—
2024-T4	Cold, immediately after quenching	**2024-T31**	37③	16	—
2117-T4	Cold, as received	**2117-T3**	29③	12	—
5056-H32	Cold, as received	**5056-H321**	26③	11	—
6053-T61	Cold, as received	**6053-T61**	20③	8.5	—
6061-T4	Cold, immediately after quenching	**6061-T31**	21③	9	—
6061-T4	Hot, 990° to 1,050°F	**6061-T43**	21③	9	—
6061-T6	Cold, as received	**6061-T6**	26③	11④	—
7277-T4	Hot, 850° to 975°F	**7277-T41**	33③	14	—
BOLTS					
2024-T4			37	16⑤	26
7075-T73			40	17⑤	28

① Suggested allowable stresses for building structures.
② Effective area is root area if bolt threads are in shear plane; otherwise gross area.
③ Considered to be equal to the typical shear strength divided by 1.15.
④ This allowable stress applies also to shear on effective area of 6061-T6 pins.
⑤ This allowable shear stress applies to either turned bolts in reamed holes or unfinished bolts in 1/16-in. oversize holes.

TABLE 3—SUGGESTED ALLOWABLE SHEAR STRESSES IN FILLET WELDS[1]
Specification 23

Filler Alloy	1100	4043	5356 5554	5556
Minimum Shear Strength of Filler Alloy, F_{suf}	7.5	11.5	17	20
PARENT ALLOY		ALLOWABLE STRESS, ksi[2]		
1100	3.2	4.8[3]	—	—
3003	3.2	5	—	—
Alclad 3004	—	5	7	8[3]
5052	—	5	7	8.5
5083	—	—	7	8.5
5086	—	—	7	8.5
5454	—	—	7	8.5
5456	—	—	—	8.5
6061	—	5	7	8.5
6063	—	5	6.5[3]	6.5[3]
6070	—	5	7	8.5
Anoclad Extrusions Types 5, 10 and 11	—	5	6.5[3]	6.5[3]
Anoclad Sheet Type 11	3.2	5	—	—
Anoclad Sheet Types 12, 20, 30 and 40	3.2	5	—	—

[1] Suggested allowable stresses for building structures.
[2] Shear stress is considered to be equal to the load divided by the throat area.
[3] These values are controlled by the shear strength of the parent metal; all other values are controlled by the strength of the filler metal.

TABLE 4—FORMULAS FOR ALLOWABLE STRESS

Type of Stress	Type of Member or Component	Spec. No.	Allowable Stress, ksi				Allowable Stress, F_c, ksi Slenderness $\geq S_2$
			Allowable Stress, F_c, ksi, Slenderness $\leq S_1$	Slenderness Limit, S_1 [3]	Allowable Stress, ksi, Slenderness Between S_1 and S_2 [3]	Slenderness Limit, S_2 [3]	
TENSION, axial, net section	Any tension member	1	F_{tu}/n_y or $F_{tu}/(k_t n_u)$ [1]				
TENSION IN BEAMS, extreme fiber, net section	Structural shapes, rectangular tubes, built-up members bent about X-axis	2	F_{ty}/n_y or $F_{tu}/(k_t n_u)$ [1]				
	Round or oval tubes	3	$1.17F_{ty}/n_y$ or $1.24F_{tu}/(k_t n_u)$ [1]				
	Rectangular bars, plates, outstanding flanges of shapes bent about Y-axis	4	$1.30F_{tu}/n_y$ or $1.42F_{tu}/(k_t n_u)$ [1]				
BEARING	On rivets and bolts	5	F_{by}/n_y or $F_{bu}/(1.2n_u)$ [1][2]				
	On milled surfaces and pins	6	$F_{by}/(1.5n_y)$ or $F_{bu}/(1.8n_u)$ [1][2]				
COMPRESSION IN COLUMNS, axial, gross section	Columns (also see Specs. 8 to 10)	7	$\dfrac{F_{cy}}{k_c n_y}$	$\dfrac{L}{r} = \dfrac{B_c - n_u F_c}{D_c}$	$\dfrac{1}{n_u}\left(B_c - D_c\dfrac{L}{r}\right)$	$\dfrac{L}{r} = C_c$	$\dfrac{\pi^2 E}{n_u(L/r)^2}$
	Components of columns (also see Spec. 7) — Outstanding flanges and legs	8	$\dfrac{F_{cy}}{k_c n_y}$	$\dfrac{b}{t} = \dfrac{B_p - n_u F_c}{5.13 D_p}$	$\dfrac{1}{n_u}\left(B_p - 5.13 D_p\dfrac{b}{t}\right)$	$\dfrac{b}{t} = \dfrac{C_p}{5.13}$	$\dfrac{\pi^2 E}{n_u(5.13 b/t)^2}$
	Flat plates with both edges supported	9	$\dfrac{F_{cy}}{k_c n_y}$	$\dfrac{b}{t} = \dfrac{B_p - n_u F_c}{1.63 D_p}$	$\dfrac{1}{n_u}\left(B_p - 1.63 D_p\dfrac{b}{t}\right)$	$\dfrac{b}{t} = \dfrac{C_p}{1.63}$	$\dfrac{\pi^2 E}{n_u(1.63 b/t)^2}$
	Curved plates supported on both edges, walls of round or oval tubes	10	$\dfrac{F_{cy}}{k_c n_y}$	$\dfrac{R}{t} = \left(\dfrac{B_t - n_u F_c}{D_t}\right)^2$	$\dfrac{1}{n_u}\left(B_t - D_t\sqrt{\dfrac{R}{t}}\right)$	$\dfrac{R}{t} = C_t$	$\dfrac{\pi^2 E}{16 n_u \dfrac{R}{t}\left(1 + \dfrac{\sqrt{R/t}}{35}\right)^2}$
COMPRESSION IN BEAMS, extreme fiber, gross section	Extreme fibers of beams (also see Specs. 15 to 19) — Single-web beams bent about X-axis	11	$\dfrac{F_{cy}}{k_c n_y}$	$\dfrac{L_b}{r_y} = \dfrac{1.2(B_c - n_u F_c)}{D_c}$	$\dfrac{1}{n_u}\left(B_c - D_c\dfrac{L_b}{1.2r_y}\right)$	$\dfrac{L_b}{r_y} = 1.2C_c$	$\dfrac{\pi^2 E}{n_u(L_b/1.2r_y)^2}$
	Round or oval tubes	12	$\dfrac{1.17F_{cy}}{n_y}$	$\dfrac{R_b}{t} = \dfrac{(B_{tb} - n_u F_c)}{D_{tb}}$	$\dfrac{1}{n_u}\left(B_{tb} - D_{tb}\sqrt{\dfrac{R_b}{t}}\right)$	$\dfrac{R_b}{t} = C_{tb}$	Same as Specification No. 10 (See p. 21)
	Solid rectangular beams bent about X-axis	13	$\dfrac{1.30F_{cy}}{n_y}$	$\dfrac{d}{t}\sqrt{\dfrac{L_b}{d}} = \dfrac{B_b - n_u F_c}{2.3D_b}$	$\dfrac{1}{n_u}\left(B_b - 2.3D_b\dfrac{d}{t}\sqrt{\dfrac{L_b}{d}}\right)$	$\dfrac{d}{t}\sqrt{\dfrac{L_b}{d}} = \dfrac{C_b}{2.3}$	$\dfrac{\pi^2 E}{5.29 n_u(d/t)^2(L_b/d)}$
	Rectangular tubes and box sections	14	$\dfrac{F_{cy}}{k_c n_y}$	$\dfrac{L_b S_c}{I_y} = \left(\dfrac{B_c - n_u F_c}{1.6D_c}\right)^2$	$\dfrac{1}{n_u}\left(B_c - 1.6D_c\sqrt{\dfrac{L_b S_c}{I_y}}\right)$	$\dfrac{L_b S_c}{I_y} = \left(\dfrac{C_c}{1.6}\right)^2$	$\dfrac{\pi^2 E}{2.56 n_u(L_b S_c/I_y)}$

			No.					
COMPRESSION IN BEAMS, extreme fiber, gross section	Components of beams, component under uniform compression (also see Specs. 11 to 14)		**15**	$\dfrac{F_{cy}}{k_c n_y}$	$\dfrac{b}{t} = \dfrac{B_p - n_u F_c}{4.5 D_p}$	$\dfrac{1}{n_u}\left(B_p - 4.5 D_p \dfrac{b}{t}\right)$	$\dfrac{b}{t} = \dfrac{C_p}{4.5}$	$\dfrac{\pi^2 E}{n_u (4.5 b/t)^2}$
	Flat plates with both edges supported		**16**	$\dfrac{F_{cy}}{k_c n_y}$	$\dfrac{b}{t} = \dfrac{B_p - n_u F_c}{1.63 D_p}$	$\dfrac{1}{n_u}\left(B_p - 1.63 D_p \dfrac{b}{t}\right)$	$\dfrac{b}{t} = \dfrac{C_p}{1.63}$	$\dfrac{\pi^2 E}{n_u (1.63 b/t)^2}$
	Flat plates with compression edge free, tension edge supported		**17**	$\dfrac{1.30 F_{cy}}{n_y}$	$\dfrac{b}{t} = \dfrac{B_p - n_u F_c}{3.5 D_p}$	$\dfrac{1}{n_u}\left(B_p - 3.5 D_p \dfrac{b}{t}\right)$	$\dfrac{b}{t} = \dfrac{C_b}{3.5}$	$\dfrac{\pi^2 E}{n_u (3.5 b/t)^2}$
	Components of beams, component under bending in its own plane (also see Specs. 11 to 14) — Flat plates with both edges supported		**18**	$\dfrac{F_{cy}}{k_c n_y}$	$\dfrac{h}{t} = \dfrac{B_b - n_u F_c}{0.6 D_b}$	$\dfrac{1}{n_u}\left(B_b - 0.6 D_b \dfrac{h}{t}\right)$	$\dfrac{h}{t} = \dfrac{C_b}{0.6}$	$\dfrac{\pi^2 E}{n_u (0.6 h/t)^2}$
	Flat plates with horizontal stiffener, both edges supported		**19**	$\dfrac{F_{cy}}{k_c n_y}$	$\dfrac{h}{t} = \dfrac{B_b - n_u F_c}{0.29 D_b}$	$\dfrac{1}{n_u}\left(B_b - 0.29 D_b \dfrac{h}{t}\right)$	$\dfrac{h}{t} = \dfrac{C_b}{0.29}$	$\dfrac{\pi^2 E}{n_u (0.29 h/t)^2}$
SHEAR IN WEBS, gross section	Unstiffened flat webs		**20**	$\dfrac{F_{sy}}{n_y}$ or $\dfrac{F_{su}}{n_u}$ [1]	$\dfrac{h}{t} = \dfrac{B_s - n_u F_c}{1.25 D_s}$	$\dfrac{1}{n_u}\left(B_s - 1.25 D_s \dfrac{h}{t}\right)$	$\dfrac{h}{t} = \dfrac{C_s}{1.25}$	$\dfrac{\pi^2 E}{n_u (1.25 h/t)^2}$
	Stiffened flat webs		**21**	$\dfrac{F_{sy}}{n_y}$ or $\dfrac{F_{su}}{n_u}$ [1]	$\dfrac{a_e}{t} = \dfrac{B_s - n_u F_c}{1.25 D_s}$	$\dfrac{1}{n_u}\left(B_s - 1.25 D_s \dfrac{a_e}{t}\right)$	$\dfrac{a_e}{t} = \dfrac{C_s}{1.25}$	$\dfrac{\pi^2 E}{n_u (1.25 a_e/t)^2}$

$$a_e = a_1 / \sqrt{1 + 0.7 (a_1/a_2)^2}$$

[1] Use smaller of allowable stresses given by two expressions.

[2] This value applies for a ratio of edge distance to bolt diameter of 2 or greater. For smaller ratios, multiply this allowable stress by the ratio, (edge distance)/(twice the rivet or bolt diameter).

[3] In cases for which S_1 is greater than S_2, the allowable stress F_c applies for all values of slenderness less than the limit S_3, defined as the slenderness value at which $F_c = F_r$ (see last column of above table). For slenderness values greater than S_3, the allowable stress is F_c.

TABLE 5
FORMULAS FOR ALLOWABLE SHEAR STRESSES IN CONNECTIONS

Specification No.	Type of Connection	Allowable Shear Stress, ksi
22	Rivets and Bolts	$\dfrac{F_{su}[1]}{1.2\,n_u}$
23	Fillet Welds	$\dfrac{F_{suf}[2]}{1.2\,n_u}$ or $\dfrac{\sqrt{2}\,F_{suw}[3][4]}{1.2\,n_u}$

[1] F_{su} in this case is the minimum shear strength of the rivet or bolt material.

[2] F_{suf} is the minimum shear strength of a longitudinal fillet weld as determined on the throat area.

[3] F_{suw} in this case is the minimum shear strength of the parent metal adjacent to the fillet weld.

[4] The smaller of the stresses given by the two expressions is used as the allowable stress on the throat area.

TABLE 6—FACTORS OF SAFETY[1]

Factor of safety on:	Symbol	Recommended Values	
		Bridge Structures[2]	Building Structures[3]
Ultimate Strength	n_u	2.2	1.95
Yielding	n_y	1.85	1.65
Appearance of Buckling	n_a	1.35	1.2

[1] Values listed are those used by the ASCE Task Committee on Lightweight Alloys in Refs. 1 and 2. Other values may be used for structures not covered by the two classifications listed.

[2] Including other types of structures that are generally designed in accordance with allowable stresses for bridges (e.g., highway sign-support structures).

[3] Including other types of structures that are generally designed in accordance with allowable stresses for buildings (e.g., electrical substations).

TABLE 7
VALUES OF COEFFICIENTS k_t AND k_c[1]

ALLOY AND TEMPER	Regions Farther Than 1.0 in. from a Weld		Regions Within 1.0 in. of a Weld	
	k_t	k_c	k_t	k_c[2]
2014-T6, -651	1.25	1.12	—	—
Alclad 2014-T6, -T651	1.25	1.12	—	—
6061-T6, -T651, -T6510, -T6511	1.0	1.12	1.0	1.0
6063-T5, -T6, -T83	1.0	1.12	1.0	1.0
6070-T6	1.1	1.12	1.1	1.0
6071-T6, -T651	1.1	1.12	1.1	1.0
Anoclad Extrusions Types 5-T5, 10-T5 and 11-T5	1.0	1.12	1.0	1.0
All others listed in Table 9	1.0	1.1	1.0	1.0

[1] These coefficients are used in the formulas in Table 4.

[2] If the weld yield strength exceeds 0.9 of the parent metal yield strength, the value of k_c used for welds should be increased so that the allowable stress within 1.0 in. of a weld does not exceed the allowable stress for nonwelded material.

TABLE 8 – FORMULAS FOR BUCKLING CONSTANTS

PRODUCTS NOT ARTIFICIALLY AGED

(All nonheat-treated products, and all heat-treated products except those whose temper designations begin with -T5, -T6, -T7, -T8 or -T9)

Type of Member and Stress	Intercept, ksi	Slope, ksi	Intersection
Compression in Columns and Beam Flanges	$B_c = F_{cy}\left[1 + \left(\dfrac{F_{cy}}{1000}\right)^{1/2}\right]$	$D_c = \dfrac{B_c}{20}\left(\dfrac{6B_c}{E}\right)^{1/2}$	$C_c = \dfrac{2B_c}{3D_c}$
Compression in Flat Plates	$B_p = F_{cy}\left[1 + \dfrac{(F_{cy})^{1/3}}{7.6}\right]$	$D_p = \dfrac{B_p}{20}\left(\dfrac{6B_p}{E}\right)^{1/2}$	$C_p = \dfrac{2B_p}{3D_p}$
Compression in Round Tubes under Axial End Load	$B_t = F_{cy}\left[1 + \dfrac{(F_{cy})^{1/5}}{5.8}\right]$	$D_t = \dfrac{B_t}{3.7}\left(\dfrac{B_t}{E}\right)^{1/3}$	C_t ①
Compressive Bending Stress in Solid Rectangular Bars	$B_b = 1.3F_{cy}\left[1 + \dfrac{(F_{cy})^{1/3}}{7}\right]$	$D_b = \dfrac{B_b}{20}\left(\dfrac{6B_b}{E}\right)^{1/2}$	$C_b = \dfrac{2B_b}{3D_b}$
Compressive Bending Stress in Round Tubes	$B_{tb} = 1.5F_y\left[1 + \dfrac{(F_y)^{1/5}}{5.8}\right]$	$D_{tb} = \dfrac{B_{tb}}{2.7}\left(\dfrac{B_{tb}}{E}\right)^{1/3}$	$C_{tb} = \left(\dfrac{B_{tb} - B_t}{D_{tb} - D_t}\right)^2$
Shear Stress in Flat Plates	$B_s = F_{sy}\left[1 + \dfrac{(F_{sy})^{1/3}}{6.2}\right]$	$D_s = \dfrac{B_s}{20}\left(\dfrac{6B_s}{E}\right)^{1/2}$	$C_s = \dfrac{2B_s}{3D_s}$

PRODUCTS ARTIFICIALLY AGED

(All heat-treated products whose temper designations begin with -T5, -T6, -T7, -T8 or -T9)

Type of Member and Stress	Intercept, ksi	Slope, ksi	Intersection
Compression in Columns and Beam Flanges	$B_c = F_{cy}\left[1 + \left(\dfrac{F_{cy}}{2250}\right)^{1/2}\right]$	$D_c = \dfrac{B_c}{10}\left(\dfrac{B_c}{E}\right)^{1/2}$	$C_c = 0.409\dfrac{B_c}{D_c}$
Compression in Flat Plates	$B_p = F_{cy}\left[1 + \dfrac{(F_{cy})^{1/3}}{11.4}\right]$	$D_p = \dfrac{B_p}{10}\left(\dfrac{B_p}{E}\right)^{1/2}$	$C_p = 0.409\dfrac{B_p}{D_p}$
Compression in Round Tubes under Axial End Load	$B_t = F_{cy}\left[1 + \dfrac{(F_{cy})^{1/5}}{8.7}\right]$	$D_t = \dfrac{B_t}{4.5}\left(\dfrac{B_t}{E}\right)^{1/3}$	C_t ①
Compressive Bending Stress in Solid Rectangular Bars	$B_b = 1.3F_{cy}\left[1 + \dfrac{(F_{cy})^{1/3}}{7}\right]$	$D_b = \dfrac{B_b}{20}\left(\dfrac{6B_b}{E}\right)^{1/2}$	$C_b = \dfrac{2B_b}{3D_b}$
Compressive Bending Stress in Round Tubes	$B_{tb} = 1.5F_y\left[1 + \dfrac{(F_y)^{1/5}}{8.7}\right]$	$D_{tb} = \dfrac{B_{tb}}{2.7}\left(\dfrac{B_{tb}}{E}\right)^{1/3}$	$C_{tb} = \left(\dfrac{B_{tb} - B_t}{D_{tb} - D_t}\right)^2$
Shear Stress in Flat Plates	$B_s = F_{sy}\left[1 + \dfrac{(F_{sy})^{1/3}}{9.3}\right]$	$D_s = \dfrac{B_s}{10}\left(\dfrac{B_s}{E}\right)^{1/2}$	$C_s = 0.409\dfrac{B_s}{D_s}$

① C_t can be found from a plot of the curves of allowable stress based on elastic and inelastic buckling or by a trial and error solution.

TABLE 9—PROPERTIES OF NONWELDED MATERIAL

ALLOY AND TEMPER[1]	PRODUCT AND THICKNESS RANGE, in.	MINIMUM MECHANICAL PROPERTIES[2]							COMPRESSIVE MODULUS OF ELASTICITY, E, ksi
		TENSION		COMPRESSION	SHEAR		BEARING[4]		
		F_{tu}, ksi	F_{ty}[3], ksi	F_{cy}[3], ksi	F_{su}, ksi	F_{sy}, ksi	F_{bu}, ksi	F_{by}[5], ksi	
1100 – H12	SHEET & PLATE 0.017 – 2.000	14	11	10	9	6.5	28	18	10,100
1100 – H12	ROLLED ROD & BAR up thru 0.374	14	11	10	9	6.5	28	18	10,100
1100 – H12	DRAWN TUBE 0.010 – 0.500	14	11	10	9	6.5	28	18	10,100
1100 – H14	SHEET & PLATE 0.009 – 1.000	16	14	13	10	8	32	21	10,100
1100 – H14	ROLLED ROD & BAR up thru 0.313	16	14	13	10	8	32	21	10,100
1100 – H14	DRAWN TUBE 0.010 – 0.500	16	14	13	10	8	32	21	10,100
2014 – T6	SHEET 0.040 – 0.249	66	58	59	40	33	125	93	10,900
2014 – T6, T651	PLATE 0.250 – 2.000	67	59	58	40	34	127	94	10,900
2014 – T6, T651	PLATE 2.001 – 2.500	65	58	57	39	33	123	93	10,900
2014 – T6, T651	PLATE 2.501 – 3.000	65	57	56	39	33	123	91	10,900
2014 – T6	EXTRUSIONS[6] up thru 0.499	60	53	55	35	31	114	85	10,900
2014 – T6	EXTRUSIONS[6] 0.500 – 0.749	64	58	60	37	33	122	93	10,900
2014 – T6	EXTRUSIONS[6] 0.750 and over (25 in.2 max.)	68	60	62	39	35	109	84	10,900
2014 – T6	EXTRUSIONS[6] 0.750 and over (25 – 32 in.2)	68	58	60	39	33	109	81	10,900
2014 – T6, T651	ROLLED ROD & BAR up thru 8.000	65	55	53	38	32	124	88	10,900
2014 – T6, T651	DRAWN TUBE 0.025 – 0.500	65	55	53	38	32	124	88	10,900
ALCLAD 2014 – T6	SHEET 0.020 – 0.039	63	55	56	38	32	120	88	10,800
ALCLAD 2014 – T6	SHEET 0.040 – 0.249	64	57	58	39	33	122	91	10,800
ALCLAD 2014 – T6, T651	PLATE 0.250 – 0.499	64	57	56	39	33	122	91	10,800
ALCLAD 2014 – T6, T651	PLATE 0.500 – 2.000	64	56	55	39	32	122	90	10,800
ALCLAD 2014 – T6, T651	PLATE 2.001 – 2.500	62	55	54	37	32	118	88	10,800
ALCLAD 2014 – T6, T651	PLATE 2.501 – 3.000	62	54	53	37	31	118	86	10,800
3003 – H12	SHEET & PLATE 0.017 – 2.000	17	12	10	11	7	34	19	10,100
3003 – H12	ROLLED ROD & BAR up thru 0.374	17	12	11	11	7	34	19	10,100
3003 – H12	DRAWN TUBE 0.010 – 0.500	17	12	11	11	7	34	19	10,100
3003 – H14	SHEET & PLATE 0.009 – 1.000	20	17	14	12	10	40	25	10,100
3003 – H14	ROLLED ROD & BAR up thru 0.313	20	17	16	12	10	40	25	10,100
3003 – H14	DRAWN TUBE 0.010 – 0.500	20	17	16	12	10	40	25	10,100
3003 – H16	SHEET 0.006 – 0.162	24	21	18	14	12	46	31	10,100
3003 – H16	ROLLED ROD & BAR up thru 0.250	24	21	20	14	12	46	31	10,100
3003 – H16	DRAWN TUBE 0.010 – 0.500	24	21	19	14	12	46	31	10,100

More information on 3003 on next page.
Footnotes appear at the end of this table.

TABLE 9

BUCKLING FORMULA CONSTANTS

COMPRESSION IN COLUMNS			COMPRESSION IN FLAT PLATES			COMPRESSION IN ROUND TUBES			BENDING IN ROUND TUBES			BENDING IN RECTANGULAR BARS			SHEAR IN FLAT PLATES		
B_c, ksi	D_c, ksi	C_c	B_p, ksi	D_p, ksi	C_p	B_t, ksi	D_t, ksi	C_t	B_{tb}, ksi	D_{tb}, ksi	C_{tb}	B_b, ksi	D_b, ksi	C_b	B_s, ksi	D_s, ksi	C_s
11.0	0.044	165	12.8	0.056	153	12.7	0.372	607	19.1	0.875	160	17.0	0.085	133	8.5	0.030	188
11.0	0.044	165	12.8	0.056	153	12.7	0.372	607	19.1	0.875	160	17.0	0.085	133	8.5	0.030	188
11.0	0.044	165	12.8	0.056	153	12.7	0.372	607	19.1	0.875	160	17.0	0.085	133	8.5	0.030	188
14.5	0.067	144	17.0	0.086	133	16.7	0.536	461	25.1	1.260	133	22.6	0.131	115	10.6	0.042	168
14.5	0.067	144	17.0	0.086	133	16.7	0.536	461	25.1	1.260	133	22.6	0.131	115	10.6	0.042	168
14.5	0.067	144	17.0	0.086	133	16.7	0.536	461	25.1	1.260	133	22.6	0.131	115	10.6	0.042	168
68.6	0.544	52	79.1	0.674	48	74.3	3.132	94	109.5	8.754	39	119.4	1.530	52	44.4	0.283	64
67.3	0.529	52	77.7	0.656	48	73.0	3.059	95	109.5	8.754	41	117.1	1.486	53	45.8	0.297	63
66.1	0.514	53	76.2	0.638	49	71.7	2.986	97	107.6	8.545	42	114.8	1.444	53	44.4	0.283	64
64.8	0.500	53	74.8	0.620	49	70.4	2.913	98	105.6	8.337	42	112.6	1.401	54	44.4	0.283	64
63.6	0.486	54	73.3	0.602	50	69.1	2.841	100	99.7	7.724	39	110.3	1.360	54	41.5	0.256	66
69.8	0.559	51	80.6	0.693	48	75.6	3.206	92	109.5	8.754	37	121.6	1.573	52	44.4	0.283	64
72.3	0.589	50	83.5	0.731	47	78.3	3.356	89	113.5	9.175	37	126.2	1.663	51	47.3	0.312	62
69.8	0.559	51	80.6	0.693	48	75.6	3.206	92	109.5	8.754	37	121.6	1.573	52	44.4	0.283	64
61.1	0.458	55	70.5	0.567	51	66.5	2.699	103	99.7	7.724	44	105.9	1.278	55	42.9	0.269	65
61.1	0.458	55	70.5	0.567	51	66.5	2.699	103	99.7	7.724	44	105.9	1.278	55	42.9	0.269	65
64.8	0.502	53	74.8	0.622	49	70.4	2.922	98	103.6	8.157	40	112.6	1.408	53	42.9	0.271	65
67.3	0.531	52	77.7	0.659	48	73.0	3.068	94	107.6	8.571	39	117.1	1.493	52	44.4	0.285	64
64.8	0.502	53	74.8	0.622	49	70.4	2.922	98	105.6	8.363	42	112.6	1.408	53	44.4	0.285	64
63.6	0.488	53	73.3	0.604	50	69.1	2.850	99	103.6	8.157	42	110.3	1.366	54	42.9	0.271	65
62.4	0.474	54	71.9	0.587	50	67.8	2.778	101	101.7	7.951	43	108.1	1.325	54	42.9	0.271	65
61.1	0.460	54	70.5	0.569	51	66.5	2.707	102	99.7	7.748	43	105.9	1.284	55	41.5	0.257	66
11.0	0.044	165	12.8	0.056	153	12.7	0.372	607	19.1	0.875	160	17.0	0.085	133	9.2	0.034	181
12.2	0.052	157	14.2	0.065	145	14.1	0.424	506	21.1	0.999	150	18.8	0.100	126	9.2	0.034	181
12.2	0.052	157	14.2	0.065	145	14.1	0.424	506	21.1	0.999	150	18.8	0.100	126	9.2	0.034	181
15.7	0.075	138	18.4	0.096	127	18.1	0.594	415	27.1	1.397	127	24.5	0.147	111	13.5	0.060	149
18.0	0.093	129	21.3	0.120	119	20.8	0.715	365	31.2	1.683	115	28.3	0.183	103	13.5	0.060	149
18.0	0.093	129	21.3	0.120	119	20.8	0.715	365	31.2	1.683	115	28.3	0.183	103	13.5	0.060	149
20.4	0.112	121	24.2	0.145	111	23.5	0.843	330	35.3	1.984	106	32.2	0.222	97	16.4	0.081	135
22.8	0.133	115	27.1	0.172	105	26.3	0.977	294	39.4	2.298	99	36.1	0.264	91	16.4	0.081	135
21.6	0.123	118	25.7	0.159	108	24.9	0.909	310	37.4	2.140	102	34.1	0.243	94	16.4	0.081	135

More information on 3003 on next page.

TABLE 9 (*Cont.*)—PROPERTIES OF NONWELDED MATERIAL

| ALLOY AND TEMPER[1] | PRODUCT AND THICKNESS RANGE, in. | MINIMUM MECHANICAL PROPERTIES[2] | | | | | | | COMPRESSIVE MODULUS OF ELASTICITY, E, ksi |
| | | TENSION | | COMPRESSION | SHEAR | | BEARING[4] | | |
		F_{tu}, ksi	F_{ty}[3], ksi	F_{cy}[3], ksi	F_{su}, ksi	F_{sy}, ksi	F_{bu}, ksi	F_{by}[5], ksi	
3003 – H18	SHEET 0.006 – 0.128	27	24	20	15	14	49	34	10,100
3003 – H18	ROLLED ROD & BAR up thru 0.204	27	24	22	15	14	49	34	10,100
3003 – H18	DRAWN TUBE 0.010 – 0.500	27	24	21	15	14	49	34	10,100
ALCLAD 3003 – H12	SHEET & PLATE 0.013 – 2.000	16	11	9	10	6.5	32	18	10,100
ALCLAD 3003 – H12	DRAWN TUBE 0.010 – 0.500	16	11	10	10	6.5	32	18	10,100
ALCLAD 3003 – H14	SHEET & PLATE 0.009 – 1.000	19	16	13	12	9	38	24	10,100
ALCLAD 3003 – H14	DRAWN TUBE 0.010 – 0.500	19	16	15	12	9	38	24	10,100
ALCLAD 3003 – H16	SHEET 0.006 – 0.162	23	20	17	14	12	44	30	10,100
ALCLAD 3003 – H16	DRAWN TUBE 0.010 – 0.500	23	20	18	14	12	44	30	10,100
ALCLAD 3003 – H18	SHEET 0.006 – 0.128	26	23	19	15	13	47	32	10,100
ALCLAD 3003 – H18	DRAWN TUBE 0.010 – 0.500	26	23	20	15	13	47	32	10,100
3004 – H14	SHEET 0.013 – 0.249	32	27	23	19	16	64	40	10,100
3004 – H16	SHEET 0.013 – 0.161	36	31	27	21	18	68	46	10,100
3004 – H18	SHEET 0.013 – 0.161	39	34	30	22	20	70	48	10,100
3004 – H32	SHEET & PLATE 0.017 – 2.000	28	21	18	17	12	56	36	10,100
3004 – H34	SHEET & PLATE 0.009 – 1.000	32	25	22	19	14	64	40	10,100
3004 – H34	DRAWN TUBE 0.018 – 0.450	32	25	24	19	14	64	40	10,100
3004 – H36	SHEET 0.006 – 0.162	35	28	25	20	16	70	45	10,100
3004 – H36	DRAWN TUBE 0.018 – 0.450	35	28	27	20	16	70	45	10,100
ALCLAD 3004 – H14	SHEET 0.013 – 0.249	31	26	22	18	15	62	39	10,100
ALCLAD 3004 – H16	SHEET 0.013 – 0.161	35	30	26	20	17	66	45	10,100
ALCLAD 3004 – H18	SHEET 0.013 – 0.161	38	33	29	22	19	68	46	10,100
ALCLAD 3004 – H291	SHEET 0.032 – 0.050	38	34	32	22	20	76	54	10,100
ALCLAD 3004 – H32	SHEET 0.017 – 0.249	27	20	17	16	12	54	34	10,100
ALCLAD 3004 – H34	SHEET 0.009 – 0.249	31	24	21	18	14	62	38	10,100
3105 – H14	SHEET 0.019 – 0.063	22	20	18	13	12	44	30	10,100
3105 – H16	SHEET 0.019 – 0.063	26	24	22	16	14	52	36	10,100
5005 – H12	SHEET & PLATE 0.017 – 2.000	17	14	13	11	8	34	22	10,100
5005 – H14	SHEET & PLATE 0.009 – 1.000	20	17	15	12	10	40	25	10,100
5005 – H32	SHEET & PLATE 0.017 – 2.000	17	12	11	11	7	34	20	10,100
5005 – H34	SHEET & PLATE 0.009 – 2.000	20	15	14	12	8.5	40	24	10,100

Footnotes appear at the end of this table.

TABLE 9

BUCKLING FORMULA CONSTANTS

COMPRESSION IN COLUMNS			COMPRESSION IN FLAT PLATES			COMPRESSION IN ROUND TUBES			BENDING IN ROUND TUBES			BENDING IN RECTANGULAR BARS			SHEAR IN FLAT PLATES		
B_c, ksi	D_c, ksi	C_c	B_p, ksi	D_p, ksi	C_p	B_t, ksi	D_t, ksi	C_t	B_{tb}, ksi	D_{tb}, ksi	C_{tb}	B_b, ksi	D_b, ksi	C_b	B_s, ksi	D_s, ksi	C_s
22.8	0.133	115	27.1	0.172	105	26.3	0.977	294	39.4	2.298	99	36.1	0.264	91	19.4	0.104	124
25.3	0.155	109	30.1	0.201	100	29.0	1.116	271	43.6	2.626	92	40.0	0.309	86	19.4	0.104	124
24.0	0.144	112	28.6	0.187	102	27.7	1.046	279	41.5	2.461	96	38.1	0.286	89	19.4	0.104	124
9.9	0.038	174	11.5	0.047	162	11.4	0.321	640	17.1	0.756	172	15.2	0.072	140	8.5	0.030	188
11.0	0.044	165	12.8	0.056	153	12.7	0.372	607	19.1	0.875	160	17.0	0.085	133	8.5	0.030	188
14.5	0.067	144	17.0	0.086	133	16.7	0.536	461	25.1	1.260	133	22.6	0.131	115	12.0	0.051	158
16.8	0.084	133	19.9	0.108	123	19.4	0.654	398	29.2	1.538	121	26.4	0.165	107	12.0	0.051	158
19.2	0.103	125	22.8	0.132	115	22.2	0.779	342	33.2	1.832	111	30.2	0.202	100	16.4	0.081	135
20.4	0.112	121	24.2	0.145	111	23.5	0.843	330	35.3	1.984	106	32.2	0.222	97	16.4	0.081	135
21.6	0.123	118	25.7	0.159	108	24.9	0.909	310	37.4	2.140	102	34.1	0.243	94	17.9	0.093	129
22.8	0.133	115	27.1	0.172	105	26.3	0.977	294	39.4	2.298	99	36.1	0.264	91	17.9	0.093	129
26.5	0.166	106	31.6	0.217	97	30.4	1.188	259	45.6	2.794	90	42.0	0.332	84	22.5	0.130	115
31.4	0.215	98	37.7	0.282	89	36.0	1.486	220	54.0	3.497	80	50.1	0.433	77	25.6	0.158	108
35.2	0.254	92	42.3	0.335	84	40.2	1.723	199	60.3	4.053	74	56.3	0.515	73	28.8	0.188	102
20.4	0.112	121	24.2	0.145	111	23.5	0.843	330	35.3	1.984	106	32.2	0.222	97	16.4	0.081	135
25.3	0.155	109	30.1	0.201	100	29.0	1.116	271	43.6	2.626	92	40.0	0.309	86	19.4	0.104	124
27.7	0.178	104	33.1	0.232	95	31.8	1.260	247	47.7	2.966	87	44.1	0.356	82	19.4	0.104	124
29.0	0.190	102	34.6	0.248	93	33.2	1.334	237	49.8	3.140	85	46.1	0.381	81	22.5	0.130	115
31.4	0.215	98	37.7	0.282	89	36.0	1.486	220	54.0	3.497	80	50.1	0.433	77	22.5	0.130	115
25.3	0.155	109	30.1	0.201	100	29.0	1.116	271	43.6	2.626	92	40.0	0.309	86	21.0	0.117	120
30.2	0.202	100	36.1	0.265	91	34.6	1.410	229	51.9	3.317	82	48.1	0.407	79	24.1	0.144	112
33.9	0.241	94	40.7	0.317	86	38.8	1.643	205	58.2	3.865	76	54.2	0.487	74	27.2	0.173	105
37.7	0.282	89	45.4	0.372	81	43.0	1.886	187	64.6	4.437	71	60.5	0.573	70	28.8	0.188	102
19.2	0.103	125	22.8	0.132	115	22.2	0.779	342	33.2	1.832	111	30.2	0.202	100	16.4	0.081	135
24.0	0.144	112	28.6	0.187	102	27.7	1.046	279	41.5	2.461	96	38.1	0.286	89	19.4	0.104	124
20.4	0.112	121	24.2	0.145	111	23.5	0.843	330	35.3	1.984	106	32.2	0.222	97	16.4	0.081	135
25.3	0.155	109	30.1	0.201	100	29.0	1.116	271	43.6	2.626	92	40.0	0.309	86	19.4	0.104	124
14.5	0.067	144	17.0	0.086	133	16.7	0.536	461	25.1	1.260	133	22.6	0.131	115	10.6	0.042	168
16.8	0.084	133	19.9	0.108	123	19.4	0.654	398	29.2	1.538	121	26.4	0.165	107	13.5	0.060	149
12.2	0.052	157	14.2	0.065	145	14.1	0.424	506	21.1	0.999	150	18.8	0.100	126	9.2	0.034	181
15.7	0.075	138	18.4	0.096	127	18.1	0.594	415	27.1	1.397	127	24.5	0.147	111	11.3	0.046	163

TABLE 9 (Cont.)—PROPERTIES OF NONWELDED MATERIAL

ALLOY AND TEMPER[1]	PRODUCT AND THICKNESS RANGE, in.	MINIMUM MECHANICAL PROPERTIES[2]							COMPRESSIVE MODULUS OF ELASTICITY, E, ksi
		TENSION		COMPRESSION	SHEAR		BEARING[4]		
		F_{tu}, ksi	F_{ty}[3], ksi	F_{cy}[3], ksi	F_{su}, ksi	F_{sy}, ksi	F_{bu}, ksi	F_{by}[5], ksi	
5050 – H32	SHEET 0.017 – 0.249	22	16	14	14	9	44	27	10,100
5050 – H32	ROLLED ROD & BAR up thru 0.374	22	16	15	13	9	44	27	10,100
5050 – H32	DRAWN TUBE 0.010 – 0.500	22	16	15	13	9	44	27	10,100
5050 – H34	SHEET 0.009 – 0.249	25	20	18	15	12	50	32	10,100
5050 – H34	ROLLED ROD & BAR up thru 0.313	25	20	19	15	12	50	32	10,100
5050 – H34	DRAWN TUBE 0.017 – 0.500	25	20	19	15	12	50	32	10,100
5052 – H291	SHEET 0.032 – 0.113	42	38	35	23	22	76	61	10,200
5052 – H32	SHEET & PLATE 0.017 – 2.000	31	23	21	19	13	60	39	10,200
5052 – H32	ROLLED ROD & BAR up thru 0.374	31	23	21	19	13	60	39	10,200
5052 – H32	DRAWN TUBE 0.010 – 0.450	31	23	21	19	13	60	39	10,200
5052 – H34	SHEET & PLATE 0.009 – 1.000	34	26	24	20	15	65	44	10,200
5052 – H34	ROLLED ROD & BAR up thru 0.313	34	26	24	20	15	65	44	10,200
5052 – H34	DRAWN TUBE 0.010 – 0.450	34	26	24	20	15	65	44	10,200
5083 – H111	EXTRUSIONS[6] up thru 0.500	40	24	21	24	14	78	41	10,400
5083 – H111	EXTRUSIONS[6] 0.501 and over	40	24	21	23	14	78	38	10,400
5083 – H321	SHEET & PLATE 0.188 – 1.500	44	31	26	26	18	84	53	10,400
5083 – H321	PLATE 1.501 – 3.000	41	29	24	24	17	78	49	10,400
5083 – H323	SHEET 0.051 – 0.249	45	34	32	26	20	88	58	10,400
5083 – H343	SHEET 0.051 – 0.249	50	39	37	29	23	95	66	10,400
5086 – H111	EXTRUSIONS[6] up thru 0.500	36	21	18	21	12	70	36	10,400
5086 – H111	EXTRUSIONS[6] 0.501 and over	36	21	18	21	12	70	34	10,400
5086 – H112	PLATE 0.250 – 0.499	36	18	17	22	10	72	31	10,400
5086 – H112	PLATE 0.500 – 1.000	35	16	16	21	9	70	28	10,400
5086 – H112	PLATE 1.001 – 2.000	35	14	15	21	8	70	28	10,400
5086 – H112	PLATE 2.001 – 3.000	34	14	15	21	8	68	28	10,400
5086 – H32	SHEET & PLATE 0.020 – 2.000	40	28	26	24	16	78	48	10,400
5086 – H32	DRAWN TUBE 0.010 – 0.450	40	28	26	24	16	78	48	10,400
5086 – H34	SHEET & PLATE 0.020 – 1.000	44	34	32	26	20	84	58	10,400
5086 – H34	DRAWN TUBE 0.010 – 0.450	44	34	32	26	20	84	58	10,400
5454 – H111	EXTRUSIONS[6] up thru 0.500	33	19	16	20	11	64	32	10,400
5454 – H111	EXTRUSIONS[6] 0.501 and over	33	19	16	19	11	64	30	10,400
5454 – H112	EXTRUSIONS[6] up thru 5.000	31	12	13	19	7	62	24	10,400
5454 – H112	PIPE 1.000 and over[7]	31	12	13	19	7	62	24	10,400

More information on 5454 on next page.
Footnotes appear at the end of this table.

TABLE 9

BUCKLING FORMULA CONSTANTS

COMPRESSION IN COLUMNS			COMPRESSION IN FLAT PLATES			COMPRESSION IN ROUND TUBES			BENDING IN ROUND TUBES			BENDING IN RECTANGULAR BARS			SHEAR IN FLAT PLATES		
B_c' ksi	D_c' ksi	C_c	B_p' ksi	D_p' ksi	C_p	B_t' ksi	D_t' ksi	C_t	B_{tb}' ksi	D_{tb}' ksi	C_{tb}	B_b' ksi	D_b' ksi	C_b	B_s' ksi	D_s' ksi	C_s
15.7	0.075	138	18.4	0.096	127	18.1	0.594	415	27.1	1.397	127	24.5	0.147	111	12.0	0.051	158
16.8	0.084	133	19.9	0.108	123	19.4	0.654	398	29.2	1.538	121	26.4	0.165	107	12.0	0.051	158
16.8	0.084	133	19.9	0.108	123	19.4	0.654	398	29.2	1.538	121	26.4	0.165	107	12.0	0.051	158
20.4	0.112	121	24.2	0.145	111	23.5	0.843	330	35.3	1.984	106	32.2	0.222	97	16.4	0.081	135
21.6	0.123	118	25.7	0.159	108	24.9	0.909	310	37.4	2.140	102	34.1	0.243	94	16.4	0.081	135
21.6	0.123	118	25.7	0.159	108	24.9	0.909	310	37.4	2.140	102	34.1	0.243	94	16.4	0.081	135
41.5	0.325	85	50.1	0.430	78	47.3	2.131	172	70.9	5.014	67	66.8	0.662	67	31.9	0.219	97
24.0	0.143	112	28.6	0.186	103	27.7	1.042	281	41.5	2.453	96	38.1	0.285	89	17.9	0.092	130
24.0	0.143	112	28.6	0.186	103	27.7	1.042	281	41.5	2.453	96	38.1	0.285	89	17.9	0.092	130
24.0	0.143	112	28.6	0.186	103	27.7	1.042	281	41.5	2.453	96	38.1	0.285	89	17.9	0.092	130
27.7	0.177	104	33.1	0.231	96	31.8	1.256	250	47.7	2.956	88	44.1	0.355	83	21.0	0.116	120
27.7	0.177	104	33.1	0.231	96	31.8	1.256	250	47.7	2.956	88	44.1	0.355	83	21.0	0.116	120
27.7	0.177	104	33.1	0.231	96	31.8	1.256	250	47.7	2.956	88	44.1	0.355	83	21.0	0.116	120
24.0	0.142	113	28.6	0.184	104	27.7	1.036	286	41.5	2.437	97	38.1	0.282	90	19.4	0.103	126
24.0	0.142	113	28.6	0.184	104	27.7	1.036	286	41.5	2.437	97	38.1	0.282	90	19.4	0.103	126
30.2	0.199	101	36.1	0.261	92	34.6	1.396	235	51.9	3.285	84	48.1	0.401	80	25.6	0.156	110
27.7	0.175	105	33.1	0.229	97	31.8	1.248	254	47.7	2.937	89	44.1	0.351	84	24.1	0.142	113
37.7	0.278	90	45.4	0.367	82	43.0	1.867	192	64.6	4.394	73	60.5	0.565	71	28.8	0.185	104
44.1	0.352	84	53.2	0.466	76	50.1	2.289	166	75.2	5.386	66	71.0	0.718	66	33.5	0.233	96
20.4	0.111	123	24.2	0.143	113	23.5	0.835	339	35.3	1.965	108	32.2	0.219	98	16.4	0.080	137
20.4	0.111	123	24.2	0.143	113	23.5	0.835	339	35.3	1.965	108	32.2	0.219	98	16.4	0.080	137
19.2	0.101	127	22.8	0.130	116	22.2	0.771	351	33.2	1.814	113	30.2	0.199	101	13.5	0.059	151
18.0	0.092	131	21.3	0.118	120	20.8	0.708	375	31.2	1.667	118	28.3	0.181	104	12.0	0.050	160
16.8	0.083	135	19.9	0.106	125	19.4	0.647	406	27.1	1.384	109	26.4	0.163	108	10.6	0.041	171
16.8	0.083	135	19.9	0.106	125	19.4	0.647	406	27.1	1.384	109	26.4	0.163	108	10.6	0.041	171
30.2	0.199	101	36.1	0.261	92	34.6	1.396	235	51.9	3.285	84	48.1	0.401	80	22.5	0.128	117
30.2	0.199	101	36.1	0.261	92	34.6	1.396	235	51.9	3.285	84	48.1	0.401	80	22.5	0.128	117
37.7	0.278	90	45.4	0.367	82	43.0	1.867	192	64.6	4.394	73	60.5	0.565	71	28.8	0.185	104
37.7	0.278	90	45.4	0.367	82	43.0	1.867	192	64.6	4.394	73	60.5	0.565	71	28.8	0.185	104
18.0	0.092	131	21.3	0.118	120	20.8	0.708	375	31.2	1.667	118	28.3	0.181	104	14.9	0.069	144
18.0	0.092	131	21.3	0.118	120	20.8	0.708	375	31.2	1.667	118	28.3	0.181	104	14.9	0.069	144
14.5	0.066	146	17.0	0.084	135	16.7	0.530	468	23.1	1.116	118	22.6	0.129	117	9.2	0.033	184
14.5	0.066	146	17.0	0.084	135	16.7	0.530	468	23.1	1.116	118	22.6	0.129	117	9.2	0.033	184

More information on 5454 on next page.

TABLE 9 (*Cont.*)—PROPERTIES OF NONWELDED MATERIAL

ALLOY AND TEMPER①	PRODUCT AND THICKNESS RANGE, in.	MINIMUM MECHANICAL PROPERTIES②							COMPRESSIVE MODULUS OF ELASTICITY, E, ksi
		TENSION		COM-PRES-SION	SHEAR		BEARING④		
		F_{tu}, ksi	F_{ty}③, ksi	F_{cy}③, ksi	F_{su}, ksi	F_{sy}, ksi	F_{bu}, ksi	F_{by}⑤, ksi	
5454 – H32	SHEET & PLATE 0.020 – 2.000	36	26	24	21	15	70	44	10,400
5454 – H32	DRAWN TUBE 0.010 – 0.450	36	26	24	21	15	70	44	10,400
5454 – H34	SHEET & PLATE 0.020 – 1.000	39	29	27	23	17	74	49	10,400
5454 – H34	DRAWN TUBE 0.010 – 0.450	39	29	27	23	17	74	49	10,400
5456 – H111	EXTRUSIONS⑥ up thru 0.500	42	26	22	25	15	82	44	10,400
5456 – H111	EXTRUSIONS⑥ 0.501 and over	42	26	22	24	15	82	42	10,400
5456 – H112	EXTRUSIONS⑥ up thru 5.000	41	19	20	24	11	82	38	10,400
5456 – H112	PIPE 1.000 and over⑦	41	19	20	24	11	82	38	10,400
5456 – H321	SHEET & PLATE 0.188 – 1.250	46	33	27	27	19	87	56	10,400
5456 – H321	PLATE 1.251 – 1.500	44	31	25	25	18	84	53	10,400
5456 – H321	PLATE 1.501 – 3.000	41	29	25	25	17	82	49	10,400
5456 – H323	SHEET 0.051 – 0.249	48	36	34	28	21	94	61	10,400
5456 – H343	SHEET 0.051 – 0.249	53	41	39	31	24	101	70	10,400
6061 – T6, T651	SHEET & PLATE 0.010 – 5.000	42	35	35	27	20	88	58	10,100
6061 – T6, T6510, T6511	EXTRUSIONS⑥ STD. STR. SHAPES⑧ up thru 3.000	38	35	35	24	20	80	56	10,100
6061 – T6, T651	ROLLED ROD & BAR up thru 8.000	42	35	35	27	20	88	56	10,100
6061 – T6	DRAWN TUBE 0.025 – 0.500	42	35	35	27	20	88	56	10,100
6061 – T6	PIPE up thru 0.999⑦	42	35	35	27	20	88	56	10,100
6061 – T6	PIPE 1.000 and over⑦	38	35	35	24	20	80	56	10,100
6063 – T5	EXTRUSIONS⑥ up thru 0.500	22	16	16	13	9	46	26	10,100
6063 – T5	EXTRUSIONS⑥ 0.501 and over	21	15	15	12	8.5	44	24	10,100
6063 – T5	PIPE up thru 0.500⑨	22	16	16	13	9	46	26	10,100
6063 – T5	PIPE 0.500 – 1.000⑨	21	15	15	12	8.5	44	24	10,100
6063 – T6	EXTRUSIONS⑥ up thru 1.000	30	25	25	19	14	63	40	10,100
6063 – T6	PIPE All	30	25	25	19	14	63	40	10,100
6063 – T83	DRAWN TUBE 0.018 – 0.259	33	30	30	20	17	69	48	10,100
6070 – T6	EXTRUSIONS⑥ up thru 3.000	48	45	45	29	26	91	72	10,100
6071 – T6, T651	SHEET & PLATE 0.010 – 2.000	50	47	48	30	27	102	73	10,100
ANOCLAD Type 5 – H12	SHEET 0.020 – 0.249	16	11	9	10	6.5	32	18	10,100
ANOCLAD Type 5 – H14	SHEET 0.020 – 0.249	19	16	13	12	9	38	24	10,100
ANOCLAD Type 10 – H12	SHEET 0.020 – 0.249	12	10	9	7	6	24	16	10,100
ANOCLAD Type 10 – H14	SHEET 0.020 – 0.249	14	12	11	8.5	7	28	18	10,100

More information on Anoclad alloys on next page.
Footnotes appear at the end of this table.

TABLE 9

BUCKLING FORMULA CONSTANTS

COMPRESSION IN COLUMNS			COMPRESSION IN FLAT PLATES			COMPRESSION IN ROUND TUBES			BENDING IN ROUND TUBES			BENDING IN RECTANGULAR BARS			SHEAR IN FLAT PLATES		
B_c, ksi	D_c, ksi	C_c	B_p, ksi	D_p, ksi	C_p	B_t, ksi	D_t, ksi	C_t	B_{tb}, ksi	D_{tb}, ksi	C_{tb}	B_b, ksi	D_b, ksi	C_b	B_s, ksi	D_s, ksi	C_s
27.7	0.175	105	33.1	0.229	97	31.8	1.248	254	47.7	2.937	89	44.1	0.351	84	21.0	0.115	121
27.7	0.175	105	33.1	0.229	97	31.8	1.248	254	47.7	2.937	89	44.1	0.351	84	21.0	0.115	121
31.4	0.212	99	37.7	0.278	91	36.0	1.472	226	54.0	3.463	82	50.1	0.426	78	24.1	0.142	113
31.4	0.212	99	37.7	0.278	91	36.0	1.472	226	54.0	3.463	82	50.1	0.426	78	24.1	0.142	113
25.3	0.152	110	30.1	0.198	101	29.0	1.105	279	43.6	2.600	94	40.0	0.304	88	21.0	0.115	121
25.3	0.152	110	30.1	0.198	101	29.0	1.105	279	43.6	2.600	94	40.0	0.304	88	21.0	0.115	121
22.8	0.131	116	27.1	0.170	107	26.3	0.967	301	37.4	2.119	93	36.1	0.260	92	14.9	0.069	144
22.8	0.131	116	27.1	0.170	107	26.3	0.967	301	37.4	2.119	93	36.1	0.260	92	14.9	0.069	144
31.4	0.212	99	37.7	0.278	91	36.0	1.472	226	54.0	3.463	82	50.1	0.426	78	27.2	0.170	107
29.0	0.187	103	34.6	0.245	94	33.2	1.321	244	49.8	3.110	86	46.1	0.376	82	25.6	0.156	110
29.0	0.187	103	34.6	0.245	94	33.2	1.321	244	49.8	3.110	86	46.1	0.376	82	24.1	0.142	113
40.3	0.307	88	48.5	0.406	80	45.9	2.033	180	68.8	4.784	70	64.7	0.624	69	30.3	0.201	101
46.7	0.383	81	56.4	0.509	74	53.0	2.464	157	79.5	5.799	63	75.3	0.784	64	35.2	0.250	94
39.4	0.246	66	45.0	0.301	61	43.2	1.558	141	64.8	4.458	55	66.8	0.665	67	25.8	0.131	81
39.4	0.246	66	45.0	0.301	61	43.2	1.558	141	64.8	4.458	55	66.8	0.665	67	25.8	0.131	81
39.4	0.246	66	45.0	0.301	61	43.2	1.558	141	64.8	4.458	55	66.8	0.665	67	25.8	0.131	81
39.4	0.246	66	45.0	0.301	61	43.2	1.558	141	64.8	4.458	55	66.8	0.665	67	25.8	0.131	81
39.4	0.246	66	45.0	0.301	61	43.2	1.558	141	64.8	4.458	55	66.8	0.665	67	25.8	0.131	81
17.3	0.072	99	19.5	0.086	93	19.2	0.529	275	28.8	1.513	95	28.3	0.183	103	11.0	0.036	124
16.2	0.065	102	18.2	0.078	96	18.0	0.484	289	26.9	1.384	99	26.4	0.165	107	10.4	0.033	128
17.3	0.072	99	19.5	0.086	93	19.2	0.529	275	28.8	1.513	95	28.3	0.183	103	11.0	0.036	124
16.2	0.065	102	18.2	0.078	96	18.0	0.484	289	26.9	1.384	99	26.4	0.165	107	10.4	0.033	128
27.6	0.145	78	31.4	0.175	73	30.5	0.978	188	45.7	2.800	70	46.1	0.381	81	17.6	0.074	98
27.6	0.145	78	31.4	0.175	73	30.5	0.978	188	45.7	2.800	70	46.1	0.381	81	17.6	0.074	98
33.5	0.193	71	38.2	0.235	67	36.8	1.259	161	55.2	3.602	62	56.3	0.515	73	21.7	0.101	88
51.4	0.366	57	59.0	0.451	53	56.1	2.207	112	84.1	6.315	47	88.2	1.010	58	34.3	0.200	70
55.0	0.406	55	63.3	0.501	52	60.0	2.413	106	88.0	6.707	43	94.8	1.125	56	35.7	0.212	69
9.9	0.038	174	11.5	0.047	162	11.4	0.321	640	17.1	0.756	172	15.2	0.072	140	8.5	0.030	188
14.5	0.067	144	17.0	0.086	133	16.7	0.536	461	25.1	1.260	133	22.6	0.131	115	12.0	0.051	158
9.9	0.038	174	11.5	0.047	162	11.4	0.321	640	17.1	0.756	172	15.2	0.072	140	7.8	0.026	196
12.2	0.052	157	14.2	0.065	145	14.1	0.424	506	21.1	0.999	150	18.8	0.100	126	9.2	0.034	181

More information on Anoclad alloys on next page.

TABLE 9 (*Cont.*)—PROPERTIES OF NONWELDED MATERIAL

ALLOY AND TEMPER[1]	PRODUCT AND THICKNESS RANGE, in.	MINIMUM MECHANICAL PROPERTIES[2]							COMPRESSIVE MODULUS OF ELASTICITY, E, ksi
		TENSION		COM-PRES-SION	SHEAR		BEARING[4]		
		F_{tu}, ksi	F_{ty}[3], ksi	F_{cy}[3], ksi	F_{su}, ksi	F_{sy}, ksi	F_{bu}, ksi	F_{by}[5], ksi	
ANOCLAD Type 11 – H12	SHEET 0.020 – 0.249	14	11	10	9	6.5	28	18	10,100
ANOCLAD Type 11 – H14	SHEET 0.020 – 0.249	16	14	13	10	8	32	21	10,100
ANOCLAD Types 12 – H12, 20 – H12, 30 – H12, 40 – H12	SHEET 0.020 – 0.113	17	12	10	11	7	34	19	10,100
ANOCLAD Types 12 – H14, 20 – H14, 30 – H14, 40 – H14	SHEET 0.020 – 0.161	20	17	14	12	10	40	25	10,100
ANOCLAD Types 5-T5, 10 – T5, 11 – T5	EXTRUSIONS[6] up thru 0.499	22	16	16	13	9	46	26	10,100

[1] Data for Anoclad alloys are given at the end of the table.
[2] Minimum tensile properties apply to the direction in which specified mechanical properties are determined. This is the principal direction of working (longitudinal direction) for all products except heat-treated sheet and plate. For heat-treated sheet and plate, specifications require that tensile properties be measured in the transverse direction, since these values are generally lower than the longitudinal properties. Compressive yield strength values apply to the principal direction of working for all products since compressive yield strength is generally lowest in this direction.
[3] Offset equals 0.2 per cent.
[4] Values for ratio of edge distance to hole diameter of 2.0. When this ratio is reduced to 1.5, the bearing ultimate strengths must be reduced 22 per cent and the bearing yield strengths reduced 15 per cent.
[5] Offset equals 2 per cent of pin diameter.
[6] Extruded rods, bars, shapes and tubes.
[7] Nominal pipe size, in.
[8] Available in -T6 temper only.
[9] Nominal wall thickness, in.

TABLE 9

BUCKLING FORMULA CONSTANTS

COMPRESSION IN COLUMNS			COMPRESSION IN FLAT PLATES			COMPRESSION IN ROUND TUBES			BENDING IN ROUND TUBES			BENDING IN RECTANGULAR BARS			SHEAR IN FLAT PLATES		
B_c, ksi	D_c, ksi	C_c	B_p, ksi	D_p, ksi	C_p	B_t, ksi	D_t, ksi	C_t	B_{tb}, ksi	D_{tb}, ksi	C_{tb}	B_b, ksi	D_b, ksi	C_b	B_s, ksi	D_s, ksi	C_s
11.0	0.044	165	12.8	0.056	153	12.7	0.372	607	19.1	0.875	160	17.0	0.085	133	8.5	0.030	188
14.5	0.067	144	17.0	0.086	133	16.7	0.536	461	25.1	1.260	133	22.6	0.131	115	10.6	0.042	168
11.0	0.044	165	12.8	0.056	153	12.7	0.372	607	19.1	0.875	160	17.0	0.085	133	9.2	0.034	181
15.7	0.075	138	18.4	0.096	127	18.1	0.594	415	27.1	1.397	127	24.5	0.147	111	13.5	0.060	149
17.3	0.072	99	19.5	0.086	93	19.2	0.529	275	28.8	1.513	95	28.3	0.183	103	11.0	0.036	124

TABLE 10
MINIMUM MECHANICAL PROPERTIES FOR WELDED MATERIAL
(TIG or MIG Welding with No Postweld Heat Treatment)

ALLOY AND TEMPER	PROD. AND THICK. RANGE, in.	FILLER WIRE①,⑤	TENSION		COMP-RES-SION	SHEAR		BEARING③	
			F_{tuw}, ksi	F_{tyw}②, ksi	F_{cyw}②, ksi	F_{suw}, ksi	F_{syw}, ksi	F_{buw}, ksi	F_{byw}④, ksi
1100 – H12, H14	⑥	1100, 4043	11	4.5	4.5	8	2.5	23	8
3003 – H12, H14, H16, H18	⑥	1100, 4043	14	7	7	10	4	30	12
ALCLAD 3003 – H12, H14, H16, H18	⑥	1100, 4043, 5356, 5556	13	6	6	10	3.5	30	11
3004 – H14, H16, H18, H32, H34, H36	⑥	4043, 5356, 5554	22	11	11	14	6.5	46	20
ALCLAD 3004 – H14, H16, H18, H291, H32	⑥	4043, 5356, 5554, 5556	21	11	11	13	6.5	44	19
3105 – H14, H16	⑥	1100, 4043	15	7	7	10	4	30	10
5005 – H12, H14, H32, H34	⑥	4043, 5356	14	7	7	9	4	28	10
5050 – H32, H34	⑥	4043, 5356	18	8	8	12	4.5	36	12
5052 – H291, H32, H34	⑥	4043, 5356, 5554	25	13	13	16	7.5	50	19
5083 – H111	EXTRUSIONS⑦ ALL	5356, 5556	39	21	20	23	12	78	32
5083 – H321	SHEET & PLATE 0.188 – 1.500	5356, 5556	40	24	24	24	14	80	36
5083 – H321	PLATE 1.501 – 3.000	5356, 5556	39	23	23	24	13	78	34
5083 – H323, H343	SHEET 0.051 – 0.249	5356, 5556	40	24	24	24	14	80	36
5086 – H111	EXTRUSIONS⑦ ALL	5356, 5556	35	18	17	21	10	70	28
5086 – H112	PLATE 0.250 – 0.499	5356, 5556	35	17	17	21	9.5	70	28
5086 – H112	PLATE 0.500 – 1.000	5356, 5556	35	16	16	21	9	70	28
5086 – H112	PLATE 1.001 – 2.000	5356, 5556	35	14	14	21	8	70	28
5086 – H32, H34	⑥	5356, 5556	35	19	19	21	11	70	28
5454 – H111	EXTRUSIONS⑦ up thru 5.000	5356, 5554, 5556	31	16	15	19	9.5	62	24
5454 – H112	⑥	5356, 5554, 5556	31	12	12	19	7	62	24
5454 – H32, H34	⑥	5356, 5554, 5556	31	16	16	19	9.5	62	24
5456 – H111	EXTRUSIONS⑦ up thru 5.000	5556	41	24	22	24	14	82	38
5456 – H112	⑥	5556	41	19	19	24	11	82	38
5456 – H321	SHEET & PLATE 0.188 – 1.500	5556	42	26	24	25	15	84	38
5456 – H321	PLATE 1.501 – 3.000	5556	41	24	23	25	14	82	36
5456 – H323, H343	SHEET 0.051 – 0.249	5556	42	26	26	25	15	84	38
6061 – T6, T651	⑥, ⑧	5356, 5556	24	20	20	15	12	50	30
6061 – T6, T651	⑥ Over 0.375	4043, 5554	24	15	15	15	9	50	30
6063 – T5, T6, T83	⑥	4043, 5356, 5554, 5556	17	11	11	11	6.5	34	22
6070, 6071 – T6, T651	⑥	5356, 5556	28	24	24	17	14	50	30
ANOCLAD TYPE 11 – H14	SHEET 0.020 – 0.249	1100, 4043	11	4.5	4.5	8	2.5	23	8

ALLOY AND TEMPER	PROD. AND THICK. RANGE, in.	FILLER WIRE[1], [5]	TENSION		COMPRESSION	SHEAR		BEARING[3]	
			F_{tuw}, ksi	F_{tyw}[2], ksi	F_{cyw}[2], ksi	F_{suw}, ksi	F_{syw}, ksi	F_{buw}, ksi	F_{byw}[4], ksi
ANOCLAD TYPES 12 – H14, 20 – H14, 30 – H14, 40 – H14	SHEET 0.020 – 0.161	1100, 4043	14	7	7	10	4	30	12
ANOCLAD TYPES 5 – T5, 10 – T5, 11 – T5	EXTRUSIONS[7] up thru 0.499	4043, 5356, 5554, 5556	17	11	11	11	6.5	34	22

[1] Filler wires listed are commonly used. They do not necessarily represent recommended filler wires for all applications.

[2] Offset equals 0.2 per cent in 10-in. gage length across a butt weld.

[3] Values for ratio of edge distance to hole diameter of 2.0. When this ratio is reduced to 1.5, the bearing ultimate strengths must be reduced 22 per cent and the bearing yield strengths reduced 15 per cent.

[4] Offset equals 2 per cent of pin diameter.

[5] Filler alloy 5183 has the same rating as 5556, except that welds made with 5183 are slightly more ductile and, in cases where the filler metal controls the weld strength, slightly less strong than welds made with 5556. Because of its lower strength, 5183 filler metal is not recommended for welding 5456.

[6] Tempers, products or thickness ranges as covered in Table 9.

[7] Extruded rods, bars, shapes and tubes.

[8] Also welds made in material 0.375-in. thick and less and welded with 4043 or 5554 filler wire.

TABLE 11
SUGGESTED ALLOWABLE STRESSES FOR
THIN, FLAT COMPONENTS, BASED ON CRIPPLING[1]

ALLOY AND TEMPER[2]	Limiting b/t [3]	Allowable Stress Based on Crippling, F_{cc}, ksi (Eqs 13a and 13b)
1100 – H14	61	270 t/b
2014 – T6, – T651	26	640 t/b
Alclad 2014 – T6, – T651	26	640 t/b
3003 – H14	59	280 t/b
3003 – H16	52	320 t/b
Alclad 3004 – H16	42	390 t/b
5052 – H34	44	370 t/b
5083 – H111	48	350 t/b
5083 – H321	43	390 t/b
5086 – H111	52	320 t/b
5086 – H34	38	440 t/b
5454 – H111	56	300 t/b
5454 – H34	42	400 t/b
5456 – H111	47	360 t/b
5456 – H321	42	400 t/b
5456 – H343	34	490 t/b
6061 – T6, – T651, – T6510, – T6511	32	480 t/b
6063 – T5	54	320 t/b
6063 – T6	39	400 t/b
6070 – T6	27	550 t/b
Anoclad Types 5 – T5, 10 – T5, 11 – T5	54	320 t/b
Anoclad Type 11 – H14	61	270 t/b
Anoclad Types 12 – H14, 20 – H14, 30 – H14, 40 – H14	59	280 t/b

[1] Formulas as given apply to sheet or plate elements supported on both unloaded edges. For outstanding flanges, replace b by equivalent width b_e, where $b_e = 3.1 \times b$ for column flanges and $2.8 \times b$ for beam flanges, b in this case being the clear width of the outstanding flange.

[2] Products and thickness ranges for the various alloys are the same as for Table 1. This table also applies to the Anoclad alloys for which suggested allowable stresses are given in Table 1.

[3] Allowable stresses in this table apply for values of b/t exceeding this limiting value. For smaller values of b/t, the allowable stress should not exceed the values given by Specifications 8, 9, 15 or 16.

PART III SUPPLEMENT

A Reprint of ASCE Proceedings Papers—Nos. 3341 and 3342

Paper No. 3341

SUGGESTED SPECIFICATIONS FOR STRUCTURES OF ALUMINUM ALLOYS 6061-T6 and 6062-T6

Report of the Task Committee on Lightweight
Alloys, Committee on Metals, Structural Division

Excerpts from Paper No. 3342

SUGGESTED SPECIFICATIONS FOR STRUCTURES OF ALUMINUM ALLOY 6063-T5 and 6063-T6

Report of the Task Committee on Lightweight
Alloys, Committee on Metals, Structural Division

Reprinted with permission from the Proceedings of

AMERICAN SOCIETY OF CIVIL ENGINEERS

Journal of the

STRUCTURAL DIVISION

Proceedings of the American Society of Civil Engineers

SUGGESTED SPECIFICATIONS FOR STRUCTURES OF
ALUMINUM ALLOYS 6061-T6 AND 6062-T6

Report of the Task Committee on Lightweight Alloys

Committee on Metals, Structural Division

COMMITTEE REPORT

The Task Committee on Lightweight Alloys (formerly the Committee on Design in Lightweight Structural Alloys) has prepared two suggested specifications for the design of structures of aluminum alloys. The first of these is for 6061-T6 and 6062-T6 alloys (Proc. Paper 3341) and supersedes the previous specifications (1), (a).[1] The second specification is for alloy 6063-T5 and 6063-T6 (Proc. Paper 3342). The task committee hopes that those who have constructive comments on, or criticism of, the suggested specifications will submit them to the Society.

POLICY OF THE STRUCTURAL DIVISION, ASCE, RELATIVE TO STRUCTURAL SPECIFICATIONS

(Adopted by the Executive Committee, Structural Division, on May 26, 1962)

No specification shall be issued in the name of, nor be endorsed by, the Structural Division of ASCE.

Specifications may be prepared by Task Committees of the Structural Division, ASCE, working alone or jointly with other groups. Such specifications may be submitted as committee reports, through the Executive Committee of the Division, for publication in the Structural Division Journal.

Note.—Discussion open until May 1, 1963. To extend the closing date one month, a written request must be filed with the Executive Secretary, ASCE. This paper is part of the copyrighted Journal of the Structural Division, Proceedings of the American Society of Civil Engineers, Vol. 88, No. ST6, December, 1962.

[1] Numerals in parentheses refer to corresponding items in Appendix I.

The Structural Division Executive Committee requests that any committee report that takes the form of a specification, and is written in the usual terse specification style, be accompanied by a commentary or discussion supporting and explaining the specification. The Executive Committee will submit such a report for publication, after the necessary review and approval.

It is the desire and intent of the Structural Division Executive Committee that the best interests of the members of ASCE and the engineering profession be served. Where this is best accomplished by publication and open discussion of design specifications in the Division Journal, this will be done. The Committee feels that no useful purpose will be served by ASCE endorsement of specifications; however, constructive criticism and discussion will add materially to the understanding and improvement of specifications.

FOREWORD

These specifications supersede two previous sets of specifications for structures of aluminum alloy 6061-T6, prepared by this committee (1),(2).

SYNOPSIS

These specifications cover allowable stresses, design rules, and fabrication procedures for structures built of the aluminum alloys known commercially as 6061-T6 and 6062-T6. Alloy 6061-T6 is available in the form of sheet, plate, shapes, tubes, rods, bars, rivets and forgings. Alloy 6062-T6 is available in the form of shapes and tubes. The two alloys have the same mechanical properties and may be used interchangeably. Two sets of allowable stresses are provided; one for bridges and other structures to which allowable stresses for bridges are normally applied; the other for buildings and other structures to which allowable stresses for buildings are normally applied. The basic allowable stresses are 17 ksi for bridge structures and 19 ksi for building structures, based on a minimum yield strength of 35 ksi and a minimum tensile strength of 38 ksi.

PART I.—GENERAL

Introduction. — These specifications cover the allowable stresses, the design rules, and the fabrication procedures for two aluminum alloys commonly used for structural purposes where a high degree of resistance to corrosion is desired. In the preparation of these specifications the Committee has made use of the available theoretical and experimental work relating to this subject and particularly to the Committee's previously published specifications.

These specifications are confined to allowable stresses, design rules, and fabrication. No attempt has been made to cover the loading, erection, inspection, or nontechnical provisions included in many specifications, because such provisions are fairly well established in current good structural practice. It is intended, of course, that structures built under these specifications will be designed, constructed, and erected by following current good practice for metal structures.

It is believed that the designer can make more effective use of a set of specifications if he knows the basis for its various provisions. For this reason the section, "Explanation of Specifications," has been added. That section contains background information and references concerning those paragraphs of the specifications for which some explanation seems required.

When the abbreviation "ksi" is used in these specifications it denotes "kips per square inch" or "thousands of pounds per square inch."

Material.—The principal materials considered in these specifications are aluminum alloys having the following nominal chemical compositions:

Composition	Percentage by weight	
	6061-T6	6062-T6
Copper	0.25	0.25
Silicon	0.6	0.6
Magnesium	1.0	1.0
Chromium	0.25	0.06
Aluminum	97.9	98.09
Total	100.0	100.0

These materials are covered by the following American Society for Testing and Materials (ASTM) specifications:

Product	ASTM Specification No.
Sheet and Plate	B209-62 (6061-T6)
Drawn Seamless Tubes	B210-62 (6061-T6 and 6062-T6)
Bars, Rods and Wire	B211-62 (6061-T6)
Extruded Bars, Rods and Shapes	B221-62 (6061-T6 and 6062-T6)
Drawn Seamless Tubes for Condensers and Heat Exchangers	B234-62 (6061-T6 and 6062-T6)
Extruded Tubes	B235-62 (6061-T6 and 6062-T6)
Pipe	B241-62 (6061-T6 and 6062-T6)
Forgings	B247-62 (6061-T6)
Standard Structural Shapes	B308-62 (6061-T6 and 6062-T6)

For products that are available in both alloys, the two alloys may be used interchangeably.

The specified minimum tensile strength of these materials is 42 ksi for sheet and plate, drawn tubes, and bars, rods and wire; and 38 ksi for all other products. The specified minimum yield strength for all products is 35 ksi. The minimum mechanical properties that have been used as a basis for the selection of allowable stresses in these specifications are listed in Table 1.

TABLE 1.—BASIC STRENGTH DATA[a]

| | | Material Affected by Heat of Welding | |
	Unaffected Parent Material	All material welded with 5356 or 5556 filler alloy and material 3/8-in. or less in thickness welded with 4043 filler alloy	Material more than 3/8-in. thick welded with 4043 filler alloy
Tensile strength	38	24[b]	24[b]
Tensile yield strength	35	20[c]	15[c]
Compressive yield strength	35	20[c]	15[c]
Shear strength	24	15	15
Shear yield strength	20	12	9
Bearing strength	80	50	50
Bearing yield strength	56	30	22

[a] Minimum strength values for Alloys 6061-T6 and 6062-T6, ksi.
[b] ASME weld qualification test value for tensile strength across a butt weld.
[c] These are expected minimum values of the yield strength across a butt weld, corresponding to 0.2% offset on a 10-in. gage length.

Materials for rivets, bolts, nuts, washers, and welding rods and electrodes are covered by the ASTM specifications listed in Table 2. Following are typical values of other physical properties of these alloys:

Modulus of elasticity, ksi	10,000
Modulus of elasticity in shear, ksi	3,800
Poisson's ratio	1/3
Coefficient of expansion, per degree Fahrenheit	0.000012
Weight, in pounds per cubic inch	0.098

Alloys 6061-T6 and 6062-T6 are the ones principally considered in the preparation of these specifications and the ones to which the allowable stresses for parts other than bolts apply. However, these specifications may be applied to structures built of other suitable aluminum alloys, provided such alloys meet the specified strengths and elongations listed in the ASTM specifications mentioned in the first paragraph of this section. Whether or not such other alloys need paint protection will depend on whether they are as resistant to corrosion as 6061-T6 and 6062-T6. The sections of this specification dealing

TABLE 2.—PERTINENT ASTM SPECIFICATIONS

Product	Alloy	ASTM Specification for Material from Which Product is Made
Rivets	6061-T6 or 6061-T4[a]	B316-62 - Rivet and Cold Heading Wire and Rods[b]
Bolts	2024-T4	B316-62 - Rivet and Cold Heading Wire and Rods[b]
Nuts	6061-T6 or 6262-T9	B211-62 - Bars, Rods and Wire, or B316-62 - Rivet and Cold Heading Wire and Rods[b]
Washers	Alclad 2024-T3 or -T4	B209-62 - Sheet and Plate
Welding Rods and Electrodes	ER4043, ER5356 or ER5556	B285-62T - Welding Rods and Bare Electrodes

[a] ASTM B316-61 includes mechanical property specifications for 6061-T6 but not 6061-T4. The heat treatment for the latter is the same as the former except that the artificial aging is omitted.

[b] ASTM B316-62 covers rods up to 0.615 in. in diameter. Rods with diameters from 0.615 to 1.000 in. are supplied with the same mechanical property limits and tolerances on diameter (+ 0.003 in., -0.001 in.) that apply to 0.615-in. rod in ASTM B316-62.

TABLE 3.—ALLOYS TO BE USED FOR RIVETS

Designation before driving	Driving procedure	Designation after driving	Typical shear strength[a]
6061-T6	Cold, as received	6061-T6	30
6061-T4	Hot, 990°F to 1,050°F	6061-T43	24

[a] Typical ultimate shear strength of the driven rivet, ksi.

with welding should not be applied to other alloys unless it has been clearly demonstrated that such alloys are suitable for welding.

Rivets used in fabricating structures designed in accordance with these specifications shall be of aluminum alloy and may be either cold driven or hot driven. The alloy used is indicated in Table 3.

Aluminum bolts used in structures designed in accordance with these specifications shall be of alloy 2024-T4. Such bolts have expected minimum tensile and shear strengths of 62 ksi and 37 ksi, respectively.

PART II.—SPECIFICATIONS FOR RIVETED AND BOLTED STRUCTURES

Section A: Summary of Allowable Stresses.—The allowable stresses to be used in proportioning the parts of a structure shall be determined from Tables

TABLE 4a.—ALLOWABLE STRESSES IN RIVETED OR BOLTED STRUCTURES IN WELDED STRUCTURES AT LOCATIONS FARTHER THAN 1.0 INCH FROM ANY WELD (6061–T6 AND 6062–T6 BRIDGE STRUCTURES NONWELDED)

Type of Stress	Specification No.	Type of Member or Component	Allowable Stress, ksi	Allowable Stress for Slenderness Less Than S_1, ksi	Slenderness Limit, S_1	Allowable Stress for Slenderness Between S_1 and S_2, ksi	Slenderness Limit, S_2	Allowable Stress for Slenderness Greater Than S_2, ksi
TENSION, axial, net section	A-1a	Any tension member	17					
TENSION in extreme fibers of beams, net section	A-2a	Structural shapes, rectangular tubes, built-up members bent about X-axis	17					
	A-3a	Round or oval tubes	21					
	A-4a	Rectangular bars and plates, and outstanding flanges of shapes bent about Y-axis	23					
BEARING	A-5a	On rivets and bolts	30 [a]					
	A-6a	On milled surfaces and pins	20					
COMPRESSION, gross section (Also see Specs. A-8a to A-10a)	A-7a	Columns		17	$\frac{L}{r} = 9.2$	$18.1 - 0.120\,\frac{L}{r}$	$\frac{L}{r} = 67$	$\dfrac{45{,}000}{(L/r)^2}$
COMPRESSION in Columns Subjected to Axial Load, Gross Section — COMPRESSION in components of columns (Also see Spec. A-7a)	A-8a	Outstanding flanges and legs		17	$\frac{b}{t} = 5.2$	$21.0 - 0.77\,\frac{b}{t}$	$\frac{b}{t} = 12$	$\dfrac{1{,}720}{(b/t)^2}$
	A-9a	Flat plates with both edges supported		17	$\frac{b}{t} = 17$	$21.0 - 0.24\,\frac{b}{t}$	$\frac{b}{t} = 38$	$\dfrac{17{,}000}{(b/t)^2}$
	A-10a	Curved plates supported on both edges and walls of round or oval tubes		17	$\frac{R}{t} = 20$	$20.0 - 0.68\,\sqrt{\frac{R}{t}}$	$\frac{R}{t} = 125$	– – – –

COMPRESSION in extreme fibers of beams, gross section (Also see Specs. A-15a to A-19a)	A-11a	Single-web structural shapes and built-up sections bent about X-axis	17	$\frac{L_b}{r_y} = 11$	$18.1 - 0.100\frac{L_b}{r_y}$	$\frac{L_b}{r_y} = 80$	$\frac{65,000}{(L_b/r_y)^2}$
	A-12a	Round or oval tubes	21	$\frac{R_b}{t} = 21$	$25.0 - 0.19\frac{R_b}{t}$	$\frac{R_b}{t} = 60$	$- - -$
	A-13a	Solid rectangular beams bent about X-axis	23	$\frac{d}{t}\sqrt{\frac{L_b}{d}} = 12$	$31.0 - 0.70\frac{d}{t}\sqrt{\frac{L_b}{d}}$	$\frac{d}{t}\sqrt{\frac{L_b}{d}} = 27$	$\frac{8,800}{(\frac{d}{t})^2(\frac{L_b}{d})}$
	A-14a	Rectangular tubes and box sections	17	$\frac{L_b S_c}{I_y} = 33$	$18.1 - 0.192\frac{L_b S_c}{I_y}$	$\frac{L_b S_c}{I_y} = 1760$	$\frac{17,700}{L_b S_c/I_y}$
COMPRESSION in Members Subjected to Bending, Gross Section — COMPRESSION in components of beams, where component is under uniform compression (Also see Specs. A-11a to A-14a)	A-15a	Flat plates with one edge free and one edge supported	17	$\frac{b}{t} = 8.0$	$21.0 - 0.67\frac{b}{t}$	$\frac{b}{t} = 14$	$\frac{2,240}{(b/t)^2}$
	A-16a	Flat plates with both edges supported	17	$\frac{b}{t} = 17$	$21.0 - 0.24\frac{b}{t}$	$\frac{b}{t} = 38$	$\frac{17,000}{(b/t)^2}$
COMPRESSION in components of beams where component is under bending in its own plane. (Also see Specs. A-11a to A-14a)	A-17a	Flat plates with compression edge free and tension edge supported, bent about X-axis	23	$\frac{b}{t} = 7.3$	$31.0 - 1.1\frac{b}{t}$	$\frac{b}{t} = 19$	$\frac{3,700}{(b/t)^2}$
	A-18a	Flat plates with both edges supported, bent about X-axis	17	$- - -$	17	$\frac{h}{t} = 110$	$\frac{205,000}{(h/t)^2}$
	A-19a	Flat plates with both edges supported, bent about X-axis with horizontal stiffener	17	$- - -$	17	$\frac{h}{t} = 227$	$\frac{880,000}{(h/t)^2}$
SHEAR in webs of beams, and also in members subjected to torsion, gross section	A-20a	Unstiffened flat webs	11	$\frac{h}{t} = 13$	$12.1 - 0.082\frac{h}{t}$	$\frac{h}{t} = 66$	$\frac{29,000}{(h/t)^2}$
	A-21a	Stiffened flat webs	11	$- - -$	11	$\frac{a_e}{t} = 65$	$\frac{47,000}{(a_e/t)^2}$

$$a_e = a_1/\sqrt{1 + 0.7(a_1/a_2)^2}$$

(a) This value applies for a ratio of edge distance to rivet or bolt diameter of 2 or greater. For smaller ratios, multiply this allowable stress by the ratio, (edge distance)/(twice the rivet or bolt diameter).

4a to 7a and 4b to 7b. The allowable stresses in Tables 4a through 7a are intended for application to bridge structures and other structures to which specifications similar to the AASHO (3) and AREA (4) specifications for steel bridges are applied. These specifications for bridge structures are designated by the numbers A-1a to A-25a and I-1a to I-24a.

The allowable stresses in Tables 4b through 7b, which appear in Appendix II, are intended for application to building structures and other structures to which specifications similar to the AISC specifications for steel buildings are applied. These specifications for building structures are designated by the numbers A-1b to A-25b and I-1b to I-24b. In subsequent sections of these specifications, when reference is made to a specification number such as "A-1," this number is intended to apply to either "A-1a" or "A-1b."

In applications where it is conventional practice to increase allowable stresses for certain types of loads, such as wind loads, the allowable stresses

TABLE 5a.—ALLOWABLE STRESSES IN RIVETS AND BOLTS
(BRIDGE STRUCTURES)

Specification Number	Description of Rivet or Bolt	Allowable Stress, ksi	
		Shear on effective shear Area	Tension on root area
A-22a	6061-T6 rivets, cold driven	10	--
A-23a	6061-T43 rivets, driven at temperatures of from 990°F to 1,050°F	8	--
A-24a	2024-T4 bolts	14[a]	23
A-25a	6061-T6 pins	10	--

[a] This allowable shear stress applies to either turned bolts in reamed holes or unfinished bolts in 1/16-in. oversize holes.

in these specifications should be increased in the same proportion as are the allowable stresses in accepted specifications for steel structures.

The terms appearing in the formulas in Tables 4a, 4b, 6a and 6b are defined as follows:

a_1 = shorter span of rectangular shear panel, in inches;

a_2 = longer span of rectangular shear panel, in inches;

a_e = equivalent span of rectangular shear panel, in inches;

b = clear width of outstanding flange or of flat plate supported on both unloaded edges, in inches;

d = depth of beam, in inches;

d_1 = distance from toe of compression flange to neutral axis, in inches;

h   = clear height of shear web, in inches;

I_y = moment of inertia of a beam (about axis parallel to web), in.^{4};

L   = length of compression member between points of lateral support or twice the length of a cantilever column (except where analysis shows that a shorter length can be used), in inches;

L_b = length of beam between points at which the compression flange is supported against lateral movement or length of cantilever beam from free end to point at which the compression flange is supported against lateral movement, in inches;

R   = outside radius of round tube or maximum outside radius for an oval tube, in inches;

R_b = outside radius of a round tube in bending or outside radius at the location of the critical compressive stress for an oval tube in bending, in inches. (The location of the critical compressive stress is at the extreme fiber for an oval tube bent about the major axis. For an oval tube bent about the minor axis, the location of the critical stress can be determined by calculating the allowable stress at several points using the formulas of Specification A-12, with R_b equal to the outside radius at each point. Bending moments corresponding to the allowable stresses at the various points are calculated, and the point resulting in the smallest bending moment is the location of the critical compressive stress.);

r   = least radius of gyration of a column, in inches;

r_y = radius of gyration of a beam about axis parallel to web, in inches. (For beams that are unsymmetrical about the horizontal axis, r_y should be calculated as though both flanges were the same as the compression flange.);

S_c = section modulus of a beam (compression side), in cubic inches; and

t   = thickness of flange, plate, web or tube, in inches. (For tapered flanges, t is the average thickness.)

Section B: Column Design.

B-1: Allowable Compressive Stress in Columns.—The allowable compressive stress on the gross section of axially loaded columns shall be determined from the formulas in Specification A-7.

Columns having cross sections involving webs and outstanding legs of such proportions that local buckling may control the design shall be checked by Specifications A-8 to A-10 or by the method outlined in Part IV, Section M.

Open section members that are unsymmetrical about one or both principal axes may be subject to failure by combined torsion and flexure. For single or double angles and tee sections, Specification A-8 provides an adequate factor of safety against this type of failure. Other unsymmetrical, open shapes, such as channels, lipped angles or hat shapes should not be used as columns unless a special analysis is made of the resistance to buckling by combined torsion and flexure (17), (43).

B-2: Columns with Slenderness Ratio Exceeding 120.—Because long columns are relatively flexible, they may be appreciably weakened by the presence

TABLE 6a.—ALLOWABLE STRESSES ON SECTIONS WITHIN 1.0 INCH OF A WELD (6061-T6 AND 6062-T6 BRIDGE STRUCTURES WELDED)

Type of Stress	Specification No.	Type of Member or Component	Allowable Stress, ksi / Allowable Stress for Slenderness Less Than S_1, ksi	Slenderness Limit, S_1	Allowable Stress for Slenderness Between S_1 and S_2, ksi	Slenderness Limit, S_2	Allowable Stress for Slenderness Greater Than S_2, ksi
TENSION, axial, net section	I-1a	Any tension member	10(b)				
TENSION in extreme fibers of beams, net section	I-2a	Structural shapes, rectangular tubes, built-up members bent about X-axis	10(b)				
	I-3a	Round or oval tubes	12(b)				
	I-4a	Rectangular bars and plates, and outstanding flanges of shapes bent about Y-axis	12(b)				
BEARING	I-5a	On rivets and bolts	16(b)(d)				
	I-6a	On milled surfaces and pins	11(b)				
COMPRESSION in Columns Subjected to Axial Load, Gross Section — COMPRESSION,(a) (Gross section (Also see Specs. I-8a to I-10a)	I-7a	Columns(a)	10(b)	- - - -	10(b)	$\frac{L}{r} = 67^{(c)}$	$\frac{45,000}{(L/r)^2}$
COMPRESSION in components of columns (Also see Spec. I-7a)	I-8a	Outstanding flanges and legs	10(b)	$\frac{b}{t} = 4.7^{(c)}$	$\frac{21.6}{\sqrt{b/t}}$	$\frac{b}{t} = 19$	$\frac{1,720}{(b/t)^2}$
	I-9a	Flat plates with both edges supported	10(b)	- - - -	10(b)	$\frac{b}{t} = 41^{(a)}$	$\frac{17,000}{(b/t)^2}$
	I-10a	Curved plates supported on both edges and walls of round or oval tubes	10(b)	$\frac{R}{t} = 13^{(a)}$	$\frac{18.9}{(R/t)^{1/4}}$	$\frac{R}{t} = 200$	- -
COMPRESSION in extreme fibers of beams, gross section (Also see Specs. I-15a to I-19a)	I-11a	Single-web structural shapes and built-up sections, bent about X-axis(a)	10(b)	- - - -	10(b)	$\frac{L_b}{r_y} = 81^{(c)}$	$\frac{65,000}{(L_b/r_y)^2}$
	I-12a	Round or oval tubes	12(b)	$\frac{R_b}{t} = 11^{(c)}$	$\frac{21.9}{(R_b/t)^{1/4}}$	$\frac{R_b}{t} = 135$	- -
	I-13a	Solid rectangular beams bent about X-axis	12(b)	$\frac{d}{t}\sqrt{\frac{L_b}{d}} = 9.8^{(c)}$	$\frac{37.5}{[(d/t)^2 L_b/d]^{1/4}}$	$\frac{d}{t}\sqrt{\frac{L_b}{d}} = 38$	$\frac{8,800}{(\frac{d}{t})^2 \frac{L_b}{d}}$
COMPRESSION in Members Subjected	I-14a	Rectangular tubes and box sections(a)	10(b)	- - - -	10(b)	$\frac{L_b S_c}{I_y} = 1770^{(c)}$	$\frac{17,700}{L_b S_c/I_y}$

Spec	Description	Sketch				
to Bending, Gross Section — COMPRESSION in components of beams, where component is under uniform compression (Also see Specs. I-11a to I-14a)						
I-15a	Flat plates with one edge free and one edge supported		$10^{(b)}$	$\frac{b}{t}=5.1^{(a)}$	$\frac{22.5}{\sqrt{b/t}}$	$\frac{b}{t}=21$ → $\frac{2,240}{(b/t)^2}$
I-16a	Flat plates with both edges supported		$10^{(b)}$	- - - -	$10^{(b)}$	$\frac{b}{t}=41$ → $\frac{\mathbf{17,000}}{(b/t)^2}$
COMPRESSION in components of beams where component is under bending in its own plane, (Also see Specs. I-11a to I-14a)						
I-17a	Flat plates with compression edge free and tension edge supported, bent about X-axis	Compression Flange	$12^{(b)}$	$\frac{b}{t}=8.3^{(a)}$	$\frac{30.2}{\sqrt{b/t}}$	$\frac{b}{t}=25$ → $\frac{3,700}{(b/t)^2}$
I-18a	Flat plates with both edges supported, bent about X-axis		$10^{(b)}$	- - - -	$10^{(b)}$	$\frac{h}{t}=143^{(c)}$ → $\frac{205,000}{(h/t)^2}$
I-19a	Flat plates with both edges supported, bent about X-axis with horizontal stiffener	Compression Flange, $0.4d_1$, Neutral Axis	$10^{(b)}$	- - - -	$10^{(b)}$	$\frac{h}{t}=300^{(c)}$ → $\frac{880,000}{(h/t)^2}$
SHEAR in webs of beams, and also in members subjected to torsion, gross section						
I-20a	Unstiffened flat webs		$6^{(b)}$	- - - -	$8^{(b)}$	$\frac{h}{t}=70^{(c)}$ → $\frac{29,000}{(h/t)^2}$
I-21a	Stiffened flat webs	$a_e = \dfrac{a_1}{\sqrt{1+0.7(a_1/a_2)^2}}$	$6^{(b)}$	- - - -	$8^{(b)}$	$\frac{a_e}{t}=88^{(c)}$ → $\frac{47,000}{(a_e/t)^2}$

(a) The allowable stresses for columns, single web beams and rectangular tubes and box sections apply to members supported at both ends and welded at the ends only. See Specification I-26 for allowable stresses in these members with welds at locations other than the ends and in cantilever columns and beams.

(b) These allowable stresses apply to all material welded with 5556 or 5356 filler alloy and to material 3/8-in. or less in thickness welded with 4043 filler alloy. For thicker material welded with 4043 filler alloy, these allowable stresses shall be reduced by multiplying them by 0.8. Allowable stresses not marked with a superscript apply to material welded with either 4043, 5556 or 5356 filler alloy.

(c) These slenderness limits apply to all material welded with 5556 or 5356 filler alloy and to material 3/8-in. or less in thickness welded with 4043 filler alloy. For thicker material welded with 4043 filler alloy, these slenderness limits must be adjusted to correspond to the reduced values of maximum allowable stresses indicated in Note (b) above.

(d) This value applies for a ratio of edge distance to rivet or bolt diameter of 2 or more. For smaller ratios, multiply this allowable stress by the ratio, (edge distance)/(twice the rivet or bolt diameter).

of lateral loads that would have little effect on the column strength of stiffer members. For this reason, columns with slenderness ratios greater than 120 should not be used unless special care is taken to insure that the effects of any lateral loads to which the member may be subjected, such as wind, dead load, or the weight of workmen and equipment, are taken into account by using the provision for combined compression and bending in Specifications B-7.

B-3: Compression Splices.—Members designed for compression, if faced for bearing, shall be spliced on four sides sufficiently to hold the abutting parts true to place. The splice shall be as near a panel point as practicable and shall be designed to transmit at least one half of the stress through the splice material. Members not faced for bearing shall be fully spliced for the computed stress. In either case, adequate provision shall be made for transmitting shear.

TABLE 7a.—ALLOWABLE SHEAR STRESSES IN FILLET WELDS
(BRIDGE STRUCTURES)

Specification Number	Filler Alloy	Allowable Shear Stress,[a] ksi	
		Transverse shear in single fillet welds or longitudinal shear[b]	Transverse shear in double fillet welds[b]
I-22a	5556	7.5	8[c]
I-23a	5356	6.5	8[c]
I-24a	4043	4.5	6

[a] Shear stress is considered to be equal to the load divided by the throat area, regardless of the direction of loading.

[b] Single fillet welds in transverse shear may be treated as double fillet welds in joints so designed as to prevent local bending of the parts adjacent to the fillet weld.

[c] These values are controlled by the shear strength of the parent material; all other values are controlled by the strength of the filler metal.

B-4: Stay Plates.—On the open sides of compression members without webs, the flanges shall be connected by lacing bars, with stay plates as near each end as practicable, or by perforated cover plates. There shall be stay plates at intermediate points where the lacing is interrupted. The length of the end stay plates shall not be less than one and one-fourth times the distance between the nearest lines of connecting rivets, bolts or welds. The thickness of stay plates shall not be less than one fortieth of the distance between lines of connections.

B-5: Diagonal Lacing.—The slenderness ratio of the part of the flange between the lacing bar connections shall not be more than three-fourths of the slenderness ratio of the member.

B-6: Perforated Cover Plates.—Perforated cover plates may be used instead of tie plates and lacing, provided that: The ratio of length (in direction of stress) to width of hole shall not exceed 2; the clear distance between holes shall not be less than the distance between nearest lines of connecting rivets, bolts or welds; the periphery of the holes at all points shall have a minimum radius of 1 1/2 in.; the thickness of the cover plate shall not be less than one fortieth of the distance between the nearest lines of connecting rivets, bolts or welds; and the stress on the net section of the column (omitting the area of the holes in the cover plate) shall not exceed the values given in Specification A-8 or I-8, where t is the thickness of the perforated cover plate and b is the distance from the edge of the hole to the nearest line of connecting rivets, bolts, or welds.

B-7: Combined Compression and Bending.—A member that carries bending moment in addition to uniform compression (as, for example, an eccentrically loaded column) shall be proportioned in accordance with the following formulas:

For members subjected to combined end load and bending, where the bending moment at the center of the span is equal to or greater than 0.9 of the maximum bending moment in the span.

$$\frac{f_a}{F_a} + \frac{f_b}{F_b \left(1 - \frac{f_a}{F_e}\right)} \leq 1 \quad \ldots \ldots \ldots \ldots \quad (1)$$

in which f_a is the average compressive stress on cross section of member produced by axial compressive load, ksi; f_b denotes the maximum bending stress (compression) caused by transverse loads or end moments in the absence of axial load, ksi; F_a refers to the allowable compressive stress for member considered as an axially loaded column, ksi; and F_b describes the allowable compressive stress for member considered as a beam, ksi.

For bridges and similar structures,

$$F_e = \frac{45,000}{\left(\frac{L}{r}\right)^2}$$

For buildings and similar structures,

$$F_e = \frac{51,000}{\left(\frac{L}{r}\right)^2}$$

in which L/r is the slenderness ratio for a member considered as a column tending to fail in the plane of the applied bending forces.

For members subjected to combined end load and bending where the bending moment at the center of the span is not more than one-half the maximum bending moment in the span.

$$\frac{f_a}{F_a} + \frac{f_b}{F_b} \leq 1 \quad \ldots \ldots \ldots \ldots \quad (2)$$

14

For members subjected to combined end load and bending where the moment at the center of the span is between 0.5 and 0.9 of the maximum moment,

$$\frac{f_a}{F_a} + \frac{f_b}{F_b \left[1 - \left(\frac{2 M_c}{M_m} - 1 \right) \frac{f_a}{F_e} \right]} \leq 1 \quad \ldots \ldots \ldots \ldots \quad (3)$$

in which M_c describes the bending moment at center of span resulting from applied bending loads, in-kips; and M_m denotes maximum bending moment in span resulting from applied bending loads, in-kips.

B-8: Transverse Shear in Columns.—In designing lacing or shear webs for columns, the maximum shear on the column shall be computed from the formula:

$$V = 0.02 \left(F_c \right)_{max} A + V_t \quad \ldots \ldots \ldots \ldots \ldots \quad (4)$$

in which V is the maximum shear on any transverse section of a column, kips; A denotes the gross area of column cross section, in square inches; $\left(F_c \right)_{max}$ is the maximum allowable compressive stress for short columns, ksi (for example, $\left(F_c \right)_{max} = 17$ for unwelded columns in bridge structures); and V_t refers to the shear caused by any transverse loads on the column, kips.

Section C: Beam and Girder Design.

C-1: Allowable Compressive Stress in Beams.—The allowable compressive stress in extreme fibers of beams shall be determined from the formulas in Specifications A-11 to A-14.

Beams whose compression flanges involve webs or outstanding legs of such proportions that local buckling may control the design shall be checked by Specifications A-15 to A-19 or by the method outlined in Part IV, Section M.

C-2: Single-Web Beams.—Because of the simplified form of the formulas for allowable stress in single-web beams and girders in Specification A-11, these formulas give very conservative values of allowable stress for certain conditions, namely for values of L_b/r_y exceeding approximately 50, for load distributions such that the bending moment near the center of the beam is appreciably less than the maximum bending moment in the beam or for beams with transverse loads applied to the bottom flange. If the designer wishes to compute more precise values of allowable stress for single-web beams and girders, he may make use of the formulas in Part IV, Section L.

C-3: Allowable Shear Stresses in Webs.—The allowable shear stress in flat webs shall not exceed the values given in Specifications A-20 for unstiffened webs or Specification A-21 for stiffened webs.

Section D: Design of Plates, Legs, and Webs in Compression.

D-1: Single-Angle, Double-Angle, Tee, or Cruciform Struts.—For struts consisting of a single angle, double angle, tee, or cruciform section, the compressive stress on the gross area shall not exceed the value given by Specification A-7 or by Specification A-8, whichever is smaller.

D-2: Flat Plate Elements of Columns.—For compression members other than those consisting of a single angle, double angle, tee, or cruciform section, the allowable compressive stress shall not exceed the value given by Specification A-7 nor shall it exceed the values given by Specifications A-9 or A-10 unless the special analysis described in Part IV, Section M is utilized.

D-3: Flat Plate Elements of Beams.—Allowable compressive stresses in flat plate elements of beams shall not exceed the values given by Specification A-15 or A-16, unless the special analysis described in Part IV, Section M, is used.

D-4: Stiffeners for Outstanding Flanges.—Outstanding flanges stiffened by lips or bulbs at the free edge shall be considered as supported on both edges if the moment of inertia of the lip or bulb meets the following requirement:

$$I_L = \frac{b^3 t}{80} \quad \dots\dots\dots\dots\dots\dots (5a)$$

in which b is the clear width of flange, in inches; t denotes the thickness of flange, in inches; and I_L refers to the moment of inertia of lip or bulb about face of flange from which lip projects, in.[4].

For rectangular lips having the same thickness as the flange, the preceding requirement may be expressed

$$b_L = \frac{1}{3} b \quad \dots\dots\dots\dots\dots\dots (5b)$$

in which b_L is the clear width of the lip, in inches. Allowable stresses for flanges with lips or bulbs meeting the foregoing requirements shall be determined from Specification A-9 or A-16. The area of stiffening lips or bulbs is included with the area of the rest of the section in calculating the stresses caused by the loads.

Section E: Plate Girder Design.

E-1: Proportioning Plate Girders.—Plate girders shall be proportioned by the moment of inertia method, with the gross section used to determine the moment of inertia.

The stress on the net area of the tension flange shall be found by multiplying the stress on the gross section by the ratio of the gross area of the tension flange to the net area. In determining this ratio the tension flange shall be considered to consist of the flange angles and cover plates plus one-sixth of the web.

E-2: Allowable Flange Stress.—The allowable compressive stress in the extreme fiber of plate girders shall be determined as outlined in Sections C and D.

E-3: Flange Cover Plates.—Cover plates shall extend far enough to allow at least two extra rivets at each end of the plate beyond the theoretical end, and the spacing of the rivets in the remainder of the plate shall be such as to develop the required strength of the plate at any section.

E-4: Flange Rivets.—The flanges of plate girders shall be connected to the web with enough rivets or bolts to transmit the longitudinal shear at any point together with any load that is applied directly on the flange.

E-5: Flange Splices.—It is preferable that flange angles be spliced with angles.

E-6: Allowable Web Stresses.—The allowable shear stress in the webs of plate girders shall not exceed the values given by Specification A-20 to A-21. The longitudinal compressive stress in webs of plate girders at the toe of the compression flange shall not exceed the values given by Specification A-18 or A-19.

E-7: Web Splices.—It is preferable that splices in the webs of plate girders be made with splice plates on both sides of the web.

E-8: Size of Vertical Stiffeners to Resist Shear Buckling.—Stiffeners applied to plate girder webs to resist shear buckling shall have a moment of inertia not less than the values given by the following formulas:

For bridges and similar structures,

$$\frac{s}{h} \leq 0.4, \quad I_s = \frac{V h^2}{16,600} \left(\frac{s}{h}\right) \qquad \ldots\ldots\ldots (6a)$$

$$\frac{s}{h} > 0.4, \quad I_s = \frac{V h^2}{104,000} \left(\frac{h}{s}\right) \qquad \ldots\ldots\ldots (7a)$$

For buildings and similar structures,

$$\frac{s}{h} \leq 0.4, \quad I_s = \frac{V h^2}{18,700} \left(\frac{s}{h}\right) \qquad \ldots\ldots\ldots (6b)$$

$$\frac{s}{h} > 0.4, \quad I_s = \frac{V h^2}{117,000} \left(\frac{h}{s}\right) \qquad \ldots\ldots\ldots (7b)$$

in which s denotes the stiffener spacing, in inches; h is the clear height of web, in inches; V refers to the shear force on the web at the stiffener location, kips; and I_s is the moment of inertia of stiffener, in.[4].

Where a stiffener is composed of a pair of members, one on each side of the web, the distance s shall be the clear distance between the stiffeners. Where a stiffener is composed of a member on one side of the web only, the distance s shall be the distance between rivet lines. In determining the allowable shear stresses in panels containing a horizontal stiffener located as indicated in Specification A-19, the vertical height of the panel, a_1 or a_2, in Specification A-21 may be taken as 90% of the clear height between flanges. For a stiffener composed of members of equal size on both sides of the web, the moment of inertia shall be taken about the centerline of the web. For a stiffener composed of a member on one side only, the moment of inertia shall be taken about the face of the web in contact with the stiffener. In determining the required moment of inertia of stiffeners, the term h shall always be taken as the full clear height between flanges, regardless of whether or not a horizontal stiffener is present.

E-9: Vertical Stiffeners at Points of Bearing.—Stiffeners shall be placed in pairs at end bearings of plate girders and at points of bearing of concentrated loads. They shall be connected to the web by enough rivets to transmit the load. Such stiffeners shall have a close bearing against the loaded flanges.

Only that part of the stiffener cross section which lies outside the fillet of the flange angle shall be considered effective in bearing. Bearing stiffeners shall not be crimped.

The moment of inertia of the stiffener shall not be less than that given by the following formulas:

For bridges and similar structures,

$$I = I_s + \frac{P\,h^2}{45,000} \quad \dots\dots\dots\dots\dots \quad (8a)$$

For buildings and similar structures,

$$I = I_s + \frac{P\,h^2}{51,000} \quad \dots\dots\dots\dots\dots \quad (8b)$$

in which I is the required moment of inertia of bearing stiffener, in.[4]; I_s denotes the moment of inertia required to resist shear buckling (Specification E-8), in.[4]; P refers to the local load concentration on the stiffener, kips; and h describes the clear height of the web between flanges, in inches.

E-10: Horizontal Stiffeners.—If a horizontal stiffener is used on a plate girder web, it shall be located so that the distance from the toe of the compression flange to the centroid of the stiffener is 0.4 of the distance from the toe of the compression flange to the neutral axis of the girder. The horizontal stiffener shall have a moment of inertia not less than that given by the formula:

$$I_h = 2\,\alpha\,f\,t\,h^3 \left[\left(1 + 6\,\frac{A_h}{h\,t}\right)\left(\frac{s}{h}\right)^2 + 0.4 \right] 10^{-6} \quad \dots\dots \quad (9)$$

in which I_h denotes the moment of inertia of the horizontal stiffener, in.[4]; α refers to a factor equal to unity for a stiffener consisting of equal members on both sides of the web and equal to 3.5 for a stiffener consisting of a member on one side only; h is the clear height of web between flanges, in inches; t describes the thickness of web, in inches; f is the compressive stress at the toe of the flange angles, ksi; s is the distance between vertical stiffeners, in inches; and A_h refers to the gross area of cross section of the horizontal stiffener, in square inches.

For a stiffener composed of members of equal size on both sides of the web, the moment of inertia shall be taken about the centerline of the web. In the case of a stiffener consisting of a member on one side only, the moment of inertia shall be taken about the face of the web in contact with the stiffener.

Eq. 9 must be solved by trial, since both the moment of inertia, I_h, and the area, A_h, of the stiffener are unknown. It is generally convenient to assume as a first approximation that the ratio $A_h/(ht)$ has the value 0.1.

Section F: Riveted and Bolted Connections.

F-1: Allowable Loads.—The allowable loads on rivets and bolts shall be calculated using the allowable shear stresses in Specifications A-22 to A-25 and the allowable bearing stresses in Specification A-5. In the latter specification, the allowable bearing stress depends on the ratio of edge distance to rivet or bolt diameter, where the edge distance is the distance from the center of the rivet or bolt to the edge of a plate or shape toward which the pressure of the rivet or bolt is directed.

F-2: Effective Diameter.—The effective diameter of rivets shall be taken as the hole diameter, but shall not exceed the nominal diameter of the rivet by more than 4% for cold driven rivets or 7% for hot driven rivets. The effective diameter of pins and bolts shall be the nominal diameter of the pin or bolt.

F-3: Shear Area.—The effective area of a rivet or bolt in any shear plane shall be based on the effective diameter, except that for bolts with threads included in the shear plane, the effective shear area shall be based on the root diameter. Shear areas of rivets are listed with recommended hole sizes in Table 8.

F-4: Bearing Area.—The effective bearing area of pins, bolts, and rivets shall be the effective diameter multiplied by the length in bearing, except that for countersunk rivets, half of the depth of the countersink shall be deducted from the length.

F-5: Arrangement and Strength of Connections.—Connections shall be arranged to minimize the eccentricity of loading on the member. Members and connections shall be proportioned to take into account any eccentricity of loading by the connections.

F-6: Net Section.—The net section of a riveted or bolted tension member is the sum of the net sections of its component parts. The net section of a part is the product of the thickness of the part multiplied by its least net width. The net width for a chain of holes extending across the part in any straight or broken line shall be obtained by deducting from the gross width the sum of the diameters of all the holes in the chain and adding $s^2/4g$ for each gage space in the chain. In the correction quantity $s^2/4g$, s denotes spacing parallel to direction of load (pitch) of any two successive holes in the chain, in inches, and g refers to spacing perpendicular to direction of load (gage) of the same holes, in inches.

The net section of the part is obtained from that chain which gives the least net width. The hole diameter to be deducted shall be the actual hole diameter for drilled or reamed holes and the hole diameter plus 1/16 in. for punched holes.

For angles, the gross width shall be the sum of the widths of the legs less the thickness. The gage for holes in opposite legs shall be the sum of the gages from the back of the angle, less the thickness.

For splice members, the thickness shall be only that part of the thickness of the member that has been developed by rivets or bolts beyond the section considered.

F-7: Effective Sections of Angles.—If an angle in tension is connected on one side of a gusset plate, the effective section shall be the net section of the connected leg plus one half of the section of the outstanding leg unless the outstanding leg is connected by a lug angle. In the latter case, the effective section shall be the entire net section of the angle. The lug angle shall be designed to develop at least one-half the total load in the member and shall be connected to the main member by at least two fasteners.

F-8: Grip of Rivets and Bolts.—If the grip of rivets or bolts carrying calculated stress exceeds four and one-half times the diameter, the allowable

TABLE 8.—RECOMMENDED HOLE SIZES FOR ALUMINUM ALLOY RIVETS

Rivet Diameter, in inches	3/8	7/16	1/2	9/16	5/8	3/4	7/8	1
COLD DRIVEN RIVETS								
Hole Diameter, in inches	0.386	0.453	0.516	0.578	0.641	0.766	0.891	1.016
Drill Size	W	29/64	33/64	37/64	41/64	49/64	57/64	1-1/64
Single Shear Area, in square inches	0.1170	0.1612	0.2091	0.2624	0.3227	0.4608	0.6235	0.8107
HOT DRIVEN RIVETS								
Hole Diameter, in inches	0.397	0.469	0.531	0.594	0.656	0.781	0.922	1.063
Drill Size	X	15/32	17/32	19/32	21/32	25/32	59/64	1-1/16
Single Shear Area, in square inches	0.1238	0.1728	0.2215	0.2771	0.3380	0.4791	0.6677	0.8875

load per rivet or bolt shall be reduced. The reduced allowable load shall be the normal allowable load divided by $(1/2 + G/9D)$ in which G is the grip, and D the nominal diameter of the rivet or bolt. If the grip of a rivet exceeds six times the diameter, special care shall be taken in driving to insure that the holes will be filled completely.

F-9: Spacing of Rivets and Bolts in Built-up Compression Members.—The pitch in the direction of stress shall be such that the allowable stress on the individual outside plates and shapes, treated as columns having a length equal to the rivet or bolt pitch in accordance with Specification A-7, exceeds the calculated stress. The gage at right angles to the direction of stresses shall be such that the allowable stress in the outside plates, treated as plates having a width b equal to the rivet or bolt gage, in accordance with Specification A-9, exceeds the calculated stress.

F-10: Stitch Rivets and Bolts.—Where two or more web plates are in contact, there shall be stitch rivets or bolts to make them act in unison. In compression members, the pitch and gage of such rivets or bolts shall be determined as outlined in Specification F-9. In tension members, the maximum pitch or gage of such rivets shall not exceed a distance, in inches, equal to $(3 + 20t)$ in which t is the thickness of the outside plates, in inches. In tension members composed of two angles in contact, the pitch of the stitch rivets or bolts shall not exceed 10 in. in the case of bridges and similar structures or 20 in. for buildings and similar structures, nor shall such a member have less than two stitch rivets or bolts.

F-11: Minimum Spacing of Rivets and Bolts.—The distance between centers of rivets shall not be less than three times the diameter of the rivets and the distance between centers of bolts shall not be less than 2 1/2 times the diameter of the bolts.

F-12: Edge Distance of Rivets or Bolts.—The distance from the center of a rivet or bolt to a sheared, sawed, rolled, or planed edge shall be not less than one and one-half times the diameter, except in flanges of beams and channels, where the minimum distance may be one and one-fourth times the diameter. For rivets or bolts under computed stress, the distance from the center of the rivet or bolt to the edge of the plate or shape toward which the pressure of the rivet or bolt is directed should normally be at least twice the nominal diameter of the rivet or bolt. In cases in which a shorter edge distance must be used, the allowable bearing stress shall be reduced in accordance with Table 4[a].

The distance from the edge of a plate to the nearest rivet or bolt line shall not exceed six times the thickness of the plate.

F-13: Extra Rivets or Bolts.—If rivets or bolts carrying calculated stress pass through fillers more than 1/4 in. thick, the fillers shall be extended beyond the connected member and the extension secured by enough additional rivets or bolts to distribute the total stress in the member uniformly over the combined section of the member and filler.

Section G: Miscellaneous Design Rules.

G-1: Reversal of Load.—Members in structures subject to reversal of load under one passage of live load shall be proportioned as follows: Determine the tensile load and the compressive load and increase each by 50% of the smaller; then proportion the member and its connections so that the allowable stresses given in Sections A through F will not be exceeded by either increased load.

G-2: Slenderness Ratio of Tension Members.—Tension members with values of slenderness ratio L/r greater than 150 shall not be used unless care is taken to insure that such members are designed to resist any lateral loads such as wind, dead load, or the weight of workmen and equipment. Stresses caused by the combined bending and tensile loadings shall not exceed allowable limits.

G-3: Stay Plates for Tension Members.—Segments of tension members not directly connected to each other shall be stayed together. The length of the stay plate shall be not less than three-fourths of the distance between the nearest lines of connecting rivets, bolts, or welds. Stay plates that are fastened by rivets or bolts shall be connected to each segment of the tension member by at least two rivets or bolts. The distance between stay plates shall be such

TABLE 9.—ALLOWABLE TENSILE STRESSES FOR REPEATED LOADS IN RIVETED OR BOLTED CONSTRUCTION

Number of Repetitions of Load Application	Allowable Maximum Tensile Stress on Net Section, F_{max}, [a] ksi	
	$F_{min} \leq 0.5 F_{max}$	$F_{min} > 0.5 F_{max}$
100,000	F	F
500,000	$0.75F + 0.17 F_{min}$	$0.53F + 0.66 F_{min}$
1,000,000	$0.67F + 0.22 F_{min}$	$0.50F + 0.68 F_{min}$
2,000,000	$0.57F + 0.26 F_{min}$	$0.42F + 0.72 F_{min}$
10,000,000	$0.37F + 0.56 F_{min}$	$0.33F + 0.73 F_{min}$

F_{max} = allowable maximum tensile stress on net section for repeated loading, ksi;
F_{min} = minimum stress on net section during loading cycle, ksi (F_{min} is the smallest tensile stress in a tension-tension cycle or the largest compressive stress in a compression-tensile cycle. In the latter case, F_{min} is negative.); and
F = allowable stress for nonrepetitive loading, from Table 4a or 4b.
(a) In addition to the limitations given in this table, F_{max} must not exceed F nor the maximum tensile stress permitted by the reversal-of-load rule in Specification G-1.

that the slenderness ratio of the individual segments of the member between stay plates does not exceed the slenderness ratio of the member as a whole.

G-4: Fatigue.—Tests indicate that riveted members designed in accordance with the requirements of these specifications and constructed so as to be free from severe re-entrant corners and other unusual stress raisers will withstand at least 100,000 repetitions of maximum live load without fatigue failure regardless of the ratio of minimum to maximum load. Where a greater number of repetitions of some particular loading cycle is expected during the life of the structure, the calculated net section tensile stresses for the loading in question shall not exceed the values given in Table 9. Table 9 applies to both of the general types of structures considered in these specifications. When using Table 9, the reversal-of-load rule in Specification G-1 should be ignored. The final member and connections selected, however, shall be strong enough to satisfy the requirements of Specification G-1. In considering fatigue action on structures, it is well to bear in mind the following points:

1. The most severe combination of loadings for which a structure is designed (dead load, maximum live load, maximum impact, maximum wind, and so forth) rarely occurs in actual service and is of little or no interest from the standpoint of fatigue.

2. The loading of most interest from the fatigue standpoint is the steady dead load with a superimposed and repeatedly applied live load having an intensity consistent with day-to-day normal operating conditions.

3. The number of cycles of load encountered in structures is usually small compared with those encountered in fatigue problems involving machine parts. For example, 100,000 cycles represent 10 cycles every day for 27 yr; 10,000,000 cycles represent 20 cycles every hour for 57 yr. Care must be taken not to overestimate grossly the number of cycles for any given load condition.

4. Careful attention to details in design and fabrication pays big dividends in fatigue life. When a fatigue failure occurs in a structure, it is usually at a point of stress concentration where the state of stress could have been improved with little or no added expense.

Section H: Fabrication.

H-1: Laying Out.

a. Hole centers may be center punched and cutoff lines may be punched or scribed. Center punching and scribing shall not be used where such marks would remain on fabricated material.

b. A temperature correction shall be applied where necessary in the layout of critical dimensions. The coefficient of expansion shall be taken as 0.000012 per degree Fahrenheit.

H-2: Cutting.

a. Material may be sheared, sawed, cut with a router, or arc cut. All edges which have been cut by the arc process shall be planed to a depth of 1/4 in. to remove edge cracks.

b. Cut edges shall be true and smooth, and free from excessive burrs or ragged breaks.

c. In bridge structures, sheared edges of plates carrying calculated stresses shall be planed to a depth of 1/4 in.

d. Re-entrant cuts shall be avoided wherever possible. If used, they shall be filleted by drilling prior to cutting.

e. Oxygen cutting of aluminum alloys is not permitted.

H-3: Heating.—Structural material shall not be heated, with the following exceptions:

a. Material may be heated to a temperature not exceeding 400°F for a period not exceeding 30 min in order to facilitate bending. Such heating shall be done only when proper temperature controls and supervision are provided to insure that the limitations on temperature and time are carefully observed.

b. Hot-driven rivets shall be heated as specified in Section H-5.

H-4: Punching, Drilling, and Reaming.—Rules for punching, drilling, and reaming are as follows:

a. In bridge structures, rivet or bolt holes in main members shall be subpunched or subdrilled and reamed to finished size after the parts are firmly bolted together or shall be drilled to finished size after the parts are firmly bolted together. The amount by which the diameter of a subpunched hole is less than that of the finished hole shall be at least 1/4 the thickness of the piece and in no case less than 1/32 in. If the metal thickness is greater than the diameter of the hole, punching shall not be used.

b. Rivet or bolt holes in secondary material not carrying calculated stress may be punched or drilled to finish size before assembly.

c. The finished diameter of holes for cold-driven rivets shall be not more than 4% greater than the nominal diameter of the rivet. Recommended hole sizes are listed in Table 8.

d. The finished diameter of holes for hot-driven rivets shall be not more than 7% greater than the nominal diameter of the rivet. Recommended hole sizes are listed in Table 8.

e. The finished diameter of holes for bolts shall be not more than 1/16 in. larger than the nominal bolt diameter.

f. If any holes must be enlarged to admit the rivets or bolts, they shall be reamed. Poor matching of holes shall be cause for rejection. Holes shall not be drifted in such a manner as to distort the metal. All chips lodged between contacting surfaces shall be removed before assembly.

H-5: Riveting.

a. The driven head of aluminum alloy rivets preferably shall be of the flat or the cone-point type, with dimensions as follows:

1. Flat heads shall have a diameter not less than 1.4 times the nominal rivet diameter and a height not less than 0.4 times the nominal rivet diameter.

2. Cone-point heads shall have a diameter not less than 1.4 times the nominal rivet diameter and a height to the apex of the cone not less than 0.65 times the nominal rivet diameter. The included angle at the apex of the cone shall be approximately 127°.

b. Rivets shall be driven hot or cold as called for on the plans, provision for heating being as follows:

1. Hot-driven rivets shall be heated in a hot-air type furnace providing uniform temperatures throughout the rivet chamber and equipped with automatic temperature controls.

2. Hot-driven rivets shall be held at from 990°F to 1,050°F for not less than 15 min and for not more than 1 hr before driving.

3. Hot rivets shall be transferred from the furnace to the work and driven with a minimum loss of time.

c. Rivets shall fill the holes completely. Rivet heads shall be concentric with the rivet holes and shall be in proper contact with the surface of the metal.

d. Defective rivets shall be removed by drilling.

H-6: Painting.—Structures of the alloy covered by these specifications are not ordinarily painted except where (1) the aluminum alloy parts are in contact with, or are fastened to, steel members or other dissimilar materials, or (2) the structures are to be exposed to extremely corrosive conditions. Painting procedure is covered in the following paragraphs, and methods of cleaning and preparation are found in Specification H-7. (Treatment and painting of the structure in accordance with United States Military Specification MIL-T-704 is also acceptable.)

a. Where the aluminum alloy parts are in contact with, or are fastened to, steel members or other dissimilar materials, the aluminum shall be kept from direct contact with the steel or other dissimilar material by painting as follows:

1. Aluminum surfaces to be placed in contact with steel shall be given one coat of zinc chromate primer in accordance with United States Military Specification MIL-P-735 or the equivalent or one coat of a suitable nonhardening joint compound capable of excluding moisture from the joint during prolonged service. Additional protection can be obtained by applying the joint compound in addition to the zinc chromate primer. Zinc chromate paint shall be allowed to dry hard before assembly of the parts. The steel surfaces to be placed in contact with aluminum shall be painted with good quality priming paint, such as red lead conforming to Federal Specification TT-P-86 or zinc chromate primer in accordance with United States Military Specification MIL-P-735, followed by one coat of paint consisting of 2 lb of aluminum paste pigment (ASTM Specification D962-49, Type II, Class B) per gallon of varnish meeting Federal Specification TT-V-81, Type II, or the equivalent. Stainless steel, or aluminized, hot-dip galvanized or electro-galvanized steel placed in contact with aluminum need not be painted.

2. Aluminum surfaces to be placed in contact with wood, concrete, or masonry construction, except where the aluminum is to be embedded in concrete, shall be given a heavy coat of an alkali-resistant bituminous paint before installation. The bituminous paint used shall meet the requirements of United States Military Specification MIL-P-6883. The paint shall be applied as it is received from the manufacturer without the addition of any thinner.

3. Aluminum surfaces to be embedded in concrete ordinarily need not be painted, unless corrosive components are added to the concrete or unless the concrete is subjected for extended periods to extremely corrosive conditions. In such cases, aluminum surfaces should be given one coat of suitable quality paint, such as zinc chromate primer conforming to United States Military Specification MIL-P-735 or equivalent, or should be wrapped with a suitable plastic tape applied in such a manner as to provide adequate protection at the overlap.

4. Water that comes in contact with aluminum after first running over a heavy metal such as copper may contain trace quantities of the dissimilar metal or its corrosion product, which will cause corrosion of the aluminum. Protection can be obtained by painting or plastic coating the dissimilar metal or by designing the structure so that the drainage from the dissimilar metal is diverted away from the aluminum.

5. Bolts and other fasteners used with aluminum shall be of aluminum, stainless steel, or aluminized, hot-dip galvanized or electro-galvanized steel.

b. Although structures of the alloy covered by these specifications are not ordinarily painted for surface protection, there may be applications where the structures are to be exposed to extremely corrosive conditions which make over-all painting advisable. In such instances, all contacting metal surfaces shall be painted before assembly with one coat of zinc chromate primer in accordance with United States Military Specification MIL-P-735 or the equivalent. The primer shall be allowed to dry hard before assembly of the parts. All other surfaces shall be given one shop coat of zinc chromate primer made in accordance with United States Military Specification MIL-P-735 or the equivalent and then shall be given a second shop coat of paint consisting of 2 1/4 lb of nonleafing aluminum paste pigment (Alcoa No. 221, Reynolds 10 LN, or equivalent) per gallon of varnish meeting Federal Specification TT-V-81, Type II, or the equivalent. The nonleafing paint shall be used to permit detection of an incomplete application of the subsequent paint coat. After erection, bare spots shall be touched-up with zinc chromate primer followed by a touch-up coat of nonleafing aluminum paint as specified previously. The completed structure shall be finished according to one of the following methods:

1. One field coat of leafing aluminum paint consisting of 2 lb of aluminum paste pigment (ASTM Specification D962-49, Type II, Class B) per gallon of varnish meeting Federal Specification TT-V-81, Type II, or equivalent.

2. One or more field coats of alkyd base enamel pigmented to meet a desired color scheme.

3. Where specific chemicals especially corrosive to aluminum are encountered (such as strong caustic or strong mineral acids), paint systems that provide superior protection against the specific chemicals involved may be used.

H-7: Cleaning and Treatment of Metal Surfaces.—All surfaces to be painted shall be cleaned as follows:

a. Surfaces of metal shall be cleaned immediately before painting, by a method that will remove all dirt, oil, grease, chips, and other foreign substances.

b. Either of the two following methods of cleaning may be used on exposed metal surfaces:

1. Chemical Cleaning: Parts may be immersed in, or swabbed with, a solution of phosphoric acid and organic solvents meeting United States Military Specification MIL-M-10578, after diluting one volume of the concentrate with three volumes of water. The solution temperature shall be between 50°F and 90°F. The solution shall remain in contact with the metal not less than 5 min and shall not be allowed to dry on the surface. Residual solution shall be thoroughly removed by flushing with clear water.

The preceding treatment will provide adequate paint adhesion for most applications. However, if unusual conditions of exposure such as continuous high humidity or highly corrosive atmospheres are anticipated, better paint adhesion will be obtained by following the treatment with application of a commercial chromate conversion solution such as those listed on Military Qualified Products list QPL-5541-16. Such solution shall be applied in accordance with the supplier's instructions.

If it is desirable to apply these treatments in the factory, the stages preceding the conversion chromate application may be modified in accordance with commercial practices for applying chromate conversion coatings.

If treatment is applied at the factory, a shop primer should be applied because handling subsequent to treatment will contaminate the treated surface. If desirable, complete finishing may be performed at the factory following factory pretreatment.

2. Sandblasting: Standard mild sandblasting methods may be used on sections more than 1/8 in. thick.

c. For contacting surfaces only, the metal may be cleaned in accordance with Specification H-7b, or with a solvent such as mineral spirits or benzine.

d. Flame cleaning is not permitted.

PART III. SPECIFICATIONS FOR WELDED STRUCTURES

Section I: Allowable Stresses for Welded Parts.—Welded members are proportioned in accordance with the general rules of Part II, except that it is necessary to reduce the allowable stresses in a "reduced strength zone" extending for a distance of 1 in. on either side of a weld. The 1-in. distance is irrespective of thickness and is measured from the centerline of a butt weld or the heel of a fillet weld.

The allowable stresses for welded cross sections whose entire area lies within 1 in. of a weld are given by Specifications I-1 to I-21 in Tables 6a and 6b. Allowable shear stresses in fillet welds are given by Specifications I-22 to I-24 in Tables 7a and 7b.

I-25: Cross Sections with Part of Area Affected by Heat of Welding.—If less than 15% of the area of a given cross section lies within 1 in. of a weld, the effect of the welds can be neglected and allowable stress for that cross section can be calculated by the formulas in Table 4. If the area of a cross section that lies within 1 in. of a weld is between 15% and 100% of the total area of the cross section, the allowable stress shall be calculated from

$$f_{pw} = f_n - \frac{A_w}{A} \left(f_n - f_w \right) \quad \cdots \cdots \cdots \cdots (10)$$

in which f_{pw} is the allowable stress on cross section, part of whose area lies within 1 in. of a weld, ksi; f_n denotes the allowable stress for same cross section if there were no welds present (see Table 4), ksi; f_w refers to the allowable stress for same cross section if entire area lies within 1 in. of a weld (see Table 6), ksi; A describes the net area of cross section of a tension member or tension flange of a beam, or gross area of cross section of a compression member or compression flange of a beam, in square inches. (A beam flange is considered to consist of that portion of the member farther than $2c/3$ from the neutral axis, where c is the distance from the neutral axis to the extreme fiber.); and A_w is the area within area A that lies within 1 in. of weld, in square inches.

I-26: Columns and Single-Web Beams with Welds at Locations Other Than Ends and Cantilever Columns and Single-Web Beams.—The allowable stresses in Specifications I-7 and I-8 apply to members supported at both ends with welds at the ends only (not farther from the supports than 0.05 of the length of the column or beam). For cantilever columns or beams and for columns and beams having welds at locations other than the ends, the allowable stress shall be determined from the following:

a. Members with welds affecting the entire cross section:

For bridges and similar structures,

$$\left.\begin{array}{ll} f_n > 16.4, & f_w = 10 \\[2em] 16.4 \geq f_n > 3.4, & f_w = \dfrac{13.0}{\sqrt{18.1 - f_n}} \\[2em] f_n \leq 3.4, & f_w = f_n \end{array}\right\} \quad \ldots\ldots\ldots(11a)$$

For buildings and similar structures,

$$\left.\begin{array}{ll} f_n > 18.4, & f_w = 11 \\[2em] 18.4 \geq f_n > 3.8, & f_w = \dfrac{15.5}{\sqrt{20.4 - f_n}} \\[2em] f_n \leq 3.8, & f_w = f_n \end{array}\right\} \quad \ldots\ldots\ldots(11b)$$

b. Members with welds affecting less than the entire cross section: The allowable stress shall be determined from Eq. 10, in which the value of f_w is given by Eqs. 11a or 11b.

Section J: Miscellaneous Design Rules.

J-1: Fatigue.--Fatigue tests indicate that welded members designed in accordance with the requirements of these specifications, and constructed so as to be free from severe re-entrant corners and other unusual stress raisers, will safely withstand at least 20,000 repetitions of maximum live load without fatigue failure regardless of the ratio of minimum to maximum load. Where a greater number of repetitions of some particular loading cycle is expected during the life of the structure, the calculated tensile stresses in welded members shall not exceed the values given in Table 10. Table 10 applies to both of the general types of structures considered in these specifications. When using Table 10, the reversal of load rule in Specification G-1 should be ignored. The final member and connections selected, however, shall be strong enough to satisfy the requirements of G-1. The comments in the listing at the end of Specification G-4 apply to welded as well as riveted or bolted structures.

Section K: Fabrication.

K-1: General.—These specifications are proposed for application to both field and shop welding operations. The general recommendations and regulations shown in the American Welding Society Specifications D2.0-47 "Welded Highway and Railway Bridges" 1947 and D1.0-46 "Code for Arc and Gas Welding in Building Construction" 1946 apply as well to welded 6061-T6 and 6062-T6 structures. Detail requirements in these specifications apply only to steel structures. Detail requirements for welded alloys 6061-T6 and 6062-T6 are given in the following paragraphs.

K-2: Preparation for Welding.—Dirt, grease, forming or machining lubricants, or any organic materials shall be removed from the areas to be welded by cleaning with a suitable solvent or by vapor degreasing.

Additional operations to remove the oxide coating just prior to welding are required when the inert gas tungsten arc welding method is used. This may be done by etching or by scratch brushing. The oxide coating may not need to be

TABLE 10.—ALLOWABLE TENSILE STRESSES FOR REPEATED LOADS IN WELDED CONSTRUCTION

Number of Repetitions of Load Application	Allowable Stress on Net Section, F_{max}[a], ksi	
	Tension on transverse or longitudinal butt welds and tension at locations adjacent to continuous longitudinal fillet welds	Tension at locations adjacent to transverse fillet welds or ends of longitudinal fillet welds, and shear on fillet welds
20,000	F	F
100,000	$F + 0.67\ F_{min}$	$0.68F + 0.67\ F_{min}$
500,000	$0.73F + 0.67\ F_{min}$	$0.40F + 0.67\ F_{min}$
1,000,000	$0.67F + 0.67\ F_{min}$	$0.34F + 0.67\ F_{min}$
2,000,000	$0.65F + 0.67\ F_{min}$	$0.29F + 0.67\ F_{min}$
10,000,000	$0.64F + 0.67\ F_{min}$	$0.23F + 0.67\ F_{min}$

F_{max} = allowable maximum tensile stress on net section for repeated loading, ksi,
F_{min} = minimum stress on net section during loading cycle, ksi (F_{min} is the smallest tensile stress in a tension-tension cycle or the largest compressive stress in a compression-tension cycle. In the latter case, F_{min} is negative.).
F = allowable stress for nonrepetitive loading, from Table 6a, 6b, 7a, or 7b.
[a] In addition to the limitations given in this table, F_{max} must not exceed F nor the maximum stress permitted by the reversal-of-load rule in Specification G-1.

removed if the welding is performed with the automatic or semiautomatic inert gas shielded metal arc.

Suitable edge preparation to assure 100% penetration in butt welds shall be used. Oxygen cutting shall not be used. Sawing, chipping, machining, shearing, or arc cutting may be used.

K-3: Welding Procedure.—Parts shall be welded with an arc or resistance welding process. No welding process that requires the use of a welding flux shall be used. The filler metal shall be aluminum alloy 5556, 5356, or 4043. Other filler metal alloys may be used provided that they are capable of meeting the qualification test requirements, and result in welds having resistance to corrosion equal to or greater than welds made with filler alloys 5556, 5356, or 4043. Preheating for welding is permissible provided the temperature does not exceed 400°F for a total time of 30 min.

K-4: Qualification of Welding Procedure and Welding Operator.—The welding process and welding operators shall both meet a qualification test. The method of qualification shall be mutually established by the inspecting agency and the contractor or shall conform to the method described in the ASME Boiler and Pressure Vessel Code, Section IX, "Welding Qualifications," Part B, 1962. Aluminum alloy 6061-T6 or 6062-T6 shall be used for the qualification test plates.

The minimum required tensile strength of reduced section specimens in the procedure qualification test is 24 ksi. In addition to the tensile test, side-bend, or face-bend and root-bend tests (either longitudinal or transverse) are required. Operators are qualified on the basis of bend tests and a fillet weld soundness test.

K-5: Rewelding Defects.—Portions of joints that have been rejected on inspection because of defects may be repaired only by rewelding. The defective area shall be removed by chipping or machining. Flame cutting shall not be used. Before rewelding, the joint shall be inspected to assure that all of the defective weld has been removed and that the joint is accessible so that the welding operator can obtain full penetration through the joint.

PART IV. SPECIAL PROVISIONS

Section L.—Single-Web Beams and Girders.—If the designer wishes to compute more precise values of allowable compressive stress for single-web beams and girders, the value of r_y in Specification A-11 may be replaced by an "effective r_y" given by one of the following formulas:

For beam spans subjected to end moment only or to transverse loads applied at the neutral axis of the beam,

$$\text{Effective } r_y = \frac{C}{1.7} \sqrt{\frac{I_y d}{S_c} \sqrt{1 + 0.152 \frac{J}{I_y} \left(\frac{L_b}{d}\right)^2}} \quad \ldots \ldots (12)$$

For beams subjected to transverse loads applied on the top flange (where the load is free to move laterally with the beam if the beam should buckle),

$$\text{Effective } r_y = \frac{C}{1.7} \sqrt{\frac{I_y d}{S_c} \left[-0.5 + \sqrt{1.25 + 0.152 \frac{J}{I_y} \left(\frac{L_b}{d}\right)^2}\right]} \quad \ldots (13)$$

For beams subjected to transverse loads applied on the bottom flange (where the load is free to move laterally with the beam if the beam should buckle),

$$\text{Effective } r_y = \frac{C}{1.7} \sqrt{\frac{I_y d}{S_c} \left[0.5 + \sqrt{1.25 + 0.152 \frac{J}{I_y} \left(\frac{L_b}{d}\right)^2}\right]} \quad \ldots (14)$$

in which C is the coefficient depending on type of loading, as given in Table 11; d is the depth of beam, in inches; I_y refers to the moment of inertia of beam about axis parallel to web, in.[4]; J denotes the torsion constant of beam, in.[4] (Values of J are published for many standard shapes (6). Values of J for plates and shapes not published may be calculated by assuming the section to be composed of rectangles and taking the sum of the terms $bt^3/3$ for each rectangle, in which b equals the length and t the thickness of the rectangle, both in inches. The value of J for a built-up member is the sum of the individual values of J for the sections of which it is composed.); and S_c describes the section modulus of beam for compression flange, in cubic inches. For a beam

TABLE 11.—VALUES OF COEFFICIENT C IN FORMULAS FOR ALLOWABLE STRESS IN SINGLE-WEB BEAMS AND GIRDERS

Description of Loading	Value of Coefficient, C
Beam restrained against lateral displacement at both ends of span	
Uniform bending moment, uniform transverse load, or two equal concentrated loads equidistant from the center of the span	1.00
Bending moment varying uniformly from a value of M at one end to β M at the other end	
$\beta = 0.5$	1.14
$\beta = 0$	1.33
$\beta = -0.5$	1.53
$\beta = -1.0$	1.60
Concentrated load at center of span	1.16
Cantilever beams	
Concentrated load at end of span	1.13
Uniform transverse load	1.43

that is unsymmetrical about the horizontal axis, I_y, S_c, and J are calculated as though the beam were symmetrical with both flanges the same as the compression flange of the actual beam.

Section M: Effective Width of Thin Plates in Compression. — Allowable compressive stresses in flat plate elements of columns or beams other than single angles, double angles, tees, or cruciform sections may be permitted to exceed the values given by Specification A-8, A-9, A-15, or A-16, provided that the following steps are taken to insure a suitable margin of safety against the weakening effects of local buckling of plates, legs, and webs:

M-1: Columns.

a. Compute the compressive stress f_c on the flat plate, leg, or web in question, based on the design loads and the gross area, without regard to local buckling. This stress must be within allowable limits as defined in Specification A-7.

b. Compute the allowable compressive stress, f_1, for the flat plate, leg, or web from Specification A-8 or A-9. If the actual stress, f_c, does not exceed this limiting value, local buckling is not a problem and the full gross area of the plate, leg, or web may be considered effective.

c. If the actual compressive stress exceeds the allowable value found in step b, only a part of the unsupported width of the flat plate, leg, or web shall be included in computing its effective area. The part of the unsupported width of any individual flat plate, leg, or web which may be considered effective shall be found from

$$b_e = b \frac{f_1}{f_c} \qquad \dots \dots \dots \dots \dots \dots (15)$$

in which b_e is that part of the unsupported width considered effective, in inches; b denotes the unsupported width, in inches; f_c describes the compressive stress based on gross area from step a, ksi; and f_1 refers to the allowable stress found in step b, ksi.

d. Compute the compressive stress on the effective area. This is simply the axial load divided by the total effective area, which, in turn, is simply the sum of the effective areas of the component parts.

e. The compressive stress on the effective area computed in accordance with step d shall not exceed allowable limits as defined in Specification A-7 for the gross area.

f. Steps c, d, and e provide a suitable factor of safety against collapse of the member as a whole, but do not necessarily provide complete protection against local buckling of individual flat surfaces at the design load. Where local buckling at the design load cannot be tolerated because of appearance, or for other reasons, the computed compressive stress on the gross area, f_c, shall not exceed 1.6 f_1, where f_1 is the compressive stress given in Specification A-8 or A-9 for the b/t ratio in question. Regardless of whether or not this limitation is placed on f_c, the member must still be checked by the method outlined in steps a through e to insure an adequate factor of safety against collapse.

M-2: Beams.—The procedure in Section M-1 can also be applied to beams. In the case of a beam or girder, the stress f_1 shall be determined from Specification A-15 or A-16 and the compressive stress on the effective area shall be determined as follows: Compute the compressive extreme fiber stress f_c for the gross section of the beam or girder and then multiply this value by the ratio of the gross compression flange area to the effective compression flange area, including in each flange area not only the flange proper, but also one-sixth of the area of the web. The stress on the effective area shall not exceed allowable limits as defined in Specifications A-11 to A-14.

PART V. EXPLANATION OF SPECIFICATIONS

Section A: Summary of Allowable Stresses.—The allowable stresses for bridges and similar structures in these specifications represent a factor of

safety of at least 1.85 on minimum yield strength and 2.2 on minimum ultimate strength. These factors of safety are reduced somewhat from those used
in the earlier specifications prepared by this committee (1),(2), on the basis
of the increased service experience and more extensive test data now available for aluminum alloy structures. The factor of safety of 1.85 on yielding
is the same as the factor of safety based on the mill coupon yield strength
value used in the AASHO and AREA specifications for steel bridges (3),(4).
The factor of safety of 2.2 on ultimate strength is conservative in comparison
with the factor of safety on collapse strength of columns and beams incorpo-
rated in the AASHO and AREA specifications for steel bridges, on the basis
of the analysis of column strength made in the Column Research Council
"Guide to Design Criteria for Metal Compression Members," (9) the results
of tests on steel beams reported by R. A. Hechtman, F. ASCE, J. S. Hattrup,
M. ASCE, E. F. Styer, and J. L. Tiedemann (10), and the mechanical properties of mild steel structural shapes as reported by L. S. Beedle, F. ASCE,
and Lambert Tall, A. M. ASCE (11).

The allowable stresses for buildings and similar structures are based on
factors of safety of at least 1.65 on minimum yield strength and 1.95 on minimum ultimate strength. These factors of safety are similar to those used in
the AISC specifications for steel buildings (5),(9),(10),(11). In the following
paragraphs, the factors of safety used to obtain allowable stresses for buildings and similar structures are listed in parentheses.

A-3: Tension in Extreme Fibers of Round or Oval Tubular Beams.—The
allowable tensile stress for round or oval tubes subjected to bending is somewhat higher than for structural shapes because analysis and tests have demonstrated that yielding or failure of tubular beams does not occur until the bending moment considerably exceeds the value that would be predicted on the basis
of the ordinary flexure formula (12),(13).

A-4: Tension in Extreme Fibers of Rectangular Bars and Plates and Single-
Web Shapes Bent About Y-Axis.—As in the case of round tubes, theory and
tests have shown that aluminum alloy members of these shapes can undergo
bending moments that are considerably higher than those predicted on the
basis of the ordinary flexure formula (13),(14),(15).

A-5: Bearing on Rivets and Bolts.—Allowable bearing stresses were determined by applying a factor of safety of 1.85 (or 1.65) to minimum bearing
yield strength and 2.2 (or 1.95) to minimum ultimate bearing strength.

A-6: Bearing on Milled Surfaces and Pins.—This allowable stress is equal
to two-thirds of the allowable bearing stress on rivets and bolts.

A-7: Compression in Columns.—The formulas in Specification A-7 approximate the tangent modulus column curves with a factor of safety of 2.2 (or
1.95) and with a cutoff at the basic allowable compressive design stress. The
tangent modulus column formula is

$$f_C = \frac{\pi^2 E_t}{\left(\frac{k L}{r}\right)^2} \qquad \dots \dots \dots \dots \dots \dots (16)$$

in which f_C denotes the column strength, ksi; E_t refers to the tangent modulus
corresponding to stress f_C, ksi; L is the length of column, in inches; r de-

scribes the least radius of gyration of column, in inches; and k refers to the factor describing the conditions of restraint at the ends of the column.

In the elastic stress range, Eq. 16 is the same as the Euler column formula. In the plastic stress range, Eq. 16 can be approximated by a straight line for aluminum alloys. The applicability of the Euler column formula and the straight line approximation to the tangent modulus curve has been extensively confirmed by tests (16).

The value of the end restraint factor k was considered to be 1.0 for all columns except cantilever columns, for which the value of k was taken to be 2.0. Studies of the effective length of columns in structures have indicated that a k value of 1.0 is conservative for most structural members (17),(18).

A-8 and A-9: Flat Plate Components of Columns.—Allowable stresses for flat plate components of columns and beams were determined by applying a factor of safety of 2.2 (or 1.95) to the strength of plates as given by the formula (20)

$$ f_C = \frac{\pi^2 \, \eta \, E}{\left(\dfrac{k' \, b}{t}\right)^2} \quad \dotfill (17) $$

in which f_C denotes the buckling strength, ksi; E is the modulus of elasticity, ksi; η denotes the modulus reduction factor for buckling of plates in the inelastic stress range; b describes the clear width of plate, in inches; t is the thickness of plate, in inches; and k' refers to a factor depending on the conditions of support at the edges of the plate. It was assumed that the supported edges of plate elements in unwelded columns are simply supported, so that k' = 5.13 for outstanding flanges and 1.63 for plates supported on both edges.

In the inelastic stress range, the factor η was considered to be given by the following formula (20):

$$ \eta = \frac{E_s}{E} \left(0.330 + 0.670 \sqrt{\frac{1}{4} + \frac{3}{4} \frac{E_t}{E_s}} \right) \quad \dotfill (18) $$

in which E_s is the secant modulus, ksi. The curve given by the foregoing formula is approximated by the formulas in Specification A-8.

A-10: Curved Plates and Tubes in Compression.—Allowable compressive stresses in curved plates and tubes are based on the results of tests of round tubes as analyzed by George Gerard and Herbert Becker (21).

A-11: Single-Web Beams.—The allowable compressive stresses in single-web structural shapes and built-up sections bent about the X-axis are based on the application of a factor of safety of 2.2 (or 1.95) to the lateral, torsional buckling strength of beams. The lateral buckling strength of aluminum alloy beams has been investigated experimentally and analytically for a number of different cross sections (19). Allowable stresses in the inelastic stress range for beams are based on the straight line approximation to the tangent modulus buckling curve that is also used for columns. In deriving the allowable stresses for beams, it was assumed that the beam is held in an upright position at the supported ends but the strengthening effect of any restraint against rotation of the flanges at the supports was neglected.

A-12: Round or Oval Tubes in Bending.—Allowable compressive stresses in extreme fibers of round or oval tubes subjected to bending are based on the results of tests of round tubes reported by R. L. Moore, F. ASCE, and M. Holt, M. ASCE (12).

A-13: Solid Rectangular Beams.—The formulas for allowable stresses in rectangular beams are based on the lateral, torsional buckling strength of such beams (14).

A-14: Box Beams.—The formulas for allowable stresses in box beams are based on the lateral, torsional buckling strength of such beams (9a). In deriving these formulas, use was made of the fact that lateral buckling will govern the design only for relatively deep, narrow box beams, and for these members the torsion constant J is roughly proportional to I_y.

A-15 and A-16: Flat Plate Components of Beams.—Outstanding flanges of beams were considered to be partially restrained against rotation at the supported edges (k' = 4.5 in Eq. 17) and flat plate compressive elements supported on both edges were considered to be simply supported (k' = 1.63 in Eq. 17), based on analysis of the elastic buckling behavior of members with typical proportions, using methods reported by K. Sutter (22).

A-17: Flat Plates with Compression Edge Free and Tension Edge Supported.—The elastic buckling strength of flat plates in bending with the compression edge free and the tension edge supported was determined from Eq. 17 with k' = 3.5. The analysis was extended into the plastic stress range on the basis of the treatment of rectangular beams (Specification A-13), because calculations and tests (38) have shown that the apparent stresses (M c/I) at which the yield strength is reached in the outer fiber of sections such as tees and angles are even higher than for rectangular beams.

A-18: Flat Plates in Bending with Both Edges Supported.—The allowable compressive stresses for flat plates with both edges supported were computed on the basis of the formula for the buckling stress with the edges half way between the fixed and simply supported conditions (23). The corresponding value of k' in Eq. 17 is 0.60. A factor of safety of 1.35 (or 1.2) was applied to the buckling strength in this case, because tests have demonstrated that the stresses in plates of this type can appreciably exceed the calculated buckling stress without affecting the behavior of the beam (23),(24).

A-19: Flat Plates in Bending with Horizontal Stiffener.—The allowable compressive stresses in webs with a horizontal stiffener were determined by applying a factor of safety of 1.35 (or 1.2) to the buckling stress for plates with simple support at the edges and at the stiffener. The value of k' in Eq. 17 for this case is 0.29, based on calculations by C. Dubas, as reported by Friedrich Bleich (17a).

A-20: Shear in Unstiffened Flat Webs.—Allowable shear stresses in unstiffened flat webs were obtained by applying a factor of safety of 2.2 (or 1.95) to the calculated buckling strength for a web with partial restraint against rotation at the attachment to the flanges (41),(42), giving a value of k' in Eq. 17 of 1.25. In the plastic stress range, the plastic reduction factor η was considered to be given by Eq. 18 with the exception that the values of the tangent modulus and secant modulus corresponding to a given shear stress were considered to be the same as the values of the tangent modulus and secant modulus corresponding to a compressive stress equal to $\sqrt{3}$ times the shear stress (41).

A-21: Shear in Stiffened Flat Webs.—Allowable stresses for stiffened flat webs were computed on the basis of assumptions similar to those used for unstiffened webs, except that a factor of safety of 1.35 (or 1.2) was applied to the buckling strength of stiffened beam webs, because tests have demonstrated that shear stresses in such webs can considerably exceed the calculated buckling strength without appreciably affecting the behavior of the beam (42).

A-22 and A-23: Allowable Shear in Rivets.—The minimum shear strength of rivets was considered to be equal to the typical strength divided by 1.15. The factors of safety applied to minimum rivet shear strengths in order to obtain allowable shear stresses were 20% higher than the basic factors of safety applied to minimum strength values elsewhere in these specifications.

A-24: Allowable Shear and Tension in Bolts.—The factors of safety applied to minimum shear strength and minimum tensile strength of 2024-T4 bolts are 20% higher than the basic factors of safety on minimum ultimate strength used elsewhere in these specifications.

A-25: Allowable Shear in Pins.—It is not anticipated that any wide use of pins will be made in aluminum alloy structures, but it is assumed that where they are used, they will be the same material as the rest of the structure and will probably be obtained in the form of rolled rod. The minimum shear strength of 6061-T6 rolled rod (25 ksi) was divided by a factor of safety of 2.2.

Section B: Column Design.

B-7: Combined Compression and Bending.—Eq. 1 is based on an interaction formula that gives good agreement with the results of tests on aluminum members subjected to combined compressive end load and uniform bending moment (26). The formula is applicable to members in which the bending is applied about either the strong or the weak axis and to members in which the strength is controlled by either overall or local buckling.

Eq. 1 becomes ultraconservative for members in which the bending moment at the center is appreciably less than the maximum bending moment in the column. For such members, Eq. 2 or Eq. 3 is satisfactory.

B-8: Transverse Shear in Columns.—Eq. 4 for transverse shear in columns is similar to an equation used in the German Specifications (44). This equation agrees well with the more complicated expression, based on the work of E. C. Hartmann, F. ASCE (27), which was used in this committee's earlier specifications.

Section D: Design of Plates, Legs, and Webs in Compression.

D-4: Stiffeners for Flat Plates in Compression.—Eqs. 5a and 5b for required size of stiffening lips or bulbs are based on theoretical and experimental studies reported by M. S. Anderson (35) and by P. S. Bulson (36).

Section E: Plate Girder Design.

E-8: Size of Vertical Stiffeners to Resist Shear Buckling.—Eqs. 9a and 9b are based on the results of tests of aluminum girders reported by Moore (40) and the theoretical analysis of Manual Stein and R. W. Fralich (29). Stiffness values calculated from Eqs. 9a and 9b are approximately the same as the values given by the more complex expression used in this committee's previous specifications.

E-9: Vertical Stiffeners at Points of Bearing.—Eq. 10 requires that the moment of inertia of a stiffener at a point of bearing should be equal to the sum of the moment of inertia required to resist the tendency of the web to buckle and the moment of inertia required for the stiffener to carry the bearing load as a column with length equal to the height of the web.

E-10: Horizontal Stiffeners.—Eq. 11, for the moment of inertia of horizontal stiffeners, is based on the theoretical work of C. Dubas, reported by Bleich (17), and on the experiments reported by C. E. L. Massonnet, F. ASCE (37), and by K. C. Rockey (25).

Section F: Riveted and Bolted Connections.

F-10: Stitch Rivets and Bolts.—The requirements for spacing of stitch rivets are based on conventional practices that have been found to give satisfactory results for thin-gage construction as well as for the thicker gages more commonly used in heavy-duty structures.

Section G: Miscellaneous Design Rules.

G-4: Fatigue.—The allowable stresses for repeated loading, given in Table 9, are based on the results of fatigue tests of riveted joints as reported by M. Holt, I. D. Eaton and R. B. Matthiesen (30). The factors of safety that have been applied to the test results are 1.35 and 1.2 for bridges and buildings, respectively.

Section I: Allowable Stresses for Welded Parts.—The allowable stresses for cross sections near welds given in Section I are based on the same principles as are the allowable stresses in Section A, with the exception that some of the allowable stresses for cross sections near welds are reduced in order

TABLE 12.—MINIMUM SHEAR STRENGTH OF FILLET WELDS[a]

Filler alloy	Transverse shear in single fillet welds and longitudinal shear	Transverse shear in double fillet welds
5556	19.5	30
5356	17	26
4043	12	16

[a] In ksi.

to account for the softening effect of the heat of welding. The basic strength values used in obtaining the allowable stresses in Tables 7a and 7b are listed in Table 1. The values of minimum shear strength of fillet welds listed in Table 12 were used in conjunction with the shear strength of the parent metal in the heat affected zone as a basis for the values of allowable shear stress in fillet welds given in Tables 7a and 7b.

In obtaining the allowable tensile stress on welds, the tensile strength value of 24 ksi for material affected by the heat of welding was multiplied by a factor of 0.9, and the resulting stress was divided by a factor of safety of 2.2 (or 1.95). The yield strength was divided by a factor of safety of 1.85 (or 1.65). The factor 0.9 was used to take account of the fact that, for welds that receive only visual inspection, the minimum strength value in Table 1 can probably not be considered to have the same reliability as the minimum mechanical properties of the parent metal, even though the weld strength value is based on ASME weld qualification test requirements (31) and on extensive tests (32). The factors of safety applied to minimum fillet weld strengths in order to obtain allowable stresses were 20% greater than the basic factors of safety applied to ultimate strength elsewhere in these specifications. Background information on the provisions of Section I, including the use of Eq. 12, can be found in the literature (33),(34).

Tests and analysis of welded aluminum columns (34) have shown that, for simply supported columns (k = 1.0), welds at the ends have little effect on the buckling strength in the range of slenderness ratios where design is controlled by buckling rather than by yielding. In deriving the allowable stresses in Specifications I-7, I-11, and I-14, therefore, end welds were not considered to affect the buckling strength. Similarly, it was considered that welds will not seriously affect the buckling strength'of flat plates supported on both edges, as in the cases covered by Specifications I-9, I-16, and I-18 to I-21. However, the allowable stresses in Specifications I-8, I-10, I-12, I-13, I-15 and I-17 are based on the conservative assumption that the buckling strengths of the members covered by these specifications are controlled by the mechanical properties of the heat-affected material immediately adjacent to the weld.

In obtaining formulas for allowable stress based on local buckling of flat plate elements, the values of k' in Eq. 17 were assumed to be the same as for unwelded plates, except that for buckling in the inelastic stress range in the case of Specifications I-8 and I-15, the values of k' were considered to be halfway between the values used for unwelded plates and the values that would apply to plates with fixed edges. This assumption was made to take into account the restraining effect of the weld bead and the surrounding metal that is not affected by the heat of welding.

Section J: Miscellaneous Design Rules.

J-1: Fatigue.—The allowable stresses for repeated loadings, given in Table 10, are based on the results of fatigue tests of welded joints (7),(8). The factors of safety that have been applied to the test results are 1.35 and 1.2 for bridge structures and building structures, respectively.

Section K: Fabrication.

K-3: Welding Procedure.—The use of alloy 5556 or 5356 as a filler metal produces welds of greater strength and ductility than are generally obtained with alloy 4043. Welds in highly restricted locations may sometimes show cracking when 5556 or 5356 filler metal is used. If this condition cannot be eliminated by adjustments of procedure or fixtures, the cracking tendency can be reduced by using 4043 filler metal. As indicated by the notes in Tables 6a and 6b, basic allowable stresses must be reduced 20% if Alloy 4043 filler wire is used to weld metal more than 3/8 in. thick.

K-4: Qualification of Welding Procedure and Welding Operator.—The minimum requirement of 24 ksi for tensile strength of a reduced-section specimen used in a welding qualification test is the same as the minimum requirement in the ASME Boiler and Pressure Vessel Code (31).

Section L: Single-Web Beams and Girders.—Eqs. 14a to 14c are derived from the general equation for elastic buckling strength of beams (19) by making the approximation that the effects of lack of symmetry of the cross section about an axis perpendicular to the web can be taken into account by calculating J, I_y, and S_c as though both flanges were the same as the compression flange. This assumption is justified by Figs. 5 to 8 of J. W. Clark, M. ASCE, and H. N. Hill, F. ASCE (19), which show that the lateral buckling stress for an I-section is not greatly affected by changes in the size of the tension flange. It was also assumed that the formula for torsion bending constant for I-sections $\left(C_s = d^2 I_y/4 \right)$ applies approximately to all sections (39).

Section M: Effective Width of Thin Plates in Compression.

M-1 and M-2: Effective Width of Thin Plates in Compression.—When a flat plate, leg, or web is built in along one or both edges to other parts of a compression member which offer partial edge restraint, the local buckling of the plate, leg, or web does not precipitate collapse of the member as a whole as it probably would in the case of a single-angle strut. For this reason, it is proper to permit a decreased factor of safety against local buckling in such cases if suitable precautions are taken to avoid collapse. Step c of this specification provides a simple method for accomplishing this result by introducing the well-known "effective width" concept. After a plate, leg, or web buckles, a part of its area is considered to be ineffective in supporting load, whereas a strip along each supported edge is considered still fully effective in working with the supporting material to which it is attached. The formula (Eq. 15) for effective width used in step c is generally more conservative than other accepted methods of computing effective width (28).

The limitation placed on the value of f_c in Step f is intended to provide a small factor of safety against local buckling at the design load.

This report is respectfully submitted by the Task Committee on Lightweight Alloys, Committee on Metals, Structural Division:

Paul E. Brandt
John M. English
Charles N. Gaylord
Edwin H. Gaylord
Glenn E. Johnson

Richard C. Kasser
S. A. Kilpatrick
Cedric Marsh
Robert B. B. Moorman
F. J. Tamanini

John W. Clark, Chairman

APPENDIX I.—BIBLIOGRAPHY ON STRUCTURES OF ALUMINUM ALLOYS 6061-T6 AND 6062-T6

1. "Specifications for Structures of a Moderate Strength Aluminum Alloy of High Resistance to Corrosion," Progress Report of the Comm. of the Structural Div. on Design in Lightweight Structural Alloys, Proc.-Sep. No. 132, ASCE, May, 1952.
2. "Specifications for Structures of Aluminum Alloy 6061-T6," 2nd Progress Report of the Comm. of the Structural Div. on Design in Lightweight Structural Alloys, Journal of the Structural Division, ASCE, Vol. 82, No. ST3, Proc. Paper 970, May, 1956.
3. "Standard Specifications for Highway Bridges," The Amer. Assn. of State Highway Officials, 1961.
4. "Specifications for Steel Railway Bridges," Amer. Railway Engrg. Assn., 1962.
5. "Specification for the Design, Fabrication and Erection of Structural Steel for Buildings," Amer. Inst. of Steel Construction, 1961.
6. "Alcoa Structural Handbook," Aluminum Co. of Amer., Pittsburgh, Pa., 1960, pp. 212-234.

7. "Static and Fatigue Tests of Arc-Welded Aluminum Alloy 61S-T Plate," by E. C. Hartmann, M. Holt, and A. N. Zamboky, The Welding Journal Research Supplement, March, 1947, pp. 129-138.

8. "Fatigue Strength Butt Joints in 3/8-in. Thick Aluminum Alloy Plates," by E. C. Hartmann, M. Holt, and I. D. Eaton, The Welding Journal Research Supplement, January, 1954, pp. 21-30.

9. "Guide to Design Criteria for Metal Compression Members," Column Research Council, Engrg. Foundation, 1960, (a) p. 57.

10. "Lateral Buckling of Rolled Steel Beams," by R. A. Hechtman, J. S. Hattrup, E. F. Styer, and J. L. Tiedemann, Transactions, ASCE, Vol. 122, 1957, p. 823.

11. "Column Research Council Symposium on Metal Compression Members: Basic Column Strength," by Lynn S. Beedle and Lambert Tall, Transactions, ASCE, Vol. 127, Part II, 1962, p. 138.

12. "Beam and Torsion Tests of Aluminum Alloy 61S-T Tubing," by R. L. Moore and M. Holt, Technical Note No. 867, Natl. Advisory Comm. for Aeronautics, Washington, D. C., 1942.

13. "Bending Strength in the Plastic Range," by F. P. Cozzone, Journal of the Aeronautical Sciences, Vol. 10, May, 1943, p. 137.

14. "The Lateral Instability of Deep Rectangular Beams," by C. Dumont and H. N. Hill, Technical Note No. 601, Natl. Advisory Comm. for Aeronautics, Washington, D. C., 1937.

15. "Inelastic Behavior of Ductile Members Under Dead Loading," by M. E. Clark, H. T. Corten, and O. M. Sidebottom, Bulletin No. 426, Univ. of Illinois Engrg. Experiment Sta., Urbana, Ill., 1954.

16. "Straight Line Column Formulas for Aluminum Alloys," by H. N. Hill and J. W. Clark, Technical Paper No. 12, Alcoa Research Labs., Aluminum Co. of Amer., Pittsburgh, Pa., 1955.

17. "Buckling Strength of Metal Structures," by Friedrich Bleich, McGraw-Hill Book Co., Inc., New York, N. Y., 1952, (a) p. 422.

18. "Column Research Council Symposium on Metal Compression Members: Effective Length of Framed Columns," by Thomas C. Kavanagh, Transactions, ASCE, Vol. 127, Part II, 1962, p. 81.

19. "Column Research Council Symposium on Metal Compression Members: Lateral Buckling of Beams," by J. W. Clark and H. N. Hill, Transactions, ASCE, Vol. 127, Part II, 1962, p. 180.

20. "Buckling Stresses for Flat Plates and Sections," by E. Z. Stowell, G. J. Heimerl, Charles Libove, and E. E. Lundquist, Transactions, ASCE, Vol. 117, 1952, p. 545.

21. "Handbook of Structural Stability: Part III - Buckling of Curved Plates and Shells," by George Gerard and Herbert Becker, Technical Note 3783, Natl. Advisory Comm. for Aeronautics, Washington, D. C., 1957.

22. "The Local Buckling of Aluminum Plate Elements," by K. Sutter, Sheet Metal Industries, January, 1960, p. 23.

23. "The Behavior of Webplates of Plate Girders Subjected to Pure Bending," by K. C. Rockey and F. Jenkins, The Structural Engineer, May, 1957, p. 176.

24. "Buckling of Webs in Deep Steel I-Girders," by George Wastlund and S. G. A. Bergman, Royal Inst. of Tech., Stockholm, Sweden, 1947.

25. "Web Buckling and the Design of Webplates," by K. C. Rockey, The Structural Engineer, February, 1958, p. 45.

26. "Designing Aluminum Alloy Members for Combined End Load and Bending," by H. N. Hill, E. C. Hartmann, and J. W. Clark, Transactions, ASCE, Vol. 121, 1956, p. 1.

27. Discussion by E. C. Hartmann of "Rational Design of Steel Columns," by D. H. Young, Transactions, ASCE, Vol. 101, 1936, p. 475.

28. "Column Research Council Symposium on Metal Compression Members: Postbuckling Behavior of Flat Plates," by J. R. Jombock and J. W. Clark, Transactions, ASCE, Vol. 127, Part II, 1962, p. 227.

29. "Critical Shear Stress of Infinitely Long, Simply Supported Plate with Transverse Stiffeners," by Manual Stein and R. W. Fralich, Technical Note 1851, Natl. Advisory Comm. for Aeronautics, Washington, D. C., 1949.

30. "Fatigue Tests of Riveted or Bolted Aluminum Alloy Joints," by M. Holt, I. D. Eaton, and R. B. Matthiesen, Journal of the Structural Division, ASCE, Vol. 83, No. ST1, Proc. Paper 1148, January, 1957.

31. "Qualification Standard for Welding Procedures, Welders and Welding Operators," ASME Boiler and Pressure Vessel Code, Section IX, 1962, Par. QN-6, p. 18.

32. "The Strength and Ductility of Welds in Aluminum Alloy Plate," by F. G. Nelson, Jr., and F. M. Howell, The Welding Journal Research Supplement, September, 1952, p. 3.

33. "Column Research Council Symposium on Metal Compression Members: Design of Welded Aluminum Structures," by H. N. Hill, J. W. Clark, and R. J. Brungraber, Transactions, ASCE, Vol. 127, Part II, 1962, p. 102.

34. "Column Research Council Symposium on Metal Compression Members: Strength of Welded Aluminum Columns," by R. J. Brungraber and J. W. Clark, Transactions, ASCE, Vol. 127, Part II, 1962, p. 202.

35. "Compressive Crippling of Structural Sections," by M. S. Anderson, Technical Note 3553, Natl. Advisory Comm. for Aeronautics, Washington, D.C., 1956.

36. "Local Instability Problems of Light Alloy Struts," by P. S. Bulson, Research Report No. 29, The Aluminium Development Assn., 1955.

37. "Stability Considerations in the Design of Steel Plate Girders," by Charles E. Massonnet, Transactions, ASCE, Vol. 127, Part II, 1962, p. 420.

38. "Theoretical and Experimental Analysis of Members Loaded Eccentrically and Inelastically," by O. M. Sidebottom and M. E. Clark, Bulletin No. 447, Univ. of Illinois Engrg. Experiment Sta., Urbana, Ill., 1958.

39. "Lateral Buckling of Channels and Z-Beams," by H. N. Hill, Transactions, ASCE, Vol. 119, 1954, p. 829.

40. "An Investigation of the Effectiveness of Stiffeners on Shear-Resistant Plate-Girder Webs," by R. L. Moore, Technical Note 862, Natl. Advisory Comm. for Aeronautics, Washington, D. C., September, 1942.

41. "Critical Stress of an Infinitely Long Plate in the Plastic Region," by E. Z. Stowell, Technical Note 1681, Natl. Advisory Comm. for Aeronautics, Washington, D. C., 1948.

42. "Observations on the Behavior of Aluminum Alloy Test Girders," by R. L. Moore, Transactions, ASCE, Vol. 112, 1947, p. 901.

43. "Structural Design with Formed Aluminium Sheet," by Cedric Marsh, Light Metals, Vol. 18, 1955, pp. 57-59, 86-88, and 124-127.

44. "German Buckling Specifications," DIN 4114, Vol. 1, 1952; English translation by T. V. Galambos and J. Jones, Column Research Council, July, 1957.

APPENDIX II.

Allowable stresses for 6061-T6 and 6062-T6 buildings and other structures to which allowable stresses for buildings are normally applied (Tables 4b, 5b, 6b, and 7b).

TABLE 5b.—ALLOWABLE SHEAR STRESSES IN RIVETS AND BOLTS
(BUILDING STRUCTURES)

Specification Number	Description of Rivet or Bolt	Allowable Stress, ksi	
		Shear on effective shear area	Tension on root area
A-22b	6061-T6 rivets, cold driven	11	--
A-23b	6061-T43 rivets, driven at temperatures of from 990°F to 1,050°F	9	--
A-24b	2024-T4 bolts	16[a]	26
A-25b	6061-T6 pins	11	--

[a] This allowable shear stress applies to either turned bolts in reamed holes or unfinished bolts in 1/16-in. oversize holes.

TABLE 7b.—ALLOWABLE SHEAR STRESSES IN FILLET WELDS
(BUILDING STRUCTURES)

Specification Number	Filler Alloy	Allowable Shear Stress,[a] ksi	
		Transverse Shear in single fillet welds or longitudinal shear[b]	Transverse shear in double fillet welds[b]
I-22b	5556	8.5	9[c]
I-23b	5356	7	9[c]
I-24b	4043	5	7

[a] Shear stress is considered to be equal to the load divided by the throat area, regardless of the direction of loading.
[b] Single fillet welds in transverse shear may be treated as double fillet welds in joints so designed as to prevent local bending of the parts adjacent to the fillet weld.
[c] These values are controlled by the shear strength of the parent material; all other values are controlled by the strength of the filler metal.

TABLE 4b.—ALLOWABLE STRESSES IN RIVETED OR BOLTED STRUCTURES AT LOCATIONS FARTHER THAN 1.0 INCH FROM ANY WELD (6061.-T6 AND 6062-T6 BUILDING STRUCTURES NONWELDED)

Type of Stress	Specification No.	Type of Member or Component	Allowable Stress, ksi	Allowable Stress for Slenderness Less Than S_1, ksi	Slenderness Limit, S_1	Allowable Stress for Slenderness Between S_1 and S_2 ksi	Slenderness Limit, S_2	Allowable Stress for Slenderness Greater Than S_2, ksi
TENSION, axial, net section	A-1b	Any tension member	19					
	A-2b	Structural shapes, rectangular tubes, built-up members bent about X-axis	19					
TENSION in extreme fibers of beams, net section	A-3b	Round or oval tubes	24					
	A-4b	Rectangular bars and plates, and outstanding flanges of shapes bent about Y-axis	26					
BEARING	A-5b	On rivets and bolts	34(a)					
	A-6b	On milled surfaces and pins	23					
COMPRESSION in Columns Subjected to Axial Load; Gross Section — COMPRESSION, gross section (Also see Specs A-8b to A-10b)	A-7b	Columns		19	$\dfrac{L}{r} = 10$	$20.4 - 0.135\,\dfrac{L}{r}$	$\dfrac{L}{r} = 87$	$\dfrac{51,000}{(L/r)^2}$
COMPRESSION in components of columns (Also see Spec. A-7b)	A-8b	Outstanding flanges and legs		19	$\dfrac{b}{t} = 5.5$	$23.7 - 0.86\,\dfrac{b}{t}$	$\dfrac{b}{t} = 12$	$\dfrac{1,940}{(b/t)^2}$
	A-9b	Flat plates with both edges supported		19	$\dfrac{b}{t} = 17$	$23.7 - 0.27\,\dfrac{b}{t}$	$\dfrac{b}{t} = 38$	$\dfrac{19,200}{(b/t)^2}$
	A-10b	Curved plates supported on both edges and walls of round or oval tubes		19	$\dfrac{R}{t} = 22$	$22.8 - 0.78\sqrt{\dfrac{R}{t}}$	$\dfrac{R}{t} = 125$	- - - -

Category	Ref	Description	Section				
COMPRESSION in extreme fibers of beams, gross section (Also see Specs. A-15b to A-19b)	A-11b	Single-web structural shapes and built-up sections bent about X-axis	19	$\frac{L_b}{r_y} = 12$	$20.4 - 0.113\frac{L_b}{r_y}$	$\frac{L_b}{r_y} = 81$	$\frac{74,000}{(L_b/r_y)^2}$
	A-12b	Round or oval tubes	24	$\frac{R_b}{t} = 19$	$28.2 - 0.22\frac{R_b}{t}$	$\frac{R_b}{t} = 60$	- - - -
	A-13b	Solid rectangular beams bent about X-axis	26	$\frac{d}{t}\sqrt{\frac{L_b}{d}} = 11$	$34.9 - 0.80\frac{d}{t}\sqrt{\frac{L_b}{d}}$	$\frac{d}{t}\sqrt{\frac{L_b}{d}} = 29$	$\frac{9,900}{\left(\frac{d}{t}\right)^2\frac{L_b}{d}}$
	A-14b	Rectangular tubes and box sections	19	$\frac{L_b S_c}{I_y} = 40$	$20.4 - 0.22\frac{L_b S_c}{I_y}$	$\frac{L_b S_c}{I_y} = 1810$	$\frac{20,000}{L_b S_c/I_y}$
COMPRESSION in Members Subjected to Bending, Gross Section	A-15b	Flat plates with one edge free and one edge supported	19	$\frac{b}{t} = 6.2$	$23.7 - 0.76\frac{b}{t}$	$\frac{b}{t} = 14$	$\frac{2,500}{(b/t)^2}$
	A-16b	Flat plates with both edges supported	19	$\frac{b}{t} = 17$	$23.7 - 0.27\frac{b}{t}$	$\frac{b}{t} = 38$	$\frac{19,200}{(b/t)^2}$
COMPRESSION in components of beams where component is under uniform compression (Also see Specs. A-11b to A-14b)	A-17b	Flat plates with compression edge free and tension edge supported, bent about X-axis	26	$\frac{b}{t} = 7.3$	$34.9 - 1.24\frac{b}{t}$	$\frac{b}{t} = 19$	$\frac{4,200}{(b/t)^2}$
COMPRESSION in components of beams where component is under bending in its own plane, (Also see Specs. A-11b to A-14b)	A-18b	Flat plates with both edges supported, bent about X-axis	19	- - - -	19	$\frac{h}{t} = 110$	$\frac{230,000}{(h/t)^2}$
	A-19b	Flat plates with both edges supported, bent about X-axis with horizontal stiffener	19	- - - -	19	$\frac{h}{t} = 228$	$\frac{990,000}{(h/t)^2}$
SHEAR in webs of beams, and also in members subjected to torsion, gross section	A-20b	Unstiffened flat webs	12	$h/t = 18$	$13.7 - 0.092\frac{h}{t}$	$\frac{h}{t} = 66$	$\frac{33,000}{(h/t)^2}$
	A-21b	Stiffened flat webs	12	- - - -	12	$\frac{a_e}{t} = 66$	$\frac{53,000}{(a_e/t)^2}$

$$a_e = a_1/\sqrt{1 + 0.7(a_1/a_2)^2}$$

(a) This value applies for a ratio of edge distance to rivet or bolt diameter of 2 or greater. For smaller ratios, multiply this allowable stress by the ratio. (edge distance)/(twice the rivet or bolt diameter).

TABLE 6b.—ALLOWABLE STRESSES ON SECTIONS WITHIN 1.0 INCH OF A WELD (6061-T6 AND 6062-T6 BUILDING STRUCTURES WELDED)

Type of Stress	Specification No.	Type of Member or Component	Allowable Stress for Slenderness Less Than S_1, ksi	Slenderness Limit, S_1	Allowable Stress for Slenderness Between S_1 and S_2, ksi	Slenderness Limit, S_2	Allowable Stress for Slenderness Greater Than S_2, ksi	Allowable Stress, ksi
TENSION, axial, net section	I-1b	Any tension member						11(b)
TENSION in extreme fibers of beams, net section	I-2b	Structural shapes, rectangular tubes, built-up members bent about X-axis						11(b)
	I-3b	Round or oval tubes						13(b)
	I-4b	Rectangular bars and plates, and outstanding flanges of shapes bent about Y-axis						13(b)
BEARING	I-5b	On rivets and bolts						18(b)(d)
	I-6b	On milled surfaces and pins						12(b)
COMPRESSION in Columns Subjected to Axial Load, Gross Section — COMPRESSION(a) gross section (Also see Specs I-8b to I-10b)	I-7b	Columns (a)	11(b)	– – –	11(b)	$\frac{L}{r} = 68$(c)	$\frac{51{,}000}{(L/r)^2}$	
COMPRESSION in components of columns (Also see Spec. I-7b)	I-8b	Outstanding flanges and legs	11(b)	$\frac{b}{t} = 4.9$(c)	$\frac{24.4}{\sqrt{b/t}}$	$\frac{b}{t} = 19$	$\frac{1{,}940}{(b/t)^2}$	
	I-9b	Flat plates with both edges supported	11(b)	– – –	11(b)	$\frac{b}{t} = 44$(c)	$\frac{19{,}200}{(b/t)^2}$	
	I-10b	Curved plates supported on both edges and walls of round or oval tubes	11(b)	$\frac{R}{t} = 14$(c)	$\frac{21.3}{(R/t)^{1/4}}$	$\frac{R}{t} = 200$	– – –	
COMPRESSION in extreme fibers of beams, gross section (Also see Specs. I-15b to I-19b)	I-11b	Single-web structural shapes and built-up sections bent about X-axis(a)	11(b)	– – –	11(b)	$\frac{L_b}{r_y} = 82$(c)	$\frac{74{,}000}{(L_b/r_y)^2}$	
	I-12b	Round or oval tubes	13(b)	$\frac{R_b}{t} = 13$(c)	$\frac{24.7}{(R_b/t)^{1/4}}$	$\frac{R_b}{t} = 135$	– – –	
	I-13b	Solid rectangular beams bent about X-axis	13(b)	$\frac{d}{t}\sqrt{\frac{L_b}{d}} = 11$(c)	$\frac{42.3}{[(d/t)^2 L_b/d]^{1/4}}$	$\frac{d}{t}\sqrt{\frac{L_b}{d}} = 38$	$\frac{9{,}900}{\left(\frac{d}{t}\right)^2 \frac{L_b}{d}}$	
COMPRESSION in Members Subjected	I-14b	Rectangular tubes and box sections(a)	11(b)	– – –	11(b)	$\frac{L_b S_c}{I_y} = 1820$(c)	$\frac{20{,}000}{L_b S_c/I_y}$	

	Spec.	Description	Diagram					
to Bending, Gross Section								
COMPRESSION in components of beams, where component is under uniform compression (Also see Specs. I-11b to I-14b)	I-15b	Flat plates with one edge free and one edge supported		$11^{(b)}$	$\dfrac{b}{t} = 5.3^{(c)}$	$\dfrac{25.4}{\sqrt{b/t}}$	$\dfrac{b}{t} = 21$	$\dfrac{2{,}500}{(b/t)^2}$
	I-16b	Flat plates with both edges supported		$11^{(b)}$	– – –	$11^{(b)}$	$\dfrac{b}{t} = 44^{(c)}$	$\dfrac{19{,}200}{(b/t)^2}$
COMPRESSION in components of beams where component is under bending in its own plane, (Also see Specs. I-11b to I-14b)	I-17b	Flat plates with compression edge free and tension edge supported, bent about X-axis		$13^{(b)}$	$\dfrac{b}{t} = 6.8^{(c)}$	$\dfrac{34.0}{\sqrt{b/t}}$	$\dfrac{b}{t} = 25$	$\dfrac{4{,}200}{(b/t)^2}$
	I-18b	Flat plates with both edges supported, bent about X-axis		$11^{(b)}$	– – –	$11^{(b)}$	$\dfrac{h}{t} = 144^{(c)}$	$\dfrac{230{,}000}{(h/t)^2}$
	I-19b	Flat plates with both edges supported, bent about X-axis with horizontal stiffener		$11^{(b)}$	– – –	$11^{(b)}$	$\dfrac{h}{t} = 300^{(c)}$	$\dfrac{990{,}000}{(h/t)^2}$
SHEAR in webs of beams, and also in members subjected to torsion, gross section	I-20b	Unstiffened flat webs		$7^{(b)}$	– – –	$7^{(b)}$	$\dfrac{h}{t} = 69^{(c)}$	$\dfrac{33{,}000}{(h/t)^2}$
	I-21b	Stiffened flat webs	$\sigma_e = \sigma_1\sqrt{1 + 0.7\left(\sigma_1/\sigma_2\right)^2}$	$7^{(b)}$	– – –	$7^{(b)}$	$\dfrac{a_e}{t} = 87^{(c)}$	$\dfrac{53{,}000}{(a_e/t)^2}$

(a) The allowable stresses for columns, single web beams and rectangular tubes and box sections apply to members supported at both ends and welded at the ends only. See Specification I-26 for allowable stresses in these members with welds at locations other than the ends and in cantilever columns and beams.

(b) These allowable stresses apply to all material welded with 5556 or 5356 filler alloy and to material 3/8-in. or less in thickness welded with 4043 filler alloy. For thicker material welded with 4043 filler alloy, these allowable stresses shall be reduced by multiplying them by 0.8. Allowable stresses not marked with a superscript apply to material welded with either 4043, 5556 or 5356 filler alloy.

(c) These slenderness limits apply to all material welded with 5556 or 5356 filler alloy and to material 3/8-in. or less in thickness welded with 4043 filler alloy. For thicker material welded with 4043 filler alloy, these slenderness limits must be adjusted to correspond to the reduced values of maximum allowable stresses indicated in Note (b) above.

(d) This value applies for a ratio of edge distance to rivet or bolt diameter of 2 or more. For smaller ratios, multiply this allowable stress by the ratio, (edge distance)/(twice the rivet or bolt diameter)

Journal of the

STRUCTURAL DIVISION

Proceedings of the American Society of Civil Engineers

SUGGESTED SPECIFICATIONS FOR STRUCTURES OF ALUMINUM ALLOY 6063-T5 AND 6063-T6

Report of the Task Committee on Lightweight Alloys

Committee on Metals, Structural Division

[Because the text of ASCE Proceedings Paper 3342 is almost identical with that of Paper 3341, only the tables from Paper 3342 are reproduced here. Tables 8, 9 and 10 are omitted because they are identical with Tables 8, 11 and 12, respectively, of Paper 3341. Paper 3342 does not contain tables similar to Tables 9 and 10 of Paper 3341.]

TABLE 1.—BASIC STRENGTH DATA[a]

	Unaffected Parent Material		Material Affected by Heat of Welding,
	6063-T5	6063-T6	6063-T5 and 6063-T6
Tensile strength	22	30	17[b]
Tensile yield strength	16	25	11[c]
Compressive yield strength	16	25	11[c]
Shear strength	13	19	11
Shear yield strength	9	14	6.5
Bearing strength	46	63	36
Bearing yield strength	25	40	17

[a] Minimum strength values for Alloy 6063-T5 and 6063-T6, ksi (thickness 0.500 in. and under).

[b] ASME weld qualification test value for tensile strength across a butt weld.

[c] These are expected minimum values of the yield strength across a butt weld, corresponding to 0.2% offset on a 10-in. gage length.

TABLE 2.—APPLICABLE ASTM SPECIFICATIONS

Product	Alloy	ASTM Specification for material from which product is made
Rivets	6061-T6 or 6061-T4[a]	B316-62 - rivet and cold heading wire and rods [b]
Bolts	2024-T4	B316-62 - rivet and cold heading wire and rods [b]
Nuts	6061-T6 or 6262-T9	B211-62 - bars, rods and wire, or B316-62 - rivet and cold heading wire and rods [b]
Washers	Alclad 2024-T3 or -T4	B209-62 - sheet and plate
Welding rods and electrodes	ER4043 or ER5356	B285-62T - welding rods and bare electrodes

[a] ASTM B316-62 includes mechanical property specifications for 6061-T6 but not 6061-T4. The heat treatment for the latter is the same as the former except that the artificial aging is omitted.

[b] ASTM B316-62 covers rods up to 0.615 in. in diameter. Rods with diameters from 0.615 to 1.000 in. are supplied with the same mechanical property limits and tolerances on diameter (+0.003 in., -0.001 in.) that apply to 0.615-in. rod in ASTM B316-62.

Material.—The principal material considered in these specifications is an aluminum alloy having the following nominal chemical composition:

Composition	Percentage By weight
Silicon	0.4
Magnesium	0.7
Others	1.0
Aluminum	97.9
Total	100.0

This material is covered by the following American Society for Testing and Materials (ASTM) specifications:

Product	ASTM Specification No.
Drawn Seamless Tubes	B210-62 (6063-T6)
Extruded Bars, Rods, and Shapes	B221-62 (6063-T5 and -T6)
Extruded Tubes	B235-62 (6063-T5 and -T6)
Pipe	B241-62 (6063-T5 and -T6)

Following are typical values of other physical properties of this alloy:

Properties	Numerical Values
Modulus of elasticity, ksi	10,000
Modulus of elasticity in shear, ksi	3,800
Poisson's ratio	1/3
Coefficient of expansion, per degree Fahrenheit	0.000012
Weight, in pounds per cubic inch	0.098

TABLE 3.—ALLOYS TO BE USED FOR RIVETS

Designation before driving	Driving procedure	Designation after driving	Typical shear strength[a]
6061-T4	Hot, 990°F to 1050°F	6061-T43	24
6053-T61	Cold, as received	6053-T61	23

[a] Typical ultimate shear strength of the driven rivet, ksi.

6063-T6

BRIDGE STRUCTURES

TABLE 4a.—ALLOWABLE STRESSES IN RIVETED OR BOLTED STRUCTURES OR IN WELDED STRUCTURES AT LOCATIONS FARTHER THAN 1.0 INCH FROM ANY WELD (6063-T6 BRIDGE STRUCTURES NONWELDED)

Type of Stress	Specification No.	Type of Member or Component	Allowable Stress, ksi	Allowable Stress for Slenderness Less Than S_1, ksi	Slenderness Limit, S_1	Allowable Stress for Slenderness Between S_1 and S_2, ksi	Slenderness Limit, S_2	Allowable Stress for Slenderness Greater Than S_2, ksi
TENSION, axial, net section	A-1a	Any tension member	13.5					
TENSION in extreme fibers of beams, net section	A-2a	Structural shapes, rectangular tubes, built-up members bent about X-axis	13.5					
	A-3a	Round or oval tubes	15					
	A-4a	Rectangular bars and plates, and outstanding flanges of shapes bent about Y-axis	17					
BEARING	A-5a	On rivets and bolts	21.5(a)					
	A-6a	On milled surfaces and pins	14.5					
COMPRESSION in Columns Subjected to Axial Load, Gross Section — COMPRESSION, gross section (Also see Specs. A-8a to A-10a)	A-7a	Columns		12	$L/r = 10$	$12.7 - 0.071\ L/r$	$L/r = 81$	$\dfrac{45{,}000}{(L/r)^2}$
COMPRESSION in components of columns (Also see Spec. A-7a)	A-8a	Outstanding flanges and legs		12	$b/t = 6.0$	$14.7 - 0.45\ b/t$	$b/t = 15$	$\dfrac{1{,}720}{(b/t)^2}$
	A-9a	Flat plates with both edges supported		12	$b/t = 19$	$14.7 - 0.141\ b/t$	$b/t = 45$	$\dfrac{17{,}000}{(b/t)^2}$
	A-10a	Curved plates supported on both edges and walls of round or oval tubes		12	$R/t = 15$	$13.6 - 0.41\sqrt{R/t}$	$R/t = 140$	----

	Ref.	Description	Sketch					
COMPRESSION in extreme fibers of beams, gross section (Also see Specs. A-15a to A-18a)	A-11a	Single-web structural shapes and built-up sections bent about X-axis		12	$L_b/r_y = 12$	$12.7 - 0.059\ L_b/r_y$	$L_b/r_y = 96$	$\dfrac{65,000}{(L_b/r_y)^2}$
	A-12a	Round or oval tubes		15	$R_b/t = 16$	$15.9 - 0.058\ R_b/t$	$R_b/t = 120$	- - -
	A-13a	Solid rectangular beams bent about X-axis		17	$\dfrac{d}{t}\sqrt{\dfrac{L_b}{d}} = 12$	$22.0 - 0.42\ \dfrac{d}{t}\sqrt{\dfrac{L_b}{d}}$	$\dfrac{d}{t}\sqrt{\dfrac{L_b}{d}} = 33$	$\dfrac{8,800}{(d/t)^2\,L_b/d}$
	A-14a	Rectangular tubes and box sections		12	$\dfrac{L_b S_c}{I_y} = 38$	$12.7 - 0.114\sqrt{\dfrac{L_b S_c}{I_y}}$	$\dfrac{L_b S_c}{I_y} = 2540$	$\dfrac{17,700}{L_b S_c/I_y}$
COMPRESSION in Members Subjected to Bending, Gross Section — COMPRESSION in components of beams, where component is under uniform compression (Also see Specs. A-11a to A-14a)	A-15a	Flat plates with one edge free and one edge supported		12	$b/t = 6.8$	$14.7 - 0.40\ b/t$	$b/t = 17$	$\dfrac{2,240}{(b/t)^2}$
	A-16a	Flat plates with both edges supported		12	$b/t = 19$	$14.7 - 0.141\ b/t$	$b/t = 45$	$\dfrac{17,000}{(b/t)^2}$
COMPRESSION in components of beams where component is under bending in its own plane, (Also see A-11a to A-14a)	A-17a	Flat plates with compression edge free and tension edge supported, bent about X-axis		17	$b/t = 7.6$	$22.0 - 0.66\ b/t$	$b/t = 22$	$\dfrac{3,700}{(b/t)^2}$
	A-18a	Flat plates with both edges supported, bent about X-axis		12	- - -	12	$h/t = 131$	$\dfrac{205,000}{(h/t)^2}$
SHEAR in webs of beams, and also in members subjected to torsion, gross section	A-19a	Unstiffened flat webs		7.5	$h/t = 20$	$8.5 - 0.049\ h/t$	$h/t = 78$	$\dfrac{29,000}{(h/t)^2}$

(a) This value applies for a ratio of edge distance to rivet or bolt diameter of 2 or more. For smaller ratios, multiply this allowable stress by the ratio, (edge distance)/(twice the rivet or bolt diameter)

TABLE 6a.—ALLOWABLE STRESSES ON SECTIONS WITHIN 1.0 INCH OF A WELD (6063-T6 BRIDGE STRUCTURES WELDED)

Type of Stress	Specification No.	Type of Member or Component	Allowable Stress, ksi
TENSION, axial, net section	I-1a	Any tension member	6
TENSION in extreme fibers of beams, net section	I-2a	Structural shapes, rectangular tubes, built-up members bent about X-axis	6
	I-3a	Round or oval tubes	6.5
	I-4a	Rectangular bars and plates, and outstanding flanges of shapes bent about Y-axis	6.5
BEARING	I-5a	On rivets and bolts	9(b)
	I-6a	On milled surfaces and pins	6

Type of Stress	Specification No.	Type of Member or Component	Allowable Stress for Slenderness Less Than S1, ksi	Slenderness Limit, S1	Allowable Stress for Slenderness Between S1 and S2, ksi	Slenderness Limit, S2	Allowable Stress for Slenderness Greater Than S2, ksi
COMPRESSION gross section (Also see Specs I-8a to I-10a) COMPRESSION in Columns Subjected to Axial Load Gross Section	I-7a	Columns (a)	6	- - -	6	$L/r = 87$	$\dfrac{45,000}{(L/r)^2}$
COMPRESSION in components of columns (Also see Spec. I-7a)	I-8a	Outstanding flanges and legs	6	$b/t = 4.1$	$\dfrac{12.1}{\sqrt{b/t}}$	$b/t = 27$	$\dfrac{1,720}{(b/t)^2}$
	I-9a	Flat plates with both edges supported	6	- - -	6	$b/t = 53$	$\dfrac{17,000}{(b/t)^2}$
	I-10a	Curved plates supported on both edges and walls of round or oval tubes	6	$R/t = 10$	$\dfrac{10.7}{(R/t)^{1/4}}$	$R/t = 125$	- - - -

Category	Spec	Description					
COMPRESSION in extreme fibers of beams, gross section (Also see Specs. I-15a to I-18a)	I-11a	Single-web structural shapes and built-up sections bent about X-axis[8]	6	- - -	6	$L_b/r_y = 104$	$\dfrac{65,000}{(L_b/r_y)^2}$
	I-12a	Round or oval tubes	6.5	$R_b/t = 13$	$\dfrac{12.3}{(R_b/t)^{1/4}}$	$R_b/t = 125$	- - -
	I-13a	Solid rectangular beams bent about X-axis	6.5	$\dfrac{d}{t}\sqrt{\dfrac{L_b}{d}} = 11$	$\dfrac{21.6}{[(d/t)^2 L_b/d]^{1/4}}$	$\dfrac{d}{t}\sqrt{\dfrac{L_b}{d}} = 55$; $\dfrac{L_bS_c}{I_y} = 920$	$\dfrac{8,800}{(d/t)^2 L_b/d}$; $\dfrac{17,700}{L_bS_c/I_y}$
	I-14a	Rectangular tubes and box sections[8]	6	- - -	6		
COMPRESSION in Members Subjected to Bending, Gross Section	I-15a	Flat plates with one edge free and one edge supported (Also see Specs I-11a to I-14a)	6	$b/t = 4.4$	$\dfrac{12.6}{\sqrt{b/t}}$	$b/t = 32$	$\dfrac{2,240}{(b/t)^2}$
	I-16a	Flat plates with both edges supported	6	- - -	6	$b/t = 53$	$\dfrac{17,000}{(b/t)^2}$
	I-17a	Flat plates with compression edge free and tension edge supported, bent about X-axis (Also see Specs. I-11a to I-14a)	6.5	$b/t = 7.2$	$\dfrac{17.4}{\sqrt{b/t}}$	$b/t = 35$	$\dfrac{3,700}{(b/t)^2}$
	I-18a	Flat plates with both edges supported, bent about X-axis	6	- - -	6	$h/t = 185$	$\dfrac{205,000}{(h/t)^2}$
SHEAR in webs of beams, and also in members subjected to torsion, gross section	I-19a	Unstiffened flat webs	3.5	- - -	3.5	$h/t = 91$	$\dfrac{29,000}{(h/t)^2}$

(a) The allowable stresses for columns, single web beams and rectangular tubes and box sections apply to members supported at both ends and welded at the ends only. See Specification I-26 for allowable stresses in these members with welds at locations other than the ends and in cantilever columns and beams.

(b) This value applies for a ratio of edge distance to rivet or bolt diameter of 2 or more. For smaller ratios, multiply this allowable stress by the ratio, (edge distance)/(twice the rivet or bolt diameter).

TABLE 5a.—ALLOWABLE STRESSES IN RIVETS AND BOLTS
(BRIDGE STRUCTURES OF 6063-T6)

Specification Number	Description of Rivet or Bolt	Allowable Stress, ksi	
		Shear on effective shear area	Tension on root area
A-20a	6053-T61	7.5	--
A-21a	6061-T43 rivets, driven at temperatures of from 990°F to 1050°F	8	--
A-22a	2024-T4 bolts	14[a]	23

[a] This allowable shear stress applies to either turned bolts in reamed holes or unfinished bolts in 1/16-in. oversize holes.

TABLE 7a.—ALLOWABLE SHEAR STRESSES IN FILLET WELDS
(BRIDGE STRUCTURES OF 6063-T6)

Specification Number	Filler Alloy	Allowable Shear Stress,[a] ksi	
		Transverse shear in single fillet welds or longitudinal shear[b]	Transverse shear in double fillet welds[b]
I-20a	5356 5556	6[c]	6[c]
I-21a	4043	4.5	6[c]

[a] Shear stress is considered to be equal to the load divided by the throat area, regardless of the direction of loading.

[b] Single fillet welds in transverse shear may be treated as double fillet welds in joints so designed as to prevent local bending of the parts adjacent to the fillet weld.

[c] These values are controlled by the shear strength of the parent material; all other values are controlled by the strength of the filler metal.

6063-T5

BRIDGE STRUCTURES

TABLE 4b.—ALLOWABLE STRESSES IN RIVETED OR BOLTED STRUCTURES OR IN WELDED STRUCTURES AT LOCATIONS FARTHER THAN 1.0 INCH FROM ANY WELD (6063-T5 BRIDGE STRUCTURES <u>NONWELDED</u>)

Type of Stress	Specification No.	Type of Member or Component	Allowable Stress, ksi
TENSION, axial, net section	A-1b	Any tension member	8.5
	A-2b	Structural shapes, rectangular tubes, built-up members bent about X-axis	8.5
TENSION in extreme fibers of beams, net section	A-3b	Round or oval tubes	9.5
	A-4b	Rectangular bars and plates, and outstanding flanges of shapes bent about Y-axis	11.5
BEARING	A-5b	On rivets and bolts	13.5(a)
	A-6b	On milled surfaces and pins	9

Type of Stress	Spec. No.	Type of Member or Component	Allowable Stress for Slenderness Less Than S_1, ksi	Slenderness Limit, S_1	Allowable Stress for Slenderness Between S_1 and S_2 ksi	Slenderness Limit, S_2	Allowable Stress for Slenderness Greater Than S_2, ksi
COMPRESSION, gross section (Also see Specs. A-8b to A-10b). COMPRESSION in Columns Subjected to Axial Load, Gross Section	A-7b	Columns	7.5	$L/r = 14$	$8.0 - 0.035\ L/r$	$L/r = 100$	$\dfrac{45{,}000}{(L/r)^2}$
COMPRESSION in components of columns (Also see Spec. A-7b)	A-8b	Outstanding flanges and legs	7.5	$b/t = 7.2$	$9.1 - 0.22\ b/t$	$b/t = 19$	$\dfrac{1{,}720}{(b/t)^2}$
	A-9b	Flat plates with both edges supported	7.5	$b/t = 23$	$9.1 - 0.070\ b/t$	$b/t = 58$	$\dfrac{17{,}000}{(b/t)^2}$
	A-10b	Curved plates supported on both edges and walls of round or oval tubes	7.5	$R/t = 16$	$8.2 - 0.177\ \sqrt{R/t}$	$R/t = 200$	- - - -

Group	Item	Description		$L_b/r_y = 17$ type	Formula	$L_b/r_y = 120$ type	Formula
COMPRESSION in extreme fibers of beams, gross section (Also see Specs. A-15b to A-18b)	A-11b	Single-web structural shapes and built-up sections bent about X-axis	7.5	$L_b/r_y = 17$	$8.0 - 0.029\,L_b/r_y$	$L_b/r_y = 120$	$\dfrac{65{,}000}{(L_b/r_y)^2}$
	A-12b	Round or oval tubes	9.5	$R_b/t = 18$	$10.0 - 0.028\,R_b/t$	$R_b/t = 140$	- - -
	A-13b	Solid rectangular beams bent about X-axis	11.5	$\dfrac{d}{t}\sqrt{\dfrac{L_b}{d}} = 11$	$13.8 - 0.21\dfrac{d}{t}\sqrt{\dfrac{L_b}{d}}$	$\dfrac{d}{t}\sqrt{\dfrac{L_b}{d}} = 44$	$\dfrac{8{,}800}{(d/t)^2\,L_b/d}$
	A-14b	Rectangular tubes and box sections	7.5	$\dfrac{L_b S_c}{I_y} = 80$	$8.0 - 0.056\sqrt{\dfrac{L_b S_c}{I_y}}$	$\dfrac{L_b S_c}{I_y} = 3{,}940$	$\dfrac{17{,}700}{L_b S_c/I_y}$
COMPRESSION in Members Subjected to Bending, Gross Section	A-15b	Flat plates with one edge free and one edge supported	7.5	$b/t = 8.3$	$9.1 - 0.194\,b/t$	$b/t = 21$	$\dfrac{2{,}240}{(b/t)^2}$
	A-16b	Flat plates with both edges supported (Also see Specs. A-11b to A-14b)	7.5	$b/t = 23$	$9.1 - 0.070\,b/t$	$b/t = 58$	$\dfrac{17{,}000}{(b/t)^2}$
	A-17b	Flat plates with compression edge free and tension edge supported, bent about X-axis	11.5	$b/t = 7.0$	$13.8 - 0.33\,b/t$	$b/t = 28$	$\dfrac{3{,}700}{(b/t)^2}$
	A-18b	Flat plates with both edges supported, bent about X-axis (Also see Specs. A-11b to A-14b)	7.5	- - -	7.5	$h/t = 165$	$\dfrac{205{,}000}{(h/t)^2}$
SHEAR in webs of beams, and also in members subjected to torsion, gross section	A-19b	Unstiffened flat webs	5	$h/t = 13$	$5.3 - 0.024\,h/t$	$h/t = 100$	$\dfrac{29{,}000}{(h/t)^2}$

(a) This value applies for a ratio of edge distance to rivet or bolt diameter of 2 or more. For smaller ratios, multiply this allowable stress by the ratio, (edge distance)/(twice the rivet or bolt diameter).

TABLE 6b.—ALLOWABLE STRESSES ON SECTIONS WITHIN 1.0 INCH OF A WELD (6063-T5 BRIDGE STRUCTURES WELDED)

Type of Stress	Specification No.	Type of Member or Component		Allowable Stress, ksi
TENSION, axial, net section	I-1b	Any tension member		8
TENSION in extreme fibers of beams, net section	I-2b	Structural shapes, rectangular tubes, built-up members bent about X-axis		8
	I-3b	Round or oval tubes		8.5
	I-4b	Rectangular bars and plates, and outstanding flanges of shapes bent about Y-axis		8.5
BEARING	I-5b	On rivets and bolts		9(b)
	I-6b	On milled surfaces and pins		8

Type of Stress	Spec. No.	Type of Member or Component		Allowable Stress for Slenderness Less Than S_1, ksi	Slenderness Limit, S_1	Allowable Stress for Slenderness Between S_1 and S_2, ksi	Slenderness Limit, S_2	Allowable Stress for Slenderness Greater Than S_2, ksi
COMPRESSION in Columns Subjected to Axial Load Gross Section — COMPRESSION, gross section (Also see Specs. I-8b to I-10b)	I-7b	Columns (a)		8	$L/r = 57$	$8.0 - 0.035\,L/r$	$L/r = 100$	$\dfrac{45{,}000}{(L/r)^2}$
COMPRESSION in components of columns (Also see Spec. I-7b)	I-8b	Outstanding flanges and legs		8	$b/t = 4.1$	$\dfrac{12.1}{\sqrt{b/t}}$	$b/t = 27$	$\dfrac{1{,}720}{(b/t)^2}$
	I-9b	Flat plates with both edges supported		8	$b/t = 44$	$9.1 - 0.070\,b/t$	$b/t = 58$	$\dfrac{17{,}000}{(b/t)^2}$
	I-10b	Curved plates supported on both edges and walls of round or oval tubes		8	$R/t = 10$	$\dfrac{10.7}{(R/t)^{1/4}}$	$R/t = 125$	- - - -

	Description					
I-11b	Single-web structural shapes and built-up sections bent about X-axis(a)	8	$L_b/r_y = 89$	$8.0 - 0.029\, L_b/r_y$	$L_b/r_y = 120$	$\dfrac{85,000}{(L_b/r_y)^2}$
I-12b	Round or oval tubes	8.5	$R_b/t = 13$	$\dfrac{12.3}{(R_b/t)^{1/4}}$	$R_b/t = 125$	- - -
I-13b	Solid rectangular beams bent about X-axis (Also see Specs. I-15b to I-18b)	8.5	$\dfrac{d}{t}\sqrt{\dfrac{L_b}{d}} = 11$	$\dfrac{21.6}{[(d/t)^2 L_b/d]^{1/4}}$	$\dfrac{d}{t}\sqrt{\dfrac{L_b}{d}} = 55$	$\dfrac{8,800}{(d/t)^2 L_b/d}$
I-14b	Rectangular tubes and box sections(a)	8	$\dfrac{L_b S_c}{I_y} = 1280$	$8.0 - 0.056\sqrt{\dfrac{L_b S_c}{I_y}}$	$\dfrac{L_b S_c}{I_y} = 3940$	$\dfrac{17,700}{L_b S_c/I_y}$
I-15b	Flat plates with one edge free and one edge supported	8	$b/t = 4.4$	$\dfrac{12.6}{\sqrt{b/t}}$	$b/t = 32$	$\dfrac{2,240}{(b/t)^2}$
I-16b	Flat plates with both edges supported (Also see Specs. I-11b to I-14b)	6	$b/t = 44$	$9.1 - 0.070\, b/t$	$b/t = 58$	$\dfrac{17,000}{(b/t)^2}$
I-17b	Flat plates with compression edge free and tension edge supported, bent about X-axis	6.5	$b/t = 7.2$	$\dfrac{17.4}{\sqrt{b/t}}$	$b/t = 35$	$\dfrac{3,700}{(b/t)^2}$
I-18b	Flat plates with both edges supported, bent about X-axis (Also see Specs. I-11b to I-14b)	8	- - - -	8	$h/t = 185$	$\dfrac{205,000}{(h/t)^2}$
I-19b	Unstiffened flat webs	3.5	$h/t = 75$	$5.3 - 0.024\, h/t$	$h/t = 100$	$\dfrac{29,000}{(h/t)^2}$

Row categories (left margin):

COMPRESSION in extreme fibers of beams, gross section (Also see Specs. I-15b to I-18b) — applies to I-11b through I-14b.

COMPRESSION in Members Subjected to Bending, Gross Section — COMPRESSION in components of beams, where component is under uniform compression (Also see Specs. I-11b to I-14b) — I-15b, I-16b. COMPRESSION in components of beams where component is under bending in its own plane, (Also see Specs. I-11b to I-14b) — I-17b, I-18b.

SHEAR in webs of beams, and also in members subjected to torsion, gross section — I-19b.

(a) The allowable stresses for columns, single web beams and rectangular tubes and box sections apply to members supported at both ends and welded at the ends only. See Specification I-26 for allowable stresses in these members with welds at locations other than the ends and in cantilever columns and beams.

(b) This value applies for a ratio of edge distance to rivet or bolt diameter of 2 or more. For smaller ratios, multiply this allowable stress by the ratio, (edge distance)/(twice the rivet or bolt diameter)

TABLE 5b.—ALLOWABLE STRESSES IN RIVETS AND BOLTS
(BRIDGE STRUCTURES OF 6063-T5)

Specification Number	Description of Rivet or Bolt	Allowable Stress, ksi	
		Shear on effective shear area	Tension on root area
A-20b	6053-T61 rivets, cold driven	7.5	--
A-21b	6061-T43 rivets, driven at temperatures of from 990°F to 1050°F	8	--
A-22b	2024-T4 bolts	14[a]	23

[a] This allowable shear stress applies to either turned bolts in reamed holes or unfinished bolts in 1/16-in. oversize holes.

TABLE 7b.—ALLOWABLE SHEAR STRESSES IN FILLET WELDS
(BRIDGE STRUCTURES OF 6063-T5)

Specification Number	Filler Alloy	Allowable Shear Stress,[a] ksi	
		Transverse shear in single fillet welds or longitudinal shear[b]	Transverse shear in double fillet welds[b]
I-20b	5356 5556	6[c]	6[c]
I-21b	4043	4.5	6[c]

[a] Shear stress is considered to be equal to the load divided by the throat area, regardless of the direction of loading.

[b] Single fillet welds in transverse shear may be treated as double fillet welds in joints so designed as to prevent local bending of the parts adjacent to the fillet weld.

[c] These values are controlled by the shear strength of the parent material; all other values are controlled by the strength of the filler metal.

6063-T6

BUILDING STRUCTURES

TABLE 4c.—ALLOWABLE STRESSES IN RIVETED OR BOLTED STRUCTURES OR IN WELDED STRUCTURES AT LOCATIONS FARTHER THAN 1.0 INCH FROM ANY WELD (6063-T6 BUILDING STRUCTURES NONWELDED)

Type of Stress	Specification No.	Type of Member or Component	Allowable Stress, ksi	Allowable Stress for Slenderness Less Than S_1 ksi	Slenderness Limit, S_1	Allowable Stress for Slenderness Between S_1 and S_2 ksi	Slenderness Limit, S_2	Allowable Stress for Slenderness Greater Than S_2, ksi
TENSION, axial, net section	A-1c	Any tension member	15					
TENSION in extreme fibers of beams, net section	A-2c	Structural shapes, rectangular tubes, built-up members bent about X-axis	15					
	A-3c	Round or oval tubes	17					
	A-4c	Rectangular bars and plates, and outstanding flanges of shapes bent about Y-axis	19					
BEARING	A-5c	On rivets and bolts	24[e]					
	A-6c	On milled surfaces and pins	18					
COMPRESSION in Columns Subjected to Axial Load, Gross Section. COMPRESSION, gross section (Also see Specs. A-8c to A-10c)	A-7c	Columns		13.5	$L/r = 11$	$14.4 - 0.080\,L/r$	$L/r = 80$	$\dfrac{51{,}000}{(L/r)^2}$
COMPRESSION in components of Columns (Also see Spec. A-7c)	A-8c	Outstanding flanges and legs		13.5	$b/t = 6.0$	$16.5 - 0.50\,b/t$	$b/t = 15$	$\dfrac{1{,}940}{(b/t)^2}$
	A-9c	Flat plates with both edges supported		13.5	$b/t = 19$	$16.5 - 0.160\,b/t$	$b/t = 46$	$\dfrac{19{,}200}{(b/t)^2}$
	A-10c	Curved plates supported on both edges and walls of round or oval tubes		13.5	$R/t = 16$	$15.4 - 0.47\sqrt{R/t}$	$R/t = 140$	- - - -

COMPRESSION in extreme fibers of beams, gross section (Also see Specs. A-15c to A-18c)	A-11c	Single-web structural shapes and built-up sections bent about X-axis	13.5	$L_b/r_y = 14$; $\;14.4 - 0.066\,L_b/r_y$	$L_b/r_y = 96$	$\dfrac{74{,}000}{(L_b/r_y)^2}$
	A-12c	Round or oval tubes	17	$R_b/t = 16$; $\;18.0 - 0.064\,R_b/t$	$R_b/t = 120$	$-\;-\;-$
	A-13c	Solid rectangular beams bent about X-axis	19	$\dfrac{d}{t}\sqrt{\dfrac{L_b}{d}} = 12$; $\;24.8 - 0.48\,\dfrac{d}{t}\sqrt{\dfrac{L_b}{d}}$	$\dfrac{d}{t}\sqrt{\dfrac{L_b}{d}} = 33$	$\dfrac{9{,}900}{(d/t)^2\,L_b/d}$
	A-14c	Rectangular tubes and box sections	13.5	$\dfrac{L_b S_c}{I_y} = 49$; $\;14.4 - 0.123\,\dfrac{L_b S_c}{I_y}$	$\dfrac{L_b S_c}{I_y} = 2{,}510$	$\dfrac{20{,}000}{L_b S_c/I_y}$
COMPRESSION in Members Subjected to Bending, Gross Section — COMPRESSION in components of beams, where component is under uniform compression (Also see Specs. A-11c to A-14c)	A-15c	Flat plates with one edge free and one edge supported	13.5	$b/t = 6.8$; $\;16.5 - 0.44\,b/t$	$b/t = 16$	$\dfrac{2{,}500}{(b/t)^2}$
	A-16c	Flat plates with both edges supported	13.5	$b/t = 19$; $\;16.5 - 0.160\,b/t$	$b/t = 46$	$\dfrac{19{,}200}{(b/t)^2}$
COMPRESSION in components of beams where component is under bending in its own plane, (Also see Specs. A-11c to A-14c)	A-17c	Flat plates with compression edge free and tension edge supported, bent about X-axis	19	$b/t = 7.6$; $\;24.8 - 0.74\,b/t$	$b/t = 22$	$\dfrac{4{,}200}{(b/t)^2}$
	A-18c	Flat plates with both edges supported, bent about X-axis	13.5	$-\;-\;-$; $\;13.5$	$h/t = 130$	$\dfrac{230{,}000}{(h/t)^2}$
SHEAR in webs of beams, and also in members subjected to torsion, gross section	A-19c	Unstiffened flat webs	8.5	$h/t = 19$; $\;9.5 - 0.054\,h/t$	$h/t = 79$	$\dfrac{33{,}000}{(h/t)^2}$

(a) This value applies for a ratio of edge distance to rivet or bolt diameter of 2 or more. For smaller ratios, multiply this allowable stress by the ratio, (edge distance)/(twice the rivet or bolt diameter).

TABLE 6c.—ALLOWABLE STRESSES ON SECTIONS WITHIN 1.0 INCH OF A WELD (6063–T6 BUILDING STRUCTURES WELDED)

Type of Stress	Specification No.	Type of Member or Component	Allowable Stress, ksi
TENSION, axial, net section	I-1c	Any tension member	6.5
TENSION in extreme fibers of beams, net section	I-2c	Structural shapes, rectangular tubes, built-up members bent about X-axis	6.5
	I-3c	Round or oval tubes	7.5
	I-4c	Rectangular bars and plates, and outstanding flanges of shapes bent about Y-axis	7.5
BEARING	I-5c	On rivets and bolts	10(b)
	I-6c	On milled surfaces and pins	7

Type of Stress	Specification No.	Type of Member or Component	Allowable Stress for Slenderness Less Than S_1, ksi	Slenderness Limit, S_1	Allowable Stress for Slenderness Between S_1 and S_2, ksi	Slenderness Limit, S_2	Allowable Stress for Slenderness Greater Than S_2, ksi
COMPRESSION in Columns Subjected to Axial Load Gross Section — COMPRESSION, gross section (Also see Specs. I-8c to I-10c)	I-7c	Columns(a)	6.5	– – – –	6.5	$L/r = 88$	$\dfrac{51,000}{(L/r)^2}$
COMPRESSION in components of columns (Also see Spec. I-7c)	I-8c	Outstanding flanges and legs	6.5	$b/t = 4.4$	$\dfrac{13.6}{\sqrt{b/t}}$	$b/t = 27$	$\dfrac{1,940}{(b/t)^2}$
	I-9c	Flat plates with both edges supported	6.5	– – – –	6.5	$b/t = 54$	$\dfrac{19,200}{(b/t)^2}$
	I-10c	Curved plates supported on both edges and walls of round or oval tubes	6.5	$R/t = 12$	$\dfrac{12.0}{(R/t)^{1/4}}$	$R/t = 125$	– – – –

Category	Spec	Member	Value	Ratio condition	Formula	Limit ratio	Formula
COMPRESSION in Members Subjected to Bending, Gross Section — COMPRESSION in extreme fibers of beams, gross section (Also see Specs. I-15c to I-18c)	I-11c	Single-web structural shapes and built-up sections bent about X-axis(a)	6.5	- - - -	6.5	$L_b/r_y = 107$	$\dfrac{74,000}{(L_b/r_y)^2}$
	I-12c	Round or oval tubes	7.5	$R_b/t = 12$	$\dfrac{13.9}{(R_b/t)^{1/4}}$	$R_b/t = 125$	- - - -
	I-13c	Solid rectangular beams bent about X-axis	7.5	$\dfrac{d}{t}\sqrt{\dfrac{L_b}{d}} = 11$	$\dfrac{24.3}{[(d/t)^2 L_b/d]^{1/4}}$; 6.5	$\dfrac{d}{t}\sqrt{\dfrac{L_b}{d}} = 55$; $\dfrac{L_b S_c}{I_y} = 3080$	$\dfrac{9,900}{(d/t)^2 L_b/d}$; $\dfrac{20,000}{L_b S_c/I_y}$
	I-14c	Rectangular tubes and box sections(a)	6.5	- - - -	6.5		
COMPRESSION in components of beams where component is under uniform compression (Also see Specs. I-11c to I-14c)	I-15c	Flat plates with one edge free and one edge supported	6.5	$b/t = 4.8$	$\dfrac{14.2}{\sqrt{b/t}}$	$b/t = 31$	$\dfrac{2,500}{(b/t)^2}$
	I-16c	Flat plates with both edges supported	6.5	- - - -	6.5	$b/t = 54$	$\dfrac{19,200}{(b/t)^2}$
COMPRESSION in components of beams where component is under bending in its own plane. (Also see Specs. I-11c to I-14c)	I-17c	Flat plates with compression edge free and tension edge supported, bent about X-axis	7.5	$b/t = 8.9$	$\dfrac{19.6}{\sqrt{b/t}}$	$b/t = 36$	$\dfrac{4,200}{(b/t)^2}$
	I-18c	Flat plates with both edges supported, bent about X-axis	6.5	- - - -	6.5	$h/t = 188$	$\dfrac{230,000}{(h/t)^2}$
SHEAR in webs of beams, and also in members subjected to torsion, gross section	I-19c	Unstiffened flat webs	4	- - - -	4	$h/t = 91$	$\dfrac{33,000}{(h/t)^2}$

(a) The allowable stresses for columns, single web beams and rectangular tubes and box sections apply to members supported at both ends and welded at the ends only. See Specification I-26 for allowable stresses in these members with welds at locations other than the ends and in cantilever columns and beams.

(b) This value applies for a ratio of edge distance to rivet or bolt diameter of 2 or more. For smaller ratios, multiply this allowable stress by the ratio, (edge distance)/(twice the rivet or bolt diameter).

TABLE 5c.—ALLOWABLE SHEAR STRESSES IN RIVETS AND BOLTS
(BUILDING STRUCTURES OF 6063-T6)

Specification Number	Description of Rivet or Bolt	Allowable Stress, ksi	
		Shear on effective shear area	Tension on root area
A-20c	6053-T61 rivets, cold driven	8.5	--
A-21c	6061-T43 rivets, driven at temperatures of from 990°F to 1050°F	9	--
A-22c	2024-T4 bolts	16[a]	26

[a] This allowable shear stress applies to either turned bolts in reamed holes or unfinished bolts in 1/16-in. oversize holes.

TABLE 7c.—ALLOWABLE SHEAR STRESSES IN FILLET WELDS
(BUILDING STRUCTURES OF 6063-T6)

Specification Number	Filler Alloy	Allowable Shear Stress,[a] ksi	
		Transverse shear in single fillet welds or longitudinal shear[b]	Transverse shear in double fillet welds[b]
I-20c	5356 5556	6.5[c]	6.5[c]
I-21c	4043	5	6.5[c]

[a] Shear stress is considered to be equal to the load divided by the throat area, regardless of the direction of loading.

[b] Single fillet welds in transverse shear may be treated as double fillet welds in joints so designed as to prevent local bending of the parts adjacent to the fillet weld.

[c] These values are controlled by the shear strength of the parent material; all other values are controlled by the strength of the filler metal.

6063-T5

BUILDING STRUCTURES

TABLE 4d.—ALLOWABLE STRESSES IN RIVETED OR BOLTED STRUCTURES OR IN WELDED STRUCTURES AT LOCATIONS FARTHER THAN 1.0 INCH FROM ANY WELD (6063-T5 BUILDING STRUCTURES NONWELDED)

Type of Stress	Specification No.	Type of Member or Component	Allowable Stress, ksi		Allowable Stress for Slenderness Less Than S_1, ksi	Slenderness Limit, S_1	Allowable Stress for Slenderness Between S_1 and S_2, ksi	Slenderness Limit, S_2	Allowable Stress for Slenderness Greater Than S_2, ksi
TENSION, axial, net section	A-1d	Any tension member	9.5						
TENSION in extreme fibers of beams, net section	A-2d	Structural shapes, rectangular tubes, built-up members bent about X-axis	9.5						
	A-3d	Round or oval tubes	11						
	A-4d	Rectangular bars and plates, and outstanding flanges of shapes bent about Y-axis	13.5						
BEARING	A-5d	On rivets and bolts	15(a)						
	A-6d	On milled surfaces and pins	10						
COMPRESSION in Columns Subjected to Axial Load, Gross Section	A-7d	Columns (COMPRESSION, gross section) (Also see Specs. A-8d to A-10d)			8.5	$L/r = 13$	$9.0 - 0.039\, L/r$	$L/r = 100$	$\dfrac{51{,}000}{(L/r)^2}$
	A-8d	Outstanding flanges and legs (COMPRESSION in components of columns (Also see Spec. A-7d))			8.5	$b/t = 6.8$	$10.2 - 0.25\, b/t$	$b/t = 19$	$\dfrac{1{,}940}{(b/t)^2}$
	A-9d	Flat plates with both edges supported			8.5	$b/t = 22$	$10.2 - 0.079\, b/t$	$b/t = 58$	$\dfrac{19{,}200}{(b/t)^2}$
	A-10d	Curved plates supported on both edges and walls of round or oval tubes			8.5	$R/t = 12$	$9.2 - 0.198\,\sqrt{R/t}$	$R/t = 200$	- - - -

Spec.		Description	(diagram)	Allowable	Lower limit	Formula	Upper limit	Above upper limit
A-11d	COMPRESSION in extreme fibers of beams gross section (Also see Specs. A-15d to A-18d)	Single-web structural shapes and built-up sections bent about X-axis		8.5	$L_b/r_y = 16$	$9.0 - 0.032\,L_b/r_y$	$L_b/r_y = 120$	$\dfrac{74{,}000}{(L_b/r_y)^2}$
A-12d		Round or oval tubes		11	$R_b/t = 9.4$	$11.3 - 0.032\,R_b/t$	$R_b/t = 140$	- - -
A-13d		Solid rectangular beams bent about X-axis		13.5	$\dfrac{d}{t}\sqrt{\dfrac{L_b}{d}} = 8.8$ $\dfrac{L_bS_c}{I_y} = 65$	$15.6 - 0.24\,\dfrac{d}{t}\sqrt{\dfrac{L_b}{d}}$ $\sqrt{\dfrac{L_bS_c}{I_y}}$	$\dfrac{d}{t}\sqrt{\dfrac{L_b}{d}} = 44$ $\dfrac{L_bS_c}{I_y} = 3920$	$\dfrac{9{,}900}{(d/t)^2 L_b/d}$ $\dfrac{20{,}000}{L_bS_c/I_y}$
A-14d		Rectangular tubes and box sections		8.5	$\dfrac{L_bS_c}{I_y} = 65$	$9.0 - 0.062\,\dfrac{L_bS_c}{I_y}$	$\dfrac{L_bS_c}{I_y} = 3920$	$\dfrac{20{,}000}{L_bS_c/I_y}$
A-15d	COMPRESSION in Members Subjected to Bending, Gross Section — COMPRESSION components of beams, where component is under uniform compression (Also see Specs. A-11d to A-14d)	Flat plates with one edge free and one edge supported		8.5	$b/t = 7.7$	$10.2 - 0.22\,b/t$	$b/t = 22$	$\dfrac{2{,}500}{(b/t)^2}$
A-16d		Flat plates with both edges supported		8.5	$b/t = 22$	$10.2 - 0.079\,b/t$	$b/t = 58$	$\dfrac{19{,}200}{(b/t)^2}$
A-17d	COMPRESSION components of beams where component is under bending in its own plane, (Also see Specs. A-11d to A-14d)	Flat plates with compression edge free and tension edge supported, bent about X-axis		13.5	$b/t = 5.7$	$15.6 - 0.37\,b/t$	$b/t = 28$	$\dfrac{4{,}200}{(b/t)^2}$
A-18d		Flat plates with both edges supported, bent about X-axis		8.5	- - - -	8.5	$h/t = 184$	$\dfrac{230{,}000}{(h/t)^2}$
A-19d	SHEAR in webs of beams, and also in members subjected to torsion, gross section	Unstiffened flat webs		5.5	$h/t = 15$	$5.9 - 0.027\,h/t$	$h/t = 103$	$\dfrac{33{,}000}{(h/t)^2}$

(8) This value applies for a ratio of edge distance to rivet or bolt diameter of 2 or more. For smaller ratios, multiply this allowable stress by the ratio, (edge distance)/(twice the rivet or bolt diameter)

TABLE 3D

TABLE 6d.—ALLOWABLE STRESSES ON SECTIONS WITHIN 1.0 INCH OF A WELD (6063-T5 BUILDING STRUCTURES WELDED)

Type of Stress	Specification No.	Type of Member or Component	Allowable Stress, ksi	Allowable Stress for Slenderness Less Than S_1, ksi	Slenderness Limit, S_1	Allowable Stress for Slenderness Between S_1 and S_2, ksi	Slenderness Limit, S_2	Allowable Stress for Slenderness Greater Than S_2, ksi
TENSION, axial, net section	I-1d	Any tension member	8.5					
	I-2d	Structural shapes, rectangular tubes, built-up members bent about X-axis	8.5					
TENSION in extreme fibers of beams, net section	I-3d	Round or oval tubes	7.5					
	I-4d	Rectangular bars and plates, and outstanding flanges of shapes bent about Y-axis	7.5					
BEARING	I-5d	On rivets and bolts	10(b)					
	I-6d	On milled surfaces and pins	7					
COMPRESSION in Columns Subjected to Axial Load, Gross Section — COMPRESSION in gross section (Also see Specs. I-8d to I-10d)	I-7d	Columns(a)		8.5	$L/r = 64$	$9.0 - 0.039\,L/r$	$L/r = 100$	$\dfrac{51{,}000}{(L/r)^2}$
COMPRESSION in components of columns (Also see Spec. I-7d)	I-8d	Outstanding flanges and legs		8.5	$b/t = 4.4$	$\dfrac{13.6}{\sqrt{b/t}}$	$b/t = 27$	$\dfrac{1{,}940}{(b/t)^2}$
	I-9d	Flat plates with both edges supported		8.5	$b/t = 47$	$10.2 - 0.079\,b/t$	$b/t = 58$	$\dfrac{19{,}200}{(b/t)^2}$
	I-10d	Curved plates supported on both edges and walls of round or oval tubes		8.5	$R/t = 12$	$\dfrac{12.0}{(R/t)^{1/4}}$	$R/t = 125$	– – – –

COMPRESSION(a) in extreme fibers of beams, gross section (Also see Specs I-15d to I-18d)	I-11d	Single-web structural shapes and built-up sections bent about X-axis(a)		6.5	$L_b/r_y = 78$	$9.0 - 0.032\, L_b/r_y$	$L_b/r_y = 120$	$\dfrac{74,000}{(L_b/r_y)^2}$
	I-12d	Round or oval tubes		7.5	$R_b/t = 12$	$\dfrac{13.9}{(R_b/t)^{1/4}}$	$R_b/t = 125$	- - - -
	I-13d	Solid rectangular beams bent about X-axis		7.5	$\dfrac{d}{t}\sqrt{\dfrac{L_b}{d}} = 11$	$\dfrac{24.3}{[(d/t)^2 L_b/d]^{1/4}}$	$\dfrac{d}{t}\sqrt{\dfrac{L_b}{d}} = 55$	$\dfrac{9,900}{(d/t)^2 L_b/d}$
	I-14d	Rectangular tubes and box sections(a)		6.5	$\dfrac{L_b S_c}{I_y} = 1620$	$9.0 - 0.062\sqrt{\dfrac{L_b S_c}{I_y}}$	$\dfrac{L_b S_c}{I_y} = 3920$	$\dfrac{20,000}{L_b S_c/I_y}$
COMPRESSION in Members Subjected to Bending, Gross Section, components of beams, where component is under uniform compression (Also see Specs. I-11d to I-14d)	I-15d	Flat plates with one edge free and one edge supported		6.5	$b/t = 4.8$	$\dfrac{14.2}{\sqrt{b/t}}$	$b/t = 31$	$\dfrac{2,500}{(b/t)^2}$
	I-16d	Flat plates with both edges supported		6.5	$b/t = 47$	$10.2 - 0.079\, b/t$	$b/t = 58$	$\dfrac{19,200}{(b/t)^2}$
COMPRESSION in components of beams where component is under bending in its own plane, (Also see Specs. I-11d to I-14d)	I-17d	Flat plates with compression edge free and tension edge supported, bent about X-axis	Compression Flange	7.5	$b/t = 6.9$	$\dfrac{19.6}{\sqrt{b/t}}$	$b/t = 36$	$\dfrac{4,200}{(b/t)^2}$
	I-18d	Flat plates with both edges supported, bent about X-axis		6.5	- - - -	6.5	$h/t = 188$	$\dfrac{230,000}{(h/t)^2}$
SHEAR in webs of beams, and also in members subjected to torsion, gross section	I-19d	Unstiffened flat webs		4	$h/t = 70$	$5.9 - 0.027\, h/t$	$h/t = 103$	$\dfrac{33,000}{(h/t)^2}$

(a) The allowable stresses for columns, single web beams and rectangular tubes and box sections apply to members supported at both ends and welded at the ends only. See Specification I-26 for allowable stresses in these members with welds at locations other than the ends and in cantilever columns and beams.

(b) This value applies for a ratio of edge distance to rivet or bolt diameter of 2 or greater. For smaller ratios, multiply this allowable stress by the ratio, (edge distance)/(twice the rivet or bolt diameter).

TABLE 5d.—ALLOWABLE SHEAR STRESSES IN RIVETS AND BOLTS
(BUILDING STRUCTURES OF 6063-T5)

Specification Number	Description of Rivet or Bolt	Allowable Stress, ksi	
		Shear on effective shear area	Tension on root area
A-20d	6053-T61 rivets, cold driven	8.5	--
A-21d	6061-T43 rivets, driven at temperatures of from 990° F to 1050° F	9	--
A-22d	2024-T4 bolts	16[a]	26

[a] This allowable shear stress applies to either turned bolts in reamed holes or unfinished bolts in 1/16-in. oversize holes.

TABLE 7d.—ALLOWABLE SHEAR STRESSES IN FILLET WELDS
(BUILDING STRUCTURES OF 6063-T5)

Specification Number	Filler Alloy	Allowable Shear Stress,[a] ksi	
		Transverse shear in single fillet welds or longitudinal shear[b]	Transverse shear in double fillet welds[b]
I-20d	5356 5556	6.5[c]	6.5[c]
I-21d	4043	5	6.5[c]

[a] Shear stress is considered to be equal to the load divided by the throat area, regardless of the direction of loading.

[b] Single fillet welds in transverse shear may be treated as double fillet welds in joints so designed as to prevent local bending of the parts adjacent to the fillet weld.

[c] These values are controlled by the shear strength of the parent material; all other values are controlled by the strength of the filler metal.

Alcoa Products and Services

INGOTS

Aluminizing Ingot

Deoxidizing Ingot
  D-OX-IT Shot
  Granulated
  Notch-Bar

Fabricating Ingot
  Extrusion
  Forging
  Sheet
  Wire Bar

Remelt Ingot
  Casting Alloy
  Electrical
    Conductor
    and Rotor Alloy
  Rich Alloy
  Unalloyed

WIRE, ROD AND BAR

Alcoa produces the most complete line of aluminum wire, rod, bar and rolled structurals.
Bar—square, rectangular, hexagonal, cold-finished, special-shaped
Rod—brazing, redraw, cold-finished, special
Screw Machine Stock—round, hexagonal, hollow
Mechanical Tube
Forging Stock—round, square, rectangular
Wire—round, flat, all forms and sizes

SHEET AND PLATE

Sheet available in all lengths, widths and tempers available in commercial alloys. Sheet available in coils, flat, circles, shapes, rings, blanks and tapered sheet.

Plate available in circles, rings, special shapes, rolling slabs and tapered plate.

Special sheet products include:
  Anoclad® Sheet
  Alumilite* Sheet
  Boral Sheet (for atomic applications)
  Brazing Sheet
  Closure Sheet
  Corrugated Sheet
  Duranel® Sheet (stainless-clad aluminum for cooking utensils)
  Fin Stock
  Industrial and Rural Roofing and Siding
  Key Stock
  Lighting Sheet (specular and diffuse finishes)
  Litho Sheet
  Mobile Home Sheet
  Patterned Sheet

* Trade Name of Aluminum Company of America

SHEET AND PLATE—Continued

Painted Sheet (coiled, flat and corrugated)
Porcelain-Enameling Sheet
Recording Sheet Circles
Reflector Sheet
Rigid Container Sheet
Trailer Roof and Panel Sheet
Vinyl-Laminated Sheet (both polyvinyl chloride and polyvinyl fluoride films available)
Patterned and
  Abrasive Armor
  Plate
Reflector Plate
Tooling Plate
Tread Plate

Plate includes;
  Anoclad Plate
  Boral Plate
  (for atomic
  applications)
  Bearing Plate

Modern rolling facilities throughout the country for fast delivery.

ELECTRICAL PRODUCTS

Aerial Cable
Aluminum Bus Bar
  and Conductor
Aluminum Cable—
  Steel Reinforced
  (ACSR)
Armor Wire
Borehole Cable
Building Wire and
  Cable
Cable: Aluminum
  and Copper
Cable: High and
  Low Voltage
CATV Cable
Coaxial Cable
Conduit: Aluminum
  and Steel
Control and Signal
  Cable
Dredger Cable
Duct Cable
Elevator Cable
Grounding Cable
Hook-up Wire
Instrumentation
  Cable
Lead-Covered Cable
Lighting Cable
Locomotive Cable
Mining Machine
  Cable

Missile Cable
Nonmetallic Sheathed
  Cable
Portable Cord and
  Cable
Preassembled Pipe
  Cable
Service Entrance
  Cable
Shot-Firing
  Cord
Shovel Cable
Switchboard Wire
Telemetering Cable
Tie Wire
Transmission and
  Distribution
  Accessories
Tree Wire
Trimline Primary Distribution System
Twin-Reel Shuttle-
  Car Cable
Underground Cable
Underground Residential Distribution
  Cable (URD)
Weatherproof Wire
  and Cable
Welding Cable

CASTINGS

Die
Permanent-Mold
(including
magnesium)
Sand
Semipermanent-Mold
Plaster
Premium-Engineered

Dependable quality and service from the most modern and complete facilities backed by engineering and research.

PASTE, POWDER AND PIGMENT PRODUCTS

Albron® Products   Atomized Powders
Paste and Flake   Pigments
   Powder   Pastes

FORGINGS

Die: Hammer, Press   Hand
Upset   Rolled Rings

Largest sizes available. All-aluminum, magnesium and titanium alloys. Specification quality. Commercial forgings. Prompt quotations and delivery. Plants at Cleveland, Ohio and Vernon, Calif. Also special Alcoa products such as forged disc wheels, forged manhole steps and other forged products.

IMPACT EXTRUSIONS

The Alcoa Impact process basically combines forging and extrusion in a single operation to produce Alcoa Impacts in alloys ranging from strain-hardened to the highest strength heat-treatable alloys. Currently, the approximate size limits are 12 in. in diameter and 60 in. in length.

Alcoa Impact Extrusions
—offer the most efficient use of metallurgically sound metal.

—are generally produced in one operation on high-speed press equipment.

—save machining costs since they have no draft; have close tolerances; and have efficient distribution of metal, very often eliminating a number of machining operations as well as saving metal.

*Trade Name of Aluminum Company of America

IMPACT EXTRUSIONS — Continued

—tool costs are generally lower than those for comparable processes.

—often eliminate assembly operations by combining several parts into a single piece, offering the engineer designs unique in wrought materials.

—reduce finishing costs because of their exceptionally smooth surface and absence of parting line.

EXTRUSIONS

Quality extrusions from Alcoa-developed alloys. Largest extrusions commercially available for special products. Wide variety of standard extrusions available including:

Angles   I-Beams
Rods   Tees
Bars   Zees
Channels   Special Shapes
H-Beams

Structural shapes are extruded. Special extrusions for all industries and all design purposes.

TUBULAR PRODUCTS
(Extruded or Drawn)

Irrigation Tube   Duotrace® Pipe
Drill Pipe   Unitrace® Pipe
Oval Tube   Unistrength* Pipe
Square Tube   Construction Tube
Rectangular Tube   Mechanical Tube
Streamlined Tube   Hollow Screw
Wave-Guide Tube   Machine Stock
Extruded Tube   Coiled Utilitube®
Drawn Tube   Tube
Welded Tube   Lighting Standard
Coiled Seamless   Tube
  Tube   Heat Exchanger
Pipe, Structural   Tube
  (conduit) and   Hydraulic Tube
  Seamless

FASTENERS AND
SCREW MACHINE PRODUCTS

All types and sizes of standard and special fasteners including:

FASTENERS AND SCREW
MACHINE PRODUCTS — Continued

Bolts

| Cap-Head | Economy | Heavy-Series |
| Carriage | Hex | Bearing |

Cotter Pins

Nuts

Cap	Wing	Aircraft, castle
Hex	Aircraft,	Aircraft, shear
Square	plain	"Compression"
	Jam	

Screws

Machine	Cap
Wood	Flattened Thumb
Sheet Metal	Knurled Thumb
Special	Hexagonal Socket

Nails

| Plain | Painted |

Rivets

Solid	Semitubular
Solid-Shoulder	Semitubular
Cutlery	Shoulder

Washers

| Plain | Lock | Finishing |

Binding Posts and Screws

Special Fasteners for Every Industry

Available in bright, Alumilite* or painted finishes. Made from strong Alcoa-developed alloys. Standard or special threads, rigid inspection. All types of screw machine and cold-headed products.

PACKAGING
AND FOIL

Foil:

Alcoa Wrap —	Insulations Liner
Household	Stock
Capacitor	Lacquered
Cigarette	Laminated
Christmas Tree	Lithographic
Colored	Nameplate
Container	Pie Plate
Converted	Plain
Dairy Closure	Printed
Embossed	Textured
Freezer	

* Trade Name of Aluminum Company of America

Closures:

Drum and Dust	Screw Caps
Cover Caps	Special Closures
Flavor-Lok® RO®	Standard RO
Goldy®	Stericaps
Hidden-Thread	TopSide RO®
Pilferproof RO	Weighing Dishes

Aluminum
Containers

Formed Containers	Rigid Container
Rigid Container	Impacts
Sheet	Collapsible Tube
Rigid Container	Slugs
Slugs	Beer Barrels
	Drums

Machines, Sealing (closures) — Sales and Rentals

Machines, Foil-Laminating — Sales and Rentals

Alcoa Foil service includes a complete package design assistance using plain, embossed, textured, laminated and lacquered and printed foil.

CHEMICAL
PRODUCTS

Alflake® (chemical reactant)
Aluminum Fluoride Fluo-Flux®
Aluminas
    Activated
    Calcined
    Calcined Low-Soda
    Catalytic
    Chromatographic
    Hydrated
    Pigment-Grade Trihydrated Hydral®
    Tabular (crushed and graded)
    Tabular (balls)

Gallium

Calcium Aluminate Cement
Calcined Dust
Quick Lime

Aluminas for abrasives, ceramic and refractory purposes. Activated aluminas for desiccant and catalytic applications. Hydrated aluminas for subsequent processing.

Alcoa Products and Services — Continued

BUILDING INDUSTRY PRODUCTS

Alply® Panels
Alshade* Sunscreen
Alumalure® Sheet
Coping
Foil for Insulation
Formed Siding (Insulated and Noninsulated)
Industrial Siding and Accessories
Industrial Roofing and Accessories
Corrugated
E-Rib
  Perforated Corrugated
  Ribbed
  V-Beam
Sealants for Roofing and Siding
Rural Roofing
Rural Siding
  Colorib
  Corrugated
  5-V Crimp
  Ribbed

Colorib® Panels
Electrical Wire and Cable
Fasteners
Sol-Dec® Sunscreen
Stair Treads
Thresholds
Vault Frames
Window Sills
Wire and Cable
Soffit
Fascia
Residental Siding
Gravel Stops
Gutters and Downspouts
Handrails and Fittings
Highway Signs and Structures
Bridge-Rail Systems
Guard-Rail Systems
Manhole Steps

MANUFACTURED PRODUCTS

Alcoa makes a wide variety of specially fabricated products for a number of in-

* Trademark of Aluminum Company of America

MANUFACTURED PRODUCTS — Continued

dustries including process, trucking, railroad, defense and building products. These products are available through Alcoa's sales offices and include:

Beer Barrels
Bridge-Rail Systems
Extruded Flooring for Trucks and Trailers
Special Farm Gates
Alcoa Forged Disc Truck Wheels
Forged Meathooks
Highway Signs
Loader Beams
Manhole Steps and Rungs and Manhole Covers
Picnic Shelters
Railroad Crossbucks Signs
Rest Rooms and Comfort Stations
Shipping Containers
Special Forged, Cast, Extruded and Rolled Aluminum Products
Special Research and Development Products for Defense Applications
Special Structures such as Transmission Towers
Stair Treads
Standard and Special Storage Tanks
Structural Assemblies
Telephone Booths
Welding, Brazing and Soldering Products

Most modern fabricating facilities available. Close proximity to Alcoa's research and development facilities.

Sales Offices

ALABAMA
Birmingham, 35223
   #10 Office Park, Mountain Brook

ARIZONA
Phoenix, 85014
   5045 North 12th Street, Suite 105

ARKANSAS
Little Rock, 72202.....1515 West Seventh Street

CALIFORNIA
Los Angeles, 90017.....1145 Wilshire Boulevard
Oakland, 94608...............1001 46th Street
San Diego, 92103...........2962 Fifth Avenue
San Francisco (Burlingame), 94010
   1840 Ogden Drive

COLORADO
Denver, 80222........1777 South Bellaire Street

CONNECTICUT
Bridgeport, 06606
   Commerce Park, 4695 Main Street
Hartford, 06105
   IBM Building, 1049 Asylum Avenue

DELAWARE
Wilmington, 19801
   825 Bank of Delaware Building

DISTRICT OF COLUMBIA
Washington, 20036........1200 Ring Building

FLORIDA
Miami (Hialeah), 33010......490 Hialeah Drive
Tampa, 33609.......4302 Henderson Boulevard

GEORGIA
Atlanta, 30309
   Alcoa Building, 1615 Peachtree Street, N.E.

IDAHO
Boise, 83705................1220 Vista Avenue

ILLINOIS
Chicago, 60611
   Equitable Bldg., 401 North Michigan Avenue
Peoria, 61602
   614 Commercial National Bank Building

INDIANA
Fort Wayne, 46807 .. 2924 South Calhoun Street
Indianapolis, 46205.......3969 Meadows Drive
Lafayette, 47902..E. Main Street (U.S. Route 52)
South Bend, 46637.......51591 U. S. 31 North

IOWA
Davenport, 52801............601 Brady Street

KANSAS
Wichita, 67208.............. 5309 East Central

KENTUCKY
Louisville, 40207 ..... Mall Office Center Bldg.,
   400 Sherburn Lane

LOUISIANA
New Orleans, 70112...1309 Whitney Bank Bldg.

MARYLAND
Baltimore, 21204..305 West Chesapeake Avenue

MASSACHUSETTS
Boston, 02181...........Wellesley Office Park
Worcester, 01608............28 Pleasant Street

MICHIGAN
Detroit, 48202........610 New Center Building
Flint, 48502.....904 Mott Foundation Building
Grand Rapids, 49502
   812 Michigan National Bank Building
Jackson, 49201.....310 National Bank Building

MINNESOTA
Minneapolis, 55424......4010 West 65th Street

MISSOURI
Kansas City, 64112......4601 Madison Avenue
St. Louis, 63105........8301 Maryland Avenue

NEBRASKA
Omaha, 68114
   Suite 282, Swanson Bldg., 8401 West Dodge Rd.

NEW JERSEY
Newark (East Orange), 07018..100 Halsted Street

NEW YORK
Albany, 12206...............40 Colvin Avenue
Buffalo, 14240............ 2427 Sheridan Drive
Garden City (L. I.), 11530
   1001 Franklin Avenue
New York, 10017............200 Park Avenue
Rochester, 14618...............Erdle Building
Syracuse, 13203...............731 James Street

NORTH CAROLINA
Charlotte, 28204.....1200 East Morehead Street

OHIO
Akron, 44303.........759 West Market Street
Cincinnati, 45206
   Alcoa Building, 2331 Victory Parkway
Cleveland, 44114.........One Erieview Plaza
Columbus, 43215..........230 Bryson Building
Dayton, 45405..........207 Northtown Arcade
Toledo (Sylvania), 43560....5800 Monroe Street
Youngstown, 44503...537 Ohio Edison Building

OKLAHOMA
Oklahoma City, 73103....111 N. W. 23rd Street

OREGON
Portland, 97232...............111 Lloyd Plaza

PENNSYLVANIA
Allentown, 18102.......1202 Washington Street
Philadelphia, 19102
   1800 Two Penn Center Plaza
Pittsburgh, 15220.........875 Greentree Road
York, 17401.............25 North Duke Street

TENNESSEE
Chattanooga, 37402....1237 Volunteer Building
Knoxville (Alcoa, Tenn.), 37701
   State Highway, Route 73
Memphis, 38117..........4515 Poplar Avenue
Nashville, 37215.....235 Wilson-Bates Building

TEXAS
Dallas, 75201.......1900 Fidelity Union Tower
Houston, 77027
   Suite 300, 5050 Westheimer Road
Lubbock, 79405............203 Fields Building

VIRGINIA
Richmond, 23227
   2123 West LaBurnum Avenue

WASHINGTON
Seattle, 98104............1401 Madison Street
Spokane, 99201..........507 Fidelity Building

WEST VIRGINIA
Charleston, 25301
   Nelson Bldg., 1018 Kanawha Boulevard, East

WISCONSIN
Milwaukee, 53233
   2040 West Wisconsin Avenue
Wausau, 54401............203½ Fourth Street

NEW YORK EXPORT OFFICE
New York, N. Y., 10017......200 Park Avenue

FOREIGN SALES OFFICES

HONG KONG, B.C.C.
Alcoa International (Asia) Limited
  Luk Hoi Tong Building, 31 Queen's Road Central

KINGSTON, JAMAICA
Alcoa International, Limited
   The Bernard Sunley Building

LAUSANNE, SWITZERLAND
Alcoa International, S.A.....61 Avenue d'Ouchy

TORONTO 2, ONTARIO, CANADA
Alcoa International Canada, Ltd.
   2 Carlton Street, Suite 1704

ALUMINUM COMPANY OF AMERICA
General Offices, 1501 Alcoa Building, Pittsburgh, Pennsylvania 15219